THE ENCYCLOPEDIA OF

BIRDS

A Complete Visual Guide

THE ENCYCLOPEDIA OF
BIRDS

CHIEF CONSULTANT

Dr Richard Schodde
Research Associate
Australian Biological Resources Study, Canberra
Honorary Fellow
American Ornithologists' Union

CONSULTANT

Dr Fred Cooke
President-Elect
American Ornithologists' Union
Norfolk, UK

RED
LEMON
PRESS

Red Lemon Press
Deepdene Lodge, Deepdene Avenue, Dorking,
Surrey, United Kingdom RH5 4AT

Chief Executive Officer John Owen
President Terry Newell
Publisher Sheena Coupe
Creative Director Sue Burk
Vice President International Sales Stuart Laurence
Administrator International Sales Kristine Ravn

Project Editor Jennifer Losco
Project Designer Heather Menzies
Editors Stephanie Goodwin, Angela Handley
Designers Clare Forte, Jacqueline Richards, Karen
Robertson, Juliana Titin
Cover Design Heather Menzies, Juliana Titin
Picture Researchers Joanna Collard, Annette
Crueger, Jennifer Losco, Heather Menzies
Editorial Assistant Irene Mickaiel
Text Karen McGhee, Richard Schodde,
Luba Vangelova

Species Gallery Illustrations MagicGroup s.r.o.
(Czech Republic) www.magicgroup.cz
Feature Illustrations Guy Troughton
Maps Andrew Davies Creative Communication
and Map Illustrations
Information Graphics Andrew Davies Creative
Communication
Index Sarah Plant/Puddingburn Publishing Services
Cover and Imprint images Shutterstock

Production Director Chris Hemesath
Production Coordinator Charles Mathews

ISBN: 978-1-78342-063-6

Color reproduction by Chroma Graphics
(Overseas) Pte Ltd
Printed by Livonia
Printed in Latvia
A Weldon Owen Production

10 9 8 7 6 5 4 3

CONTENTS

FOREWORD

This is a book for anyone with a thirst for knowledge about birds. It spells out what sets birds apart from other animals, from their remarkable plumage and flight to their hatching of warm-blooded young from eggs. It looks into their origins and their relationships with reptiles. It investigates their life-cycles, adaptations, and habitats. Above all, it details their diversity and threats to survival. It is a book about birdlife and the life of birds on a global scale, and is brilliantly illustrated.

How well it enlightens depends ultimately on its coverage, balance, and accuracy. Over the last decade or so, great advances have been made in our understanding of birdlife. The extraordinary range of birds' feeding and breeding strategies has become clearer. The discovery of vast deposits of fossil birds in the Cretaceous beds of China, laid down more than 100 million years ago, has shed new light on the links between birds and dinosaurs. Molecular technology, too, has rejuvenated research into evolution within birds, overturning more than a little conventional 20th-century wisdom.

All of these advances are brought into perspective here. They affect, in particular, the make-up and sequence of the orders and families of birds, especially the songbirds that comprise about half of the world's birdlife. Here we have followed the third edition of *The Howard and Moore Complete Checklist of the Birds of the World*, published in 2003, though with minor variations resulting from even more up-to-date information. Details of the status of threatened species of birds have been drawn from the June 2004 *World Bird Database of Birdlife International*, the organization that supplies bird data for the IUCN.

Yet, however informative this book may be, it will mean little if birds continue down the path to extinction. Some species have already gone; and, if current trends continue, many more are on the way. Almost every modern book dealing with biodiversity focuses on this issue and pleads for action to conserve wildlife and its habitats. And you, the involved reader, need little convincing. Those that do need convincing are governments and industry, for until they are, no concerted action can be taken on any significant scale. Let me urge all of you who are aware to take every opportunity to inform those who are not.

Richard Schodde
Research Associate, Australian Biological Resources Study, Canberra
Honorary Fellow, American Ornithologists' Union

HOW TO USE THIS BOOK

The first section of this book provides an introduction to birds: their characteristics, evolution, classification, biology, behavior, habitats, adaptations, and conservation status. The second section profiles birds according to their taxonomy. Each bird group is introduced with a study of its general characteristics. Then follows a species-by-species survey. The book concludes with a comprehensive glossary and index.

Group global distribution
A map shows the worldwide distribution of the bird group being profiled, followed by text that discusses the distribution of particular groups in more detail.

HABITAT ICONS

The 18 habitat icons below indicate at a glance the various habitats in which a species or group can be found. It should be noted that the icons are used in the same order throughout the book, rather than in their order of significance. A more detailed profile of each habitat can be found on pages 30–37.

- Tropical rain forest
- Tropical monsoon forest
- Temperate forest
- Coniferous forest
- Moorlands and heath
- Open habitat, including savanna, grassland, fields, pampas, and steppes
- Desert and semidesert
- Mountains and highlands
- Tundra
- Polar regions
- Seas and oceans
- Coral reefs
- Mangrove swamps
- Coastal areas, including beaches, oceanic cliffs, sand dunes, intertidal rock pools, and/or coastal waters (as applicable to group)
- Rivers and streams, including river and stream banks
- Wetlands, including swamps, marshes, fens, floodplains, deltas, and bogs
- Lakes and ponds
- Urban areas

Section and chapter
This indicates the group of birds under discussion.

114　PARROTS

Classification box
This shows the taxonomic groups to which birds belong.

CLASS	Aves
ORDERS	1
FAMILIES	3 or more
GENERA	85
SPECIES	364

PARROTS

Parrots and cockatoos form an ancient and highly distinct order of birds, without clear relatives. They are easily recognized by their short, hooked bills, which have incurved mandibles specialized for seed eating; and also by finely scaled feet, which have two toes pointing forward and two pointing backward, specialized for clambering. Most are brilliantly plumaged, colored in shades of green accented by splashes of red, yellow, and blue. Their visual appeal is one reason for their popularity as pets over the centuries. Another is their antics: they can perform acrobatics, hanging on perches with either feet or bills, and can mimic human voices.

Southerly distribution Parrots live primarily in the Southern Hemisphere. They are especially common in lowland tropical rain forests, but some species prefer open, arid regions. The highest concentrations of species occur in Australasia and South America. The most southerly parrot inhabits Tierra del Fuego, Argentina.

A SOCIABLE GROUP

Most parrots eat seeds and nuts (which they crack open with their heavy bills) as well as fruit. They forage among the treetops or on the ground. Lorikeets, on the other hand, are strictly arboreal; they eat soft fruit, and harvest pollen and nectar with brush-tipped tongues.

Although parrots' basic features differ little among species, there is considerable variation in size and shape. Wings can be narrow and pointed, or broad and rounded. Similarly, tails may be long and pointed or short and squarish. Some have ornate feathers. Cockatoos, a separate family from "true parrots," have prominent, erectile head crests. Usually, the sexes are alike and monogamous. Nearly all nest in tree holes and lay plain white eggs.

Parrots are very social birds. They squawk loudly and frequently, and are heard more often than seen in the wild where their green plumage camouflages them. Parrots usually pair for life and separate to breed without holding territory. Almost all nest in scrapes in tree hollows, and all lay plain, dull white eggs.

Lavish photographs
Taken by leading wildlife photographers, these portray the habits and habitats of different species.

Group dynamics A colorful gathering of orange-cheeked (*Pionopsitta barrabandi*) and blue-headed (*Pionus menstruus*) parrots at a clay (above), "lick" for salt. Parrots are gregarious and roost and feed in small parties or large flocks.

Fancy feathers Red-and-green macaws (*Ara chloroptera*) (below), though difficult to see in forest foliage, can be recognized by their colorful plumage and long tails. Their tapered wings allow them to fly faster than expected for birds of their size.

Open wide Parrots' bills have a greater range of motion and are more powerful than the bills of other birds. A well-developed hinge on the upper mandible of a parrot's jaw (below) provides leverage that enables the bird to use its bill to climb branches, and a strongly muscled, cutting-edged lower mandible to cut up and crack open large, hard-shelled nuts.

Photographic details
Photographs and text focus on unusual or intriguing aspects of bird behavior.

Sounding off Parrots can use their feet like hands, to handle objects. This palm cockatoo (*Progosciger aterrimus*) (above) creates mechanical sounds by drumming a stick against a hollow tree.

Inner view The cutaway shows the adaptations to jaw and bill.

upper hinge

lower hinge

lower bill when jaw is open

cutting tip of lower bill

crotch in upper bill for anchoring nut to be husked. The nut is braced there by a muscular tongue specialized for manipulating food

hook for grabbing food

Aloft Two brilliantly colored red-and-green macaws display a rainbow of hues when they fly. They are among the largest parrots.

Detailed diagrams
Where appropriate, diagrams are included to illustrate points about anatomy or adaptation.

CONSERVATION INFORMATION

Within the fact files, each profiled species is allocated a conservation status, using IUCN and other conservation categories, as follows:

† Indicates that a species is listed under the following categories:
Extinct (IUCN) It is beyond reasonable doubt that the last individual of a given species has died.
Extinct in the wild (IUCN) Only known to survive in captivity or as a naturalized population outside its former range.

⚑ Indicates that a species is listed under the following categories:
Critically endangered (IUCN) Facing a very high and immediate risk of extinction in the wild.
Endangered (IUCN) Facing a very high risk of extinction in the wild in the near future.

The following categories are also used:
Vulnerable (IUCN) Facing a high risk of extinction in the wild in the foreseeable future.
Near threatened (IUCN) Likely to qualify for one of the above categories in the near future.
Conservation dependent (IUCN) Dependent upon species- or habitat-specific conservation programs to keep it out of one of the above threatened categories.

Data deficient (IUCN) Inadequate information available to make an assessment of its risk.
Not known Not evaluated or little studied.
Common Widespread and abundant.
Locally common Widespread and abundant within its range.
Uncommon Occurs widely in low numbers in preferred habitat(s).
Rare Occurs in only some of preferred habitat or in small restricted areas.

FACT FILE STATISTICS

Important or interesting facts about profiled species use the following icons and information. All measurements are maximums.

Length
⤒ Tip of bill to tip of tail

Height
Head and body height

Wingspan
⤢ From tip of one wing to tip of the other

Plumage
// Sexes alike
// Sexes differ

Reproduction
• Number of eggs

Migration
↻ Migrant
Partial migrant
⊘ Sedentary
~ Nomad

Number of genera and species
The number of genera and species in the relevant taxonomic group

Fact file
This profiles one or more of the illustrated species or groups, with information about its size, appearance, habitat, range, reproduction, migratory habits, behavior, calls, or regional variations.

Distribution map
This shows the species' or group's range (and former range, where appropriate). If distributed throughout the world, a world map is shown; if regional distribution, a map of that area only is given.

Habitat icons
The icons indicate the various habitats in which the profiled bird can be found, for example polar regions or tropical rain forest. The full list is on the opposite page.

Conservation watch box
This provides information about the status of a particular species, according to the IUCN Red List of Threatened Species. These boxes may also outline factors that threaten the bird's survival.

Feature page
This explores topics of particular interest and provides insight into bird behavior through text, illustrations, and photographs.

Snippets
These highlight distinguishing aspects or characteristics of the species, such as color variations, behavior, habitat, size, and anatomical features.

Sex symbols
Where there is a difference in plumage between the sexes, the sex of the bird illustrated is indicated.

Name labels
Labels provide the common and scientific name of the illustrated birds.

INTRODUCING BIRDS

BIRDS

PHYLUM	Chordata
CLASS	Aves
ORDERS	31
FAMILIES	194
GENERA	2,161
SPECIES	9,723

Birds arose from primitively feathered reptiles by becoming warm-blooded and gaining the power of flight. Today they are among the most mobile of all animals. Although some never stray far from home, others cross oceans and continents, sometimes in a single flight on annual migrations. Birds are most common in woodlands, forests, and wetlands, but have also adapted to big cities, hot dry deserts, and even polar ice. They range in size from the tiny bee hummingbird, with a top weight of 0.07 ounce (2 g), to the imposing 9-foot (2.8-m), 300-pound (135-kg) ostrich.

FEATHER TYPES

There are several kinds of feathers. Closest to the body are the fluffy down feathers that protect a bird from the cold. Over these are the contour feathers. These are short and round, and give the bird its streamlined shape. The longer and stronger feathers on a bird's wing and tail enable it to fly and maneuver in the air.

Flight feather *The vane of a flight feather is made up of fine strands that interlock to create a smooth surface.*

hooklets

barbule

shaft

shaft | vane

barb

Purpose-built *Feathers provide warmth, protection, color, and shape, as well as the dynamics that make flight possible.*

Pheasant's tail feather | Macaw's body feather | Eagle's down feather

Obsessive groomers All birds, even those that cannot fly, have feathers—about 2,000 on average. To keep feathers at their peak for flight and insulation, most birds arrange, inspect, clean, preen, lubricate, and rearrange their plumage for hours each day.

LIFE IN THE AIR

Some modern birds, such as the emu and cassowary, have lost the power of flight. But the possession of feathers and the ability of most birds to soar into the air are the features that set them apart from other vertebrates. The capabilities of birds to fly enormous distances, at speed, and under their own power, are unparalleled.

Birds can display an astonishing range of aerial maneuvers, from swooping and soaring to hovering. Some, such as the hummingbirds, can even fly backward. Birds use flight to search for food and more favorable climates, to meet up with mates, and to avoid predators.

All birds have feathers made of keratin, the same material as hair. Feather keratin is very light, and feather shafts are hollow and usually strong, all adapted for flight. Wing and tail feathers are elongated in an airfoil shape, contributing lift and propulsion.

Bill versatility Bills perform a variety of tasks. Here (above), this green heron (*Butorides virescens*) has wielded its bill against a frog. The great blue heron (*Ardea herodias*) (right) uses its sharp bill in courtship, to spear fishes, and for making nests.

BIRDS THROUGH THE AGES

The first birds appeared more than 150 million years ago, during the Jurassic or possibly the Triassic period. Knowledge of their early history has grown rapidly with the recent discovery of vast beds of fossil birds and feathered dinosaurs in deposits in northeast China and central Asia. Although these discoveries have opened argument about whether birds descended from dinosaurs or earlier archosaurs, they have also clarified a critical question. Birds and two-legged dinosaurs known as theropods—a group that included the fearsome carnivore *Tyrannosaurus rex*—are on the same branch of the evolutionary tree. The realization that birds are, in fact, "feathered dinosaurs" came about with the spectacular discovery of new specimens of the oldest known bird, *Archaeopteryx lithographica*. Six specimens of *Archaeopteryx* have been found, all in the Solhofen limestones in southern Germany. They are dated from the Jurassic period, between 200 and 140 million years ago. These fossils show that *Archaeopteryx* grew to about the size of a crow.

FEATHERED DINOSAURS

The close relationship between *Archaeopteryx* and theropod dinosaurs means that flight, and the structural modifications needed for it, arose in swift, two-legged, predatory ancestors designed for a life of gliding in trees. Although *Archaeopteryx* displays many unmistakable bird features, much of its skeleton is akin to those of reptiles. The forelimb bones, for example, show little of the special flight modifications developed in modern birds.

Far more fossil birds have been uncovered from right through the Cretaceous (140 to 65 million years ago), which followed the Jurassic period. Some of the oldest are not much younger than *Archaeopteryx* and yet all are much more like modern birds. Most of them were also undoubtedly capable of strong flight. They fell into two groups. The first group had feet with one toe pointed forward and the other three backward, and a reptilian pelvis. These were the "opposite" or enantiornithine birds, a lineage that soon died out. The second group, the ornithurine birds, had toes and hindlimbs much like modern birds—and were their immediate ancestors.

Ancient bird Right from its discovery, in 1861, *Archaeopteryx* was considered a bird because its body was covered with feathers arranged in tracts similar to those of modern birds. Scientists still debate, however, whether it could truly fly or simply glide.

Marine dweller Several species of *Hesperornis* were among the birds that lived on the late Cretaceous seas, 70 million years ago. These fish eaters may have given rise to grebes. They had lost the power of flight and, unlike all modern birds, had teeth.

Pleistocene scavenger *Teratornis merriami* was a large, vulture-like predator that lived in western North America during the Pleistocene epoch—2 million–10,000 years ago. The fossils of many specimens have been found in California's Rancho La Brea tar pits.

DINOSAUR TO BIRD

The evolution of powered flight required major skeletal modifications, seen in this evolutionary sequence. Small meat-eating dinosaurs such as *Compsognathus* ran on their two hindlegs, leaving their arms free to catch prey. *Archaeopteryx* turned this grasping movement into a gliding movement by using its early wings. In birds today, gliding has become flapping flight.

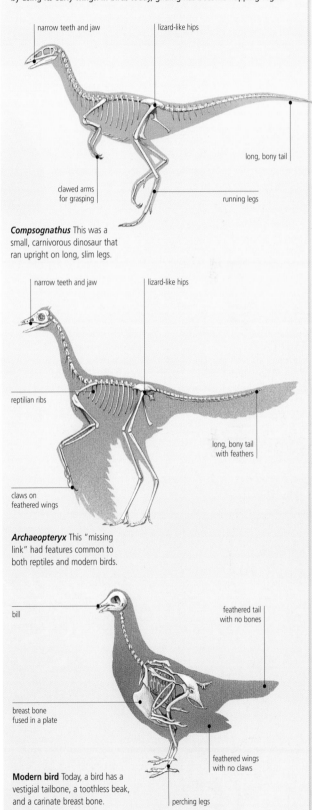

narrow teeth and jaw

lizard-like hips

long, bony tail

clawed arms for grasping

running legs

Compsognathus This was a small, carnivorous dinosaur that ran upright on long, slim legs.

narrow teeth and jaw

lizard-like hips

reptilian ribs

long, bony tail with feathers

claws on feathered wings

Archaeopteryx This "missing link" had features common to both reptiles and modern birds.

bill

feathered tail with no bones

breast bone fused in a plate

feathered wings with no claws

Modern bird Today, a bird has a vestigial tailbone, a toothless beak, and a carinate breast bone.

perching legs

RISE OF MODERN BIRDS

Modern birds are known as Neornithes—meaning new birds—and fall within two clearly defined groups. One is the paleognaths. It includes the tinamous of South and Central America; and the large, flightless ratites, such as the ostrich of Africa, South America's rheas, the emu and cassowaries of Australia and New Guinea, and New Zealand's kiwis.

Paleognaths have a long history that extends back to before the break-up of Gondwana. Several fossils from the late Cretaceous have been found in Mongolia and Europe. Numerous, long-since extinct species of relatively small paleognaths existed in Europe and North America and most were capable of powered flight.

The second modern bird group, the neognaths, accounts for all other living species. Most of their major orders were present in the Eocene—57 to 37 million years ago. Paleontologists believe that, despite a deficiency of fossils, many of these groups or their direct ancestors were present in the late Cretaceous.

One of the most primitive neognath lines includes the galliformes—chickens, pheasants, and quails—and the anseriformes—ducks, geese, and swans.

ANCESTRAL LINEAGES

Evidence indicates that waterbirds, such as penguins, loons, grebes, cormorants and their relatives, and albatrosses, shearwaters and their relatives, comprise a distinct evolutionary line that originated in the Cretaceous. Fossil penguins are well represented in Australia, South America, and New Zealand where these birds live today. It appears that even by the Eocene, these birds were already specialized for underwater "flying."

One of the most unusual fossil records is that of the pelecaniformes, to which modern pelicans belong. This group included the pseudodontorns—the false-teethed birds. They were a diverse assemblage of albatross-like gliders, all of which had bony, teeth-like projections from the jaws thought to have been used for capturing prey while skimming the ocean's surface. Some of these birds were truly enormous, with a wingspan of 20 feet (6 m), far bigger than that of any living albatross.

Another lineage of aquatic forms includes flamingos, storks, and ibises, all of which were present and widely distributed by 50 to 40 million years ago.

Big birds New Zealand was the home of moas, a group of at least 15 species of large to very large wingless birds thought to have reigned from the Pleistocene, about 2 million years ago, to within just several centuries ago. It is believed that hunting, habitat interference, and egg collecting by the Maori people—who arrived in New Zealand from Polynesia about 1,000 years ago—led to their extinction.

Easy to trick Emus (*Dromaius novaehollandiae*) (right) are members of the paleognath group (which means "ancient jawed" in reference to their primitive, heavily boned palates). These flightless, shaggy birds have strong legs and run fast but they do not attack anything taller than themselves. To escape an emu attack, a person only has to hold a stick above their head.

Avian oddity South America's hoatzin (*Opisthocomus hoazin*) (below) is the only bird that ferments plant matter in a foregut, as cows do. Wing claws, used for clambering among branches, are reminiscent of *Archaeopteryx*.

SMART CHICKS

Chickens, quails, and grouse belong to the neognaths (which means "new jawed" in reference to their more advanced palate structure). Despite popular belief, chickens are moderately intelligent birds.

Crowing call Chickens use over 30 distinct vocalizations to communicate a wealth of information to one another.

Pecking order Quails are less intelligent than many other birds. They are not innovative and have a low metabolic rate.

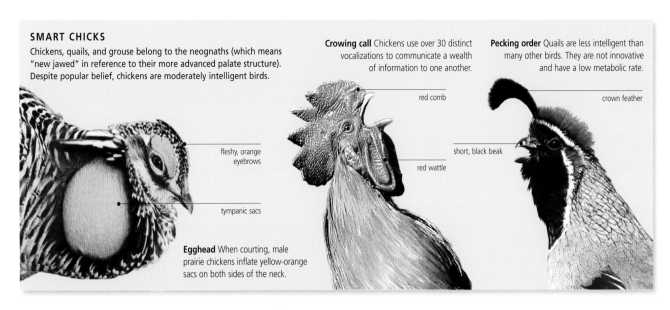

fleshy, orange eyebrows

tympanic sacs

red comb

red wattle

short, black beak

crown feather

Egghead When courting, male prairie chickens inflate yellow-orange sacs on both sides of the neck.

CLASSIFICATION

Biological classification has two main goals. The first is to identify the basic units of biological diversity—species and subspecies—and to assign them unique names. This establishes the extent of diversity among organisms, living and extinct. The second purpose is to arrange these basic units into a system of increasingly higher-level groups that reflect evolutionary relationships. Closely related species are grouped in one genus, closely related genera are grouped in one family, closely related families are grouped in one order, and so on. The vital research for this kind of classification uses morphology, behavior, ecology, and more recently, molecular genetics. The resulting sequence represents the "tree" of evolution, tables biodiversity, and provides the foundation for all biological knowledge. To avoid confusion across languages, Latinized names are used in bird classification, as they are for all other organisms.

MODERN CLASSIFICATION

Since the days of Charles Darwin in the mid-1880s, birds have been classified according to perceptions of their natural relationships. This system allows scientists to identify relationships between living species, as well as with ancient, extinct birds. All species in a genus are presumed to be descendants of a common ancestor.

These days, species are still identified as similar-looking birds that can freely interbreed. And genera, families, and orders are sorted according to structural similarities in limbs, skeletons, and feathers. In this way, birds that have a foot with two toes projecting forward and two pointing backward, and a hooked bill with vertically twisted palate bones, are all grouped in the parrot family.

Since the late 20th century, however, molecular studies have shown that many structural traits used for classifying birds are unreliable due to convergent evolution, especially within the families of passerines. For example, such studies have revealed that the wrens, flycatchers, robins, and warblers of Australasia are unrelated to their Eurasian look-alikes. Modern research suggests these Australasian groups are the old ancestral lineages of the world's songbirds.

Naming rights To avoid confusion, scientists assign a unique two-part Latinized name to each and every known bird. This given name is used in all countries and avoids the confusion created by inconsistent common names. New Guinea's spangled kookaburra, for example, is known by at least two other common names but only one scientific name—*Dacelo tyro*.

KINGDOM
Animalia
spangled kookaburra, lion, white shark, brown snake, stick insect, human, jellyfish

PHYLUM
Chordata
spangled kookaburra, lion, white shark, brown snake, human

CLASS
Aves
spangled kookaburra, ostrich, vulture, chicken, egret

ORDER
Coraciiformes
spangled kookaburra, kingfishers, rollers, bee-eaters, todies

FAMILY
Dacelonidae
spangled kookaburra, white-rumped kingfisher

GENUS
Dacelo
spangled kookaburra, rufous-bellied kookaburra

SPECIES
Dacelo tyro
spangled kookaburra

Deceptive appearances Just as birds that resemble each other are not necessarily related, birds that look completely different can be. The southern yellow-billed hornbill (*Tockus leucomelas*) (above), for example, belongs to the same order as the hoopoes, Bucerotiformes, despite its very different bill.

Great order The tree swallow (*Tachycineta bicolor*) (far right, bottom) belongs to the order Passeriformes—the perching birds. More than half of all known species of living birds belong to this enormous avian order, which is represented in every continent except Antarctica.

BIRDS

The classification system used in this book recognizes almost 10,000 species of birds. These are arranged into more than 2,000 genera, which come within almost 200 families.

Class Aves

Order Tinamiformes
Tinamous and rheas

Order Struthioniformes
Ostrich

Order Casuariiformes
Cassowaries, emus, and kiwis

Order Galliformes
Gamebirds

Order Anseriformes
Waterfowl

Order Sphenisciformes
Penguins

Order Gaviiformes
Divers

Order Casuariiformes, page 47

Order Podicipediformes
Grebes

Order Procellariiformes
Albatrosses and petrels

Order Phoenicopteriformes
Flamingos

Order Ciconiiformes
Herons and allies

Order Pelecaniformes
Pelicans and allies

Order Falconiformes
Birds of prey

Order Turniciformes
Buttonquail

Order Pelecaniformes, page 79

Order Gruiformes
Cranes and allies

Order Opisthocomiformes
Hoatzin

Order Charadriiformes
Waders and shorebirds

Order Pteroclidiformes
Sandgrouse

Order Columbiformes
Pigeons

Order Psittaciformes
Parrots and cockatoos

Order Musophagiformes
Turacos

Order Cuculiformes
Cuckoos

Order Strigiformes
Owls

Order Caprimulgiformes
Nightjars and allies

Order Apodiformes
Hummingbirds and swifts

Order Coliiformes
Mousebirds

Order Trogoniformes
Trogons

Order Coraciiformes
Kingfishers and allies

Order Bucerotiformes
Hornbills and hoopoes

Order Piciformes
Woodpeckers and allies

Order Passeriformes
Passerines

Order Passeriformes, page 152

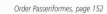

WEBBED DISCREPANCIES

Although both grebes and loons have webbed feet, they have different types of webbing which suggests the two groups are not closely related. They are an example of convergent evolution, where similar adaptations have evolved to suit similar environments and lifestyles in different lineages of birds.

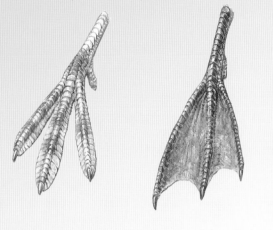

A grebe's foot showing flanged toes   **A loon's foot** showing webbed toes

BIOLOGY AND BEHAVIOR

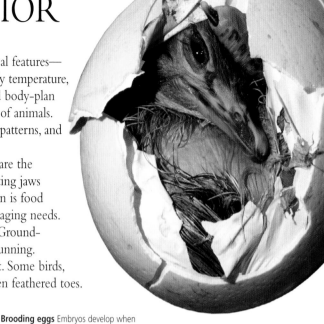

A ll birds have fundamentally similar anatomical and physiological features—a bony toothless beak, a high metabolic rate that regulates body temperature, and a skeleton that is both strong and lightweight. In fact, the bird body-plan varies far less in size and structure than that of most other groups of animals. Birds do, however, show a kaleidoscopic range of plumage colors, patterns, and outgrowths, often related to courtship and mate selection.

The other areas in which birds show a large range of variation are the shape, size, and structure of the bill and feet. The bill is the projecting jaws of a bird, encased in a horny sheath of keratin. Its primary function is food gathering and so most variations relate to different dietary and foraging needs.

Structural modifications to the legs and feet are also common. Ground-dwellers, for example, have long legs, well suited to walking and running. Legs adapted to climbing and perching in trees are short and stout. Some birds, especially those living in cold climates, have feathered legs and even feathered toes.

AVIAN REPRODUCTION

All birds have internal fertilization but embryos develop inside eggs laid outside the mother's body. When the young of some species hatch, they are well developed and become independent almost immediately. Other chicks are born blind and helpless.

Most adult male birds have no external sex organs. Testes, which remain small outside the breeding season, are located internally. When producing sperm they can swell hundreds of times in size. In nearly all species, only the ovary on the left side of the female's body is functional.

Males of most species do not have a copulatory organ, such as a penis, to deliver sperm. During copulation the cloacas—the combined urinogenital openings—of both sexes are everted and brought together for no more than seconds in a "cloacal kiss." Through this brief contact, sperm is transferred into the female's cloaca where it may be stored for up to a year. In some birds, most notably waterfowl and ratites, part of the cloaca of the male is modified to form a penis.

Fertilization of ova takes place in the upper oviduct. Then, as each egg descends the oviduct, albumen layers are deposited around it. The shell and pigment are added, to complete the egg, in the wider and greatly distensible uterus. The egg then passes through the vagina and cloaca and finally it is expelled into a nest.

Brooding eggs Embryos develop when eggs are maintained at the correct temperature, usually achieved through contact with a parent's body (below). Adults of many species develop brood patches—areas denuded of feathers and richly supplied with blood vessels.

Breaking out When ready to hatch, a chick will crack the eggshell surrounding it using a special "egg-tooth" on the tip of its bill (above). This useful feature is obvious only at hatching, and is shed or reabsorbed within a day or two.

Toco toucan

Hyacinth macaw

Bald eagle

Tufted puffin

Egrets

Bill variety From left to right: the toucan's soft bill picks fruit; a macaw's bill shells nuts and seeds; an eagle's bill tears flesh; a puffin's serrated bill secures fish; and an egret's bill is suited to stabbing among wetland plants.

SKELETON AND ORGAN SYSTEMS

Most of the main features of a bird's skeleton relate to their two independent and specialized modes of locomotion—flying and bipedal walking. Typically, girdles for both the forelimbs and hindlimbs are particularly strong because each must at some stage—either during flying or walking—support the entire weight of the body.

The skeleton of the forelimb is modified so that the arm, forearm, and hand support the wing. Each hindlimb is also specialized. Some foot bones (metatarsals) are fused and lengthened so that each leg appears to contain an extra segment.

Both lightness and strength are essential for flight. And so, the skeleton of many birds is lightened by extensive pneumatization, a condition in which bones are hollow and contain air sacs. Even though bones may be hollow, they are structurally very strong, having internal, truss-like reinforcements which add strength.

A strong, four-chambered heart is at the epicenter of the bird's circulatory system. Species capable of sustained flight, such as albatrosses, have a proportionately larger heart compared to birds that are poor fliers or fly only short distances.

The avian respiratory system is highly specialized. The small lungs comprise only about 2 percent of body volume, but connecting air sacs are well developed and, in total, may take up to 20 percent of body volume.

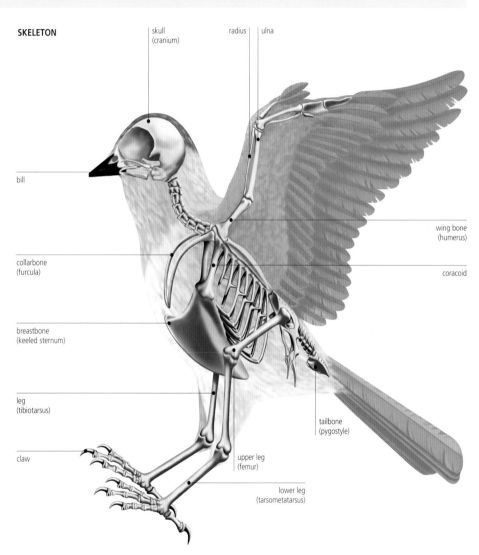

SKELETON

- skull (cranium)
- radius
- ulna
- bill
- wing bone (humerus)
- collarbone (furcula)
- coracoid
- breastbone (keeled sternum)
- leg (tibiotarsus)
- tailbone (pygostyle)
- claw
- upper leg (femur)
- lower leg (tarsometatarsus)

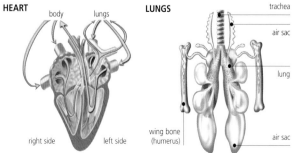

HEART
- body
- lungs
- right side
- left side

LUNGS
- trachea
- air sac
- lung
- wing bone (humerus)
- air sac

Flight adaptations Although wings are the obvious and outward feature that enable birds to fly, every part of a flying bird's body—from its heart and lungs to its powerful muscles and lightweight bones—is adapted to enable it to flap through the air. Flying requires large amounts of energy—food and oxygen—and an efficient way of transferring these fuels to the muscles. Air sacs connected to the small lungs (left) help them work more efficiently. The sacs extend into the birds' bones.

SENSES

Birds have the same five basic senses as humans. In most, eyesight and hearing are the best developed and most important. The structure of the eye is particularly complex, with added sensory cells. Unlike most other vertebrates, birds see color in an even wider range of the spectrum than humans, extending to ultraviolet wavelengths. Nocturnal birds, such as owls and nightjars, have tubular eyes to improve light-gathering capacity without loss of resolving power.

The bird's left eye views the horizon for orientation and predators, while the right eye is used for seeing close objects and social interaction.

Raptors have particularly keen eyesight. The eye of an eagle is the same size as a human eye but has a far greater density of sensory elements (rods and cones) in the retina—the rear inner surface of the eye on which the image is formed. Eagles can spy small prey on the ground from a mile (1.6 km) up in the air.

Despite the lack of external ears, the hearing range of most birds seems similar to that of humans. Some species, however, have particularly well-developed capabilities, notably the owls. The barn owl can home in on and kill a mouse in a pitch-black room within seconds because its ears are specialized for sound location.

A sense of smell plays little part in the lives of most birds. Exceptions include turkey vultures, which locate carrion using olfactory organs. New Zealand's kiwis use a keen sense of smell in nostrils at the bill tip as they probe around at night for food.

FINDING FOOD

Because of the lightweight requirements for flight, few birds accumulate large fat reserves and so a constant supply of food is critical. Whether diving for fishes, probing the water's edge for crabs, gleaning insects from the forest canopy, or searching for seeds on the ground, most birds spend a large proportion of their waking hours searching for food.

Small birds, in particular, must feed actively throughout most of the daylight hours. Indeed, some of the smallest, such as hummingbirds, have so little in reserve that they lose heat overnight and use the Sun's warmth to get going in the morning.

Few birds search cooperatively for food. Most are either solitary hunters, such as hawks and owls, or species that gather in groups where food is abundant, as finches, waterfowl, or penguins do—yet these birds do not assist each other.

Members of a mated pair may forage together and there is evidence that some birds that roost together at night may benefit by gaining information from each other about where best to feed.

Some birds, such as the marsh tit and acorn woodpecker, overcome a lack of constant food by storing it.

Bird's eye view Vision is the best developed sense in birds. The general structure of the eye is similar to that found in all vertebrates but is more complex, with extra sets of cone cells. Birds see the world even better than we do, and differently.

AVOIDING PREDATORS

A lone finch foraging in the open makes easy prey. This is one reason why so many small birds form flocks—to confuse predators. This safety-in-numbers strategy also ensures that, at all times, at least some members of the flock have their heads up, watching for threats.

Some species post sentries to watch while others forage. The first to spot a predator will raise an alarm call that members of its own species, as well as other birds nearby, recognize as a warning.

Solitary birds also have ways of avoiding predators. Snipes, which are secretive waders, sit still until predators are almost upon them. Then they dart off in a zig-zag flight pattern that is hard for predators to follow. Their plumage is streaked in shades of brown to match the long marsh grasses where they live. Like many cryptically colored birds, the snipe's main defense is camouflage.

North America's burrowing owl has evolved a particularly ingenious strategy. This species lives in the burrows of ground squirrels. Should a squirrel happen upon it, the owl gives a call that resembles the chattering sound of a rattlesnake.

Shell crackers Smashing shells onto a hard surface to crack them open is just one stage short of tool use. The song thrush (*Turdus philomelos*) (below), in particular, is noted for this kind of behavior. Each bird has a preferred stone anvil against which it smashes hard-shelled garden snails to expose the soft tissues within.

Chick protection The ground nests of sandgrouse (above) are scrapes in deserts, low scrub, and grasslands. Hatchlings rely on near-perfect camouflage to avoid the attentions of predators while their parents are off foraging. When alarmed, chicks stop dead still and drop to the ground, disappearing into the background.

Food extraction The woodpecker finch (*Camarhynchus pallidus*) (below), from the Galápagos Islands, will wield a cactus spine in its bill to extract insect larvae from holes in trees. Most animal behaviorists agree this fits the definition of tool use.

COURTSHIP AND MATING

Most birds are monogamous, with males defending territories in which food can be found for both the pair and nestlings. Among songbirds, males commonly sing to attract mates and deter rivals.

Very rarely, females court males. This occurs among the phalaropes, small Northern Hemisphere waders, in which the females sport brighter plumage during the breeding season.

Nest-building, mating, and egg-laying follow pairing. Brooding can be carried out by both parents, by the female alone or, though less commonly, by the male alone. Either or both sexes may feed and watch over the young. In some species, non-breeding birds help out too.

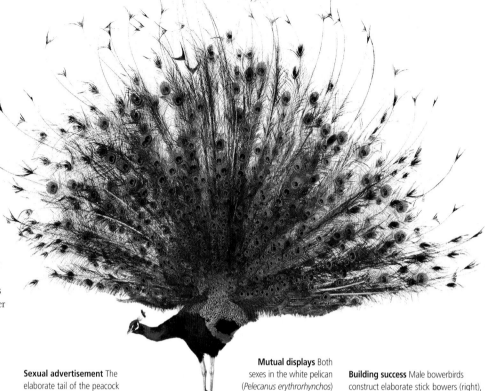

Elaborate songsters Male nightingales are famous for their exquisite singing, using up to 300 different songs to attract mates and establish breeding territories (below). They sing both day and night and usually from high perches to disperse their calls more widely.

Sexual advertisement The elaborate tail of the peacock (above) is intended to tell females it is a worthy mate. The tails are at their most spectacular during the breeding season, with feather length and quality indicating age, health, and status.

Mutual displays Both sexes in the white pelican (*Pelecanus erythrorhynchos*) (below), display with the bill. "Pouch-rippling"—when rapid opening and shutting of the bill sets the pouch quivering—is common.

Building success Male bowerbirds construct elaborate stick bowers (right), often decorated with objects such as feathers and stones. There they display for potential mates. The bower is used only for courtship and mating, and may be maintained over several seasons.

GROWING UP

The young of many birds, such as songbirds and raptors, are altricial—they are small, helpless, and naked upon hatching. They need to be fed and protected from predators until they grow enough to leave the nest, which can often take several weeks.

In other species, such as ducks and shorebirds, hatchlings are precocial—they are well developed and covered with down right from hatching. They can stand (and sometimes even run) within just minutes. The hatchlings rapidly learn to feed themselves and parents provide only shelter and protection. Precocial species usually have longer incubation periods, smaller clutch sizes, and larger eggs to advance development at hatching. Imprinting—where young become socially attached to and copy the behavior of parents shortly after birth—is also well marked among precocial birds.

Experience plays an important role in the development of all young birds, particularly after they leave the nest. A young gull, for example, learns to recognize the call of its parent and will respond with typical nestling begging behavior only when it hears that parent gull return to the colony. It also learns to peck at its parent's bill to obtain food.

Through experiences with parents and siblings, young birds learn to recognize their own species. It is these imprints that they will look to when they are more mature and seek a mate of their own. If, for example, a young male zebra finch is reared by a pair of Bengalese finches, it will prefer to court and mate with a Bengalese, rather than its own species, when it becomes an adult.

BIRD BRAINS

Much of bird behavior is instinctive. And much of bird learning is more a case of special abilities matched to habitat and lifestyle rather than a sign of wide-ranging intellectual prowess. For example, a brown thrasher can master a thousand song phrases and a marsh tit can memorize the locations of hundreds of seeds. Such activities undoubtedly require equivalent intelligence, but neither species could manage the other's tasks. Natural selection has endowed each species with special abilities where they are needed.

Birds are not, however, stupid. Like mammals, they have relatively large and highly organized brains, which underpin elaborate and varied behaviors. The evidence for learning by imitation in birds is as strong as that for most mammals other than primates.

One bird family attributed with high "intelligence" is the Corvidae—which includes crows, rooks, and magpies. In Japan and California, crows have been observed placing nuts in the paths of cars and then recovering the exposed nut meat after the nut has been driven over.

Fooling around Play behavior is most commonly associated with young mammals, particularly carnivores. It is not so well documented in birds but young predators, such as these bald eagles (*Haliaeetus leucocephalus*) (left), will often fly at each other and grapple in harmless displays of dazzling aerobatics. Such behaviors may be important for learning and experiencing the complex skills needed for capturing and subduing prey.

Begging baby A robin (right) hatches, after about two weeks' incubation, in a very underdeveloped and dependent state. Its early days are spent mostly sleeping, eating, and energetically beseeching its parents for food. As a rule, songbird hatchlings are helpless.

Mother love When goslings hatch, they will follow any large object they see. After a few days, they imprint on their mother and will follow only her (below).

HABITATS AND ADAPTATIONS

A bird's habitat is the environment it occupies, with climate and vegetation usually being deciding factors. Habitats provide food, foraging sites, cover from predators and the weather, and nesting sites. Birds have adapted to habitats as varied as the Arctic tundra, Sahara Desert, Amazon rain forest, and the open ocean. A bird's habitat may be restricted by geographical barriers. For example, bowerbirds, fairy wrens, and lyrebirds are found nowhere else but Australia and New Guinea, their distribution limited by surrounding oceans. More often, habitat restriction occurs because a species needs a particular resource. This is the case for Scandinavia's common crossbill, which is adapted to eat spruce tree seeds.

HABITAT SELECTION

Birds can have broad or narrow habitat requirements. For example, both the peregrine falcon and the barn owl have adapted to a wide range of habitats around the world. In contrast, Kirtland's warbler has highly specialized needs and lives only in jack pine woodlands recovering from fire that burnt between 6 and 13 years previously. Often, the presence of other animals, particularly predators, parasites, or competitors, can deter birds from an otherwise suitable habitat.

Many migratory birds occupy quite different habitats in breeding and non-breeding seasons. Seabirds, for example, roam across oceans for much of the year but breed in colonies on mainlands and islands.

Extreme tolerance Flamingos (far right) are able to exploit niches that other waders cannot because they are adapted to withstand waters that are exceptionally hot and highly alkaline.

Exposed habitat Characteristic of open habitats, the red-backed shrike (*Lanius collurio*) (top right) perches on field grasses, searching for prey below.

Predator peril The North Island saddleback (*Philesturnus carunculatus*) (right) is one of many native birds exterminated from New Zealand's main islands following the introduction of predators, such as stoats and rats. The saddleback is now restricted to tiny offshore islands that are free of predators.

Restrictive needs Parakeet auklets (*Cyclorrhynchus psittacula*) (below) spend most of their lives at sea, coming to islands and coasts only to breed and raise young.

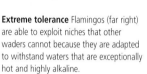

Complex environment Tropical rain forest (above) is among the most species-rich of habitats, not only for birds but also for all terrestrial animal groups. Because of its complexity, tropical rain forest offers a wide variety of niches and microhabitats.

ECOLOGICAL NICHES

An animal's ecological niche is the position it occupies in its habitat, particularly in relation to food, shelter, and enemies. Feeding behavior can determine a species' niche. For example, Eurasia's great spotted woodpecker (*Picoides major*) is a forest-dwelling, bark-gleaning and probing insect and seed eater.

The idea of a niche is particularly useful for appreciating how different species live together in any one habitat. In a forest, for example, birds that live side-by-side commonly occupy different foraging niches such as seed-eating, fruit-eating, insect-eating, nectar-eating, and carnivory. Combined diets are a feature of some species, such as the thrushes of North America and Europe which consume both fruit and invertebrates.

Different species that take the same type of food often forage at different levels within a habitat. These are known as microhabitats. Scientists studying the way that birds partition resources in similar communities around the world have observed that similar-looking but often unrelated birds fill similar niches on different continents.

SPECIES DIVERSITY

The most biologically diverse of all the world's habitats is tropical rain forest. A small area of New Guinean rain forest may be home to 200 different bird species. The best parts of the Amazon can be even richer, supporting a staggering 300 to 500 species. In comparison, an area of similar size in the richest temperate forests in North America, Europe, and southern Australia, may yield no more than 50 species.

One reason why rain forests nurture such biological diversity is their much greater array of resources—fruits, flowers, large insects—than other habitats. Birds such as parrots, fruit-doves, jacamars, motmots, and oropendolas exploit these niches. Partitioning of resources is common so that tropical rain forests abound with microhabitats.

Islands usually have fewer kinds of birds than continents. Generally, the smaller the island and the more distant it is from the mainland, the fewer species it supports. Larger islands have more habitats and therefore more ecological niches.

Particularly remote islands may have few species simply because not many birds have ever reached them. Recent research on fossil remains found on Pacific islands, however, has revealed that species diversity on these islands may have become impoverished following the arrival of humans.

Wide-ranging species Australia's striated pardalote (*Pardalotus striatus*) (top left) has a particularly wide distribution. It is found in open forests and woodlands right across the continent. This bird's preferred habitat is dominated by eucalypts because these trees provide its favorite food—sweet secretions, known as lerps, exuded as a hard protective cover by psyllid grubs. Its various disconnected populations across the country have been described as different races.

Restricted family The distribution of the large honeyeater family, Meliphagidae, is centered in Australasia. It is said that at least one species occupies every suitable habitat across Australia, from coastal heathland and mangrove forests to grasslands and arid woodlands. In all, the continent boasts more than 70 species, including the yellow-faced honeyeater (*Lichenostomus chrysops*) (center left).

Knocking on wood The pileated woodpecker (*Dryocopus pileatus*) (above) inhabits North America's coniferous and deciduous forests. Like other woodpeckers, its body is well adapted to life in the vertical pose, seen here, and it is rarely seen hopping around on the ground. Most of its diet comprises carpenter ants and beetle larvae, which it exposes by ripping bark from trees with its strong bill, then extracting them with its long tongue.

Marking territory The western meadowlark (*Sturnella neglecta*) (bottom left) lives in open grasslands through western North America. It migrates short distances to breeding grounds, the males arriving well before the females to claim a territory of about 7 acres (2.8 ha) by singing. These birds eat mainly insects—from grasshoppers to snails—but also take seeds and grains.

ADAPTIVE RADIATION

When a bird arrives on an island, or other geographically isolated areas, to find new and vacant niches, a form of evolution that is known as adaptive radiation can occur. Darwin's finches on the Pacific Ocean Galápagos Islands provide one of the best examples. No other small land birds were present when the first finches arrived from the neighboring South American mainland. But there were insects, fruits, and flowers as well as seeds available for eating. As different individuals began to exploit different resources they started evolving in diverse adaptive directions. Today, the islands support 13 different finch species, all descended from the original colonizing stock.

Water lover Egrets are common inhabitants of inland waterways and waterlogged land as well as coastal areas. They are long-legged, dagger-billed omnivores that are adapted to eat fishes, crustaceans, and herptiles, as well as algae.

URBAN HABITATS

In urban habitats humans and their activities are dominating forces, yet birds have been exploiting habitats created by humans for centuries. European storks, for example, have been building their nests on chimneys and rooftops across Europe for so long that it has now become common for homeowners to adorn their roofs with structures that will attract nesting storks.

Most birds, however, do not adapt well to living in a man-made environment. And as cities grow and their habitats spread and become increasingly less like natural environments, fewer and fewer avian species manage to cope. Most of those that do, however, do so exceptionally well and some have become so common that they are now considered pests. These include the European starling, house sparrow, house finch, and rock dove, all of which have become widespread throughout the world's cities and towns. Larger birds that do well in urban environments include crows and kites, which abound alongside highways and motorways where they dodge cars to pick at the flesh of road-killed animals.

Among all the world's habitats, cities boast some of the poorest levels of avian biodiversity. But away from highly congested city centers, where suburban sprawl accommodates increasing levels of vegetation, the environment becomes more conducive to birdlife. In Britain's graveyards, for example, robins and mistle thrush are common. And many suburban park ponds and lakes support waterfowl such as ducks, coots, gulls, and even swans.

High-rise nests The peregrine falcon (*Falco peregrinus*) (left) became endangered in the mid-20th century due to pesticide poisoning. Its numbers have recovered so well that this species is now sometimes seen nesting on the narrow ledges of city high-rise buildings.

Landfill diners Some birds do so well in disturbed environments they can reach plague proportions. Gulls (below) and ibises, for example, are found in huge numbers at many waste dumps where they squabble over discarded scraps. Many species pick up disease-causing Salmonella bacteria, which they can then carry into contact with humans.

BILLS, FEET, WINGS, AND TAILS

The body parts of birds are adapted to suit their feeding behavior and the niches they occupy. Bills display this best. The long, dagger-shaped bill of the herons, the huge pouches on the pelican's bill, the hooked bill of predatory birds, and the deep, heavy bills of seed-eating parrots are all adaptations to diet.

Feet also show adaptations to a bird's feeding behavior and environment. The talons of raptors, used for gripping large prey, and the webbed feet of ducks, specialized for swimming, are both examples. Ground-feeding birds usually have long legs and toes, whereas tree-creeping species usually have long toes and claws but short legs.

Wings and tails can be important too. Long wings provide economy during flight. However, short wings give maneuverability and are found in birds living in dense habitats or those that indulge in aggressive aerobatics. Long tails also enhance maneuverability and are present in most species of flycatchers.

Momentary pause A migratory bird, the snow goose (*Anser caerulescens*) (above) has particularly long wings. These enable it to commute between the salt marshes and coastal bays of North America's Pacific coast and breeding grounds in Arctic regions.

Water waders Birds that seek food by wading in shallow waters, such as the black-winged stilt (*Himantopus himantopus*) (below left), generally have long legs, long necks, and long bills. Stilts are found in shallow wetlands worldwide.

Versatile feeder The acrobatic flight of the blue tit (*Parus caeruleus*) (below right) is made possible by short wings and a relatively long tail. These traits help it catch flying insects. It switches to seeds during winter when invertebrates are scarce.

Sublime adaptations The osprey (*Pandion haliaetus*) (right) is a superbly adapted hunter. Its tough, hooked bill is designed for tearing flesh and long, spike-soled talons on its feet hold firmly onto slippery fishes. These birds also have keen eyesight.

BIRDS IN DANGER

Birdlife International estimates that at least 1,200 bird species—more than 10 percent—could face extinction by the century's end, unless their declining numbers can be arrested. Although all kinds of birds are at risk, the parrot family (Psittacidae) is facing particular pressures, with more than 80 species threatened. The habitat with the most at-risk species is tropical rain forest. Many of the threatened parrots, pigeons, pheasants, birds of prey, and hornbills dwell in tropical forests. Some families, such as the antbirds of Central and South America, the broadbills of Africa and Asia, and the birds of paradise of Indonesia, New Guinea, and Australia, are restricted almost entirely to forests. Species restricted to small islands are also at risk as they have nowhere else to go.

ALTERED ENVIRONMENTS

The greatest overall threat to birds today is undoubtedly habitat destruction. Almost all major habitat types have been affected by encroachment. Grasslands have been widely ploughed or subjected to intensive grazing by livestock. Wetlands have been drained and converted to farmland. And forests have been degraded, chopped down, and burnt. In some areas there has been almost complete deforestation with catastrophic effects. The Philippine island of Cebu, for example, has lost 39 bird species due to forest clearing.

Some species can survive partial clearance of their forest habitat, or may even make use of cutover secondary forest. There are many more, however, that are unable to adapt because they rely on pristine habitat for their continuing survival. One of the world's most powerful birds of prey, the harpy eagle (*Harpia harpyja*), is in dangerous decline in the tropical forests of Central and South America due to the clearance and fragmentation of its habitat.

Introduced species are another major threat. Interestingly, introduced herbivores, such as rabbits and goats, can be just as deadly to bird species as introduced predators because of the habitat changes they wreak by browsing on vegetation. Species introduced in the past can have ongoing effects. Despite efforts to eradicate them, exotic fishes have caused a decline in water plants in Madagascar which in turn threatens the survival of the Madagascan grebe (*Tachybaptus pelzelnii*).

Island threat Introduced predators, such as domestic cats (right), have been a major cause of extinction of island birds. Many such birds evolved without any predator pressure and have been unable to adapt to alien species that steal eggs and nestlings or hunt adults. Birds that have lost the ability to fly are particularly susceptible to new predators.

Forest fires After large trees are felled in the Amazon, the remaining undergrowth is often burned (above) to accelerate clearing for agriculture or urban sprawl. Some 80,000 square miles (500,000 sq. km) of tropical Amazonian rain forest has been cleared since the late 1970s.

Deadly pollution Marine pollution can have huge impacts on seabirds. Diving birds are especially vulnerable to contamination from oil spills (right). The oil clogs and interferes with the buoyancy and insulation provided by feathers. For every oiled seabird that survives long enough to wash ashore, many more die at sea.

Disappearing species New Zealand's flightless and nocturnal kakapo (*Strigops habroptilus*) (left) is the world's rarest parrot. Numbers began declining following the arrival of Polynesian people several thousand years ago. From the mid-1800s Europeans exacerbated the decline by hunting the species for its tasty flesh, introducing predators, and destroying habitat. The species is now confined to a couple of islands off New Zealand.

VARIED IMPACTS

Birds have also suffered due to hunting, particularly with the development of efficient weapons. One bird hunted to extinction was North America's passenger pigeon, a species once so common that its flocks blackened the sky. Hunting competitions were organized in which more than 30,000 dead birds were needed to claim the prize. Its demise took less than a century.

The illegal international trade in caged birds is equally devastating. Brazil's Spix's macaw, for example, was illegally trapped down to the last bird in the wild. Captive breeding efforts are attempting to rebuild the species' numbers so it can be released back into its natural habitat.

Pollution can also have a major impact on bird numbers. Pesticides, particularly chlorinated hydrocarbons such as DDT, once led to huge declines in raptors across Europe and North America.

RESTRICTED RANGES

Some birds have earned threatened conservation status because they are confined to extremely small areas, even when their numbers are healthy. The Ascension frigatebird, for example, is a seabird that now breeds only on Boatswainbird Islet. This tiny piece of land, just 7 acres (3 ha) in area, is located off the coast of the remote South Atlantic island of Ascension. The frigatebird's numbers remain high but the fact that the entire population of this species is confined to such a small area places it at risk of extinction from, for example, a natural disaster or the introduction of a predator. It could be easily and quickly threatened should predators such as cats get a foothold on the island.

Many continental species also have restricted distributions, confined to single mountaintops or tiny patches of forest. The black-breasted puffleg, which is known only from two volcanoes in north-central Ecuador, is one such species.

Threatened particularly by habitat destruction because of the close proximity of the volcanoes to the Ecuadorian capital, Quito, it is vital that birds like these are given adequate protection before it is too late.

Endangered rarity The imperial parrot (*Amazona imperialis*) (below) is found only in Dominica's mountain forest. No more than 60 birds may survive in the wild due to illegal hunting and the destruction of parts of the species' habitat by loggers.

Dietary impact Grazing deer during the 1940s and 1950s affected the nutrition of New Zealand's takahe (*Porphyrio hochstetteri*) (below), causing chick losses.

MYSTERY BIRDS

Some bird species are considered threatened or endangered because they are almost unknown. They have been seen so few times they are assumed to be extremely rare naturally and therefore vulnerable to extinction.

One recent discovery, for example, was a new shrike species from Somalia. The Bulo Burti bush shrike (*Laniarius liberatus*) has been scientifically described only on the basis of DNA analysis of blood and feathers from a single individual, captured in disturbed bushland in 1989. It is thought the species escaped detection for so long, and remains elusive, because of the usually impenetrable nature of its habitat.

Another mystery bird is the Red Sea swallow, (*Petrochelidon perdita*). It is known from only one specimen that was found dead at a lighthouse off Port Sudan in 1984.

The Fiji petrel (*Pseudobulweria macgillivrayi*) is known from only three specimens from the Fijian island of Gau, where it is believed the species may breed. Occasional reports of sightings filter through from time to time.

Fragile existence The Laysan duck (*Anas laysanensis*) (above), one of the world's rarest ducks, once occurred throughout the Hawaiian archipelago but is now confined to Laysan Island, which is managed as a wildlife refuge. The small surviving population was almost wiped out in the early 1990s by drought.

Disappearing migrants Numbers of the critically endangered slender-billed curlew (*Numenius tenuirostris*), a migratory Northern Hemisphere species, decline annually. There are old records of flocks of about 100 birds. Now, only two or three are ever seen together.

Reduced distribution The Ascension frigatebird (*Fregata aquila*) (right) once bred on Ascension Island. Egg-collecting and the introduction of alien mammals, particularly cats, have now restricted it to the cat- and people-free Boatswainbird Islet.

BACK FROM THE BRINK

Even when a species drops perilously low in numbers, it can sometimes still be rescued from the brink of extinction. The whooping crane, for example, has been at the center of a remarkable US-Canadian conservation effort that has seen the total population rise from an all-time low of just 15 wild birds in 1944 to over 340 birds in wild and captive flocks today. The crane's recovery required a complicated strategy that involved much ferrying of eggs between locations in a massive attempt to maximize the crane's reproductive rate—but the enormous effort and expense paid off.

Unfortunately, the majority of threatened birds occur in habitats within the borders of developing nations where governments are hard pressed to meet the needs of the human population, let alone find available funds for conservation programs. So it is therefore unlikely that many species can be saved once they decline to a critical state. Instead, it is vital that appropriately preventive conservation action is taken at a much earlier stage.

Sometimes it can be an unexpected but welcome surprise when birds come back from the brink. Some species have been rediscovered after being officially classified as extinct. In 2005, naturalists around the world celebrated the first confirmed sighting since the 1960s of the ivory-billed woodpecker, on the US mainland in the state of Arkansas. The species had been thought to be extinct for decades.

Losing numbers The jackass penguin (*Spheniscus demersus*) (top right) population was about 1.2 million in the 1930s. Today, it has fallen by a massive 90 percent to 120,000 and the species has been registered on the IUCN's Red List as vulnerable. These birds occur only off southern Africa. Egg harvesting by humans, commercial overfishing of their food supply, and oil pollution have all contributed to the decline.

Encouraging response The Lord Howe rail (*Gallirallus sylvestris*) (right) occurs only on a tiny island in the Tasman Sea, east of the Australian mainland. Introduced predators reduced the population to a critical 20 birds in the late 1970s and urgent captive breeding and reintroduction programs were instituted. Today, the wild population numbers between 200 and 300 birds.

FUTURE CONSERVATION

Those species of birds that are at risk of extinction, as well as those that are potentially threatened or declining, need to be rescued. Birds are critically important components of most ecosystems and are also valuable to humans for a variety of reasons. They control invertebrate pests for farmers, for example. And the physical beauty of many species provides much pleasure to people, borne out by the many thousands around the globe who bird-watch every day.

Different species have different conservation needs, but a general combination of habitat preservation, hunting bans, trade control, pollution prevention, and the elimination of introduced predatory species will help ensure the survival of many.

While conservation action to save single species can be successful for that species, conservation in the future will need to focus on key sites of special bird diversity, where several threatened species occur together. It will be these "hot spots"—or Important Bird Areas (IBAs) in Birdlife International jargon—that will reap the biggest returns for the conservation effort invested.

Conservation success Shrinking breeding and wintering grounds, separated by a hazardous 1,850-mile (3,000-km) migration route fraught with hunters and overhead powerlines, brought the whooping crane (*Grus americana*) (above) close to extinction. Conservation efforts have now saved the species.

Amazing rescue Just a single breeding pair, within a total population numbering five, was all that remained of the New Zealand black robin (*Petroica traversi*) (left) in 1980. Desperate efforts have rebuilt its stocks to more than 200.

KINDS OF BIRDS

RATITES AND TINAMOUS

CLASS	Aves
ORDERS	3
FAMILIES	5
GENERA	15
SPECIES	60

Ratites are huge, flightless birds with flat breastbones that lack the prominent, keel-like sternums of flying birds. Like other flightless birds, they are believed to have lost the ability to fly because they either lacked predators or could evade them by their size and fast legs. Included among them are three groups of large extinct birds: the New Zealand moas, the elephant bird of Madagascar, and the giant dromornithid runners of Australia. The surviving ratites are thought to have evolved from diverse ancestors, developing a similar appearance adaptively. Tinamous are a related group of flying birds with keeled sternums that share some unusual anatomical characteristics—such as a distinctive palate and jaw structure—with ratites.

Southern exposure Today, ratites and tinamous are found only on southern Gondwanan continents. Their various species are adapted to grasslands, jungles, woodlands, or high mountain ranges. The emu of Australia is the most versatile, roaming in diverse habitats.

GIANTS AND RUNNERS

Adult ratites—among them the largest of all birds, the ostrich, which may exceed 9 feet (2.8 m) in height—resemble overgrown chicks, with underdeveloped, stubby wings and soft flight feathers or quills.

Powerful runners, ratites have as few as two or three toes per foot, rather than the standard four toes of other birds. Ostriches can run faster than a racehorse and sometimes defend themselves by kicking. South American rheas occasionally raise one of their sail-like wings while running. Rheas do not have tails.

ANCIENT ORDER

Allied to rheas, the partridge-sized tinamous are an ancient order of plump, round-winged, stout-legged birds. They fly clumsily and run strongly, if only for short distances. When threatened, tinamous steal away or freeze, using their dun plumage for camouflage. Their 47 species are found in Central and South America, where they roost on the gound or in trees and feed mainly on seeds and fruit supplemented by animal matter. Tinamous forage alone but breed polygamously: several hens will often lay in a nest—a scrape on the ground—brooded by one cock.

Great tinamou
Tinamus major

Heavy legs built for running

Courting A reversal of the usual sex roles is apparent among tinamous (above), with the females taking the more aggressive lead role in courtship. Their eggs are brilliantly glossed yellow, green, and blue.

Fathers lead Like most other ratites and tinamous, the male southern cassowary (above, right) is responsible for incubating and raising the young. Male emus live off their fat reserves for the entire 8-week incubation period, not taking a break to eat, drink, or even defecate during that time.

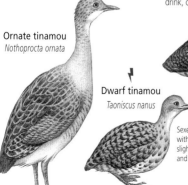

Ornate tinamou
Nothoprocta ornata

Dwarf tinamou
Taoniscus nanus

Sexes alike, with females slightly larger and brighter

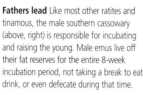

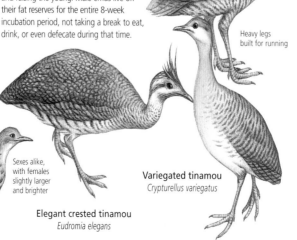

Variegated tinamou
Crypturellus variegatus

Elegant crested tinamou
Eudromia elegans

PADDING ALONG

Rheas are large, heavy birds that can reach 5 feet (1.5 m) in height. Their powerful legs bear a lot of weight when they run, but extra flesh on the soles of their toes helps absorb some of the impact. The bird's three forward-facing toes are also well adapted to running.

Contrastingly colored tail is raised and fanned in display

♂ ♀

Ostrich
Struthio camelus

Broad, flat bill for feeding on seeds and fruit

The only ratites in Africa, ostriches have only two toes

Lesser rhea
Pterocnemia pennata

Rheas, like tinamous, live only in South America

Kiwis, found only in New Zealand, have sensory nostrils at the tip of the bill

Long neck for reaching food

Greater rhea
Rhea americana

Little spotted kiwi
Apteryx owenii

Tokoeka
Apteryx australis

Northern cassowary
Casuarius unappendiculatus

Dry, spongy head casque

Emu
Dromaius novaehollandiae

Emu chicks

Emu egg

Cassowaries pad secretively over rain forest floors, searching for fallen fruit. Found in New Guinea and northeast Australia, they are keystone species for dispersing the seeds of trees

Powerful, short legs are well adapted for running. The inner toe has a spurred claw

Emus, like cassowaries, have twinned hairy feathers, vestigial wings, and three toes

Southern cassowary
Casuarius casuarius

FACT FILE

Ostrich This large bird once ranged to the Middle East and Asia, but is now limited mainly to national parks in eastern and southern Africa. Males keep a temporary harem when breeding and scrape nests on the ground.

- Up to 9½ ft (2.9 m)
- 5–11 (major hen)
- Sexes differ
- Nomad
- Locally common

C., E. & S. Africa

Greater rhea The largest species of rhea, the greater rhea has a wide, flat beak, well adapted for grazing on the plains where it roams. It is an agile runner, able to twist and turn abruptly to elude pursuers. Males fight for territory and a breeding harem.

- Up to 5¼ ft (1.6 m)
- 13–30
- Sexes alike
- Sedentary
- Near threatened

E., S.E. & C.W. South America

Tokoeka Like other kiwis, the tokoeka is nocturnal, feeding on invertebrates at night and sleeping in burrows by day. Unlike other ratites, it is monogamous and mates for life.

- Up to 26 in (66 cm)
- 1–2
- Sexes alike
- Sedentary
- Vulnerable

South & Stewart Is, New Zealand

Emu To breed, emus mate temporarily, the female then leaves the male to brood the dark olive eggs on bare ground and rear the young. This species roams open plains on its long "legs" in search of fruits, seeds, and shoots.

- Up to 6½ ft (2 m)
- 7–11
- Sexes alike
- Nomad
- Locally common

Australia, Tasmania (extinct)

CONSERVATION WATCH

Ratites IUCN lists two of the three species of cassowary as vulnerable, and all four species of kiwis as well. The Emu is common on mainland Australia; but two pygmy species that were alive on islands off southeastern Australia at the time of European settlement are now extinct. Six species and two subspecies of tinamous are also under threat.

GAMEBIRDS

CLASS	Aves
ORDERS	1
FAMILIES	5
GENERA	80
SPECIES	290

These familiar birds include chickens (domesticated forms of the southeast Asian red jungle fowl) and turkeys. Humans also hunt and eat pheasants, partridges, grouse, and quail. Gamebirds may vary in size, but all have stocky frames, relatively small heads with stout pointed bills for pecking food, and short, broad wings. They feed on the ground on mostly vegetable matter and typically flush in low and fast whirring flight. Gamebirds are favorite prey of many wild predators. To elude them, this group relies on camouflage from their patterned plumage, or else they fly or scurry away quickly. They are commonly polygamous and have large clutches of up to 20 plain, creamy, or black-spotted eggs, but species' populations tend to fluctuate greatly. Most are grain-feeders, with a crop for storing food and a muscular stomach to grind it.

Far and wide Gamebirds live in a variety of climatic zones and, depending on the species, prefer either forests, scrub, open habitats, or grasslands. Some groups are much more widespread than others: for example, quails and partridges are found on several continents across the world, whereas turkeys occur only in North America and guineafowl in Africa.

FACT FILE

Brush turkey This bird incubates its eggs by laying them in a mound of heat-generating decaying matter, adding or removing material to keep the mound's temperature constant.

- ▲ Up to 30 in (76 cm)
- ● 15–27
- ✔ Sexes alike
- ⊘ Sedentary
- ✦ Locally common

🏛 ☀

E. Australia

Great curassow This slender, forest-dwelling bird spends much of its time on the ground, foraging for fallen fruit and seeds that it picks up with its sturdy bill. It roosts and seeks refuge in trees, and also builds nests of plant matter among the branches.

- ▲ Up to 36 in (92 cm)
- ● 2
- ✔ Sexes differ
- ⊘ Sedentary
- ✦ Locally common

🏛 ☀ 🌿

E. Mexico to far N.W. South America; Cozumel I.

White-crested guan This handsome, secretive bird is confined to a fairly small area south of the Amazon River. It has a call that carries far through the forest due to a looped windpipe that is adapted for amplifying sound.

- ▲ Up to 32 in (81 cm)
- ● 3–4
- ✔ Sexes alike
- ⊘ Sedentary
- ✦ Near threatened

🏛

N.E. Amazonian Brazil

Check me out Many gamebirds stage elaborate courtship displays. Sage grouse males (*Centrocercus urophasianus*) (above) gather at strutting grounds known as leks. After each male performs, the fortunate dominant male mates with dozens of females.

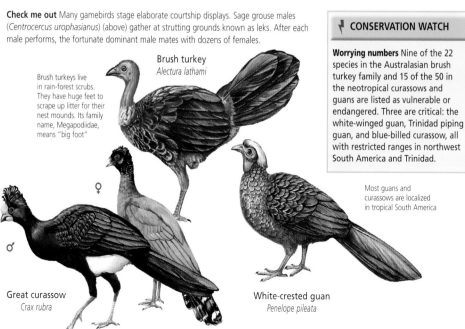

Brush turkeys live in rain-forest scrubs. They have huge feet to scrape up litter for their nest mounds. Its family name, Megapodiidae, means "big foot"

Brush turkey
Alectura lathami

♀

♂

Great curassows live in heavy rain forests at low altitudes, and feed in foliage and on the forest floor singly, in pairs, or in small groups

Great curassow
Crax rubra

White-crested guan
Penelope pileata

✦ CONSERVATION WATCH

Worrying numbers Nine of the 22 species in the Australasian brush turkey family and 15 of the 50 in the neotropical curassows and guans are listed as vulnerable or endangered. Three are critical: the white-winged guan, Trinidad piping guan, and blue-billed curassow, all with restricted ranges in northwest South America and Trinidad.

Most guans and curassows are localized in tropical South America

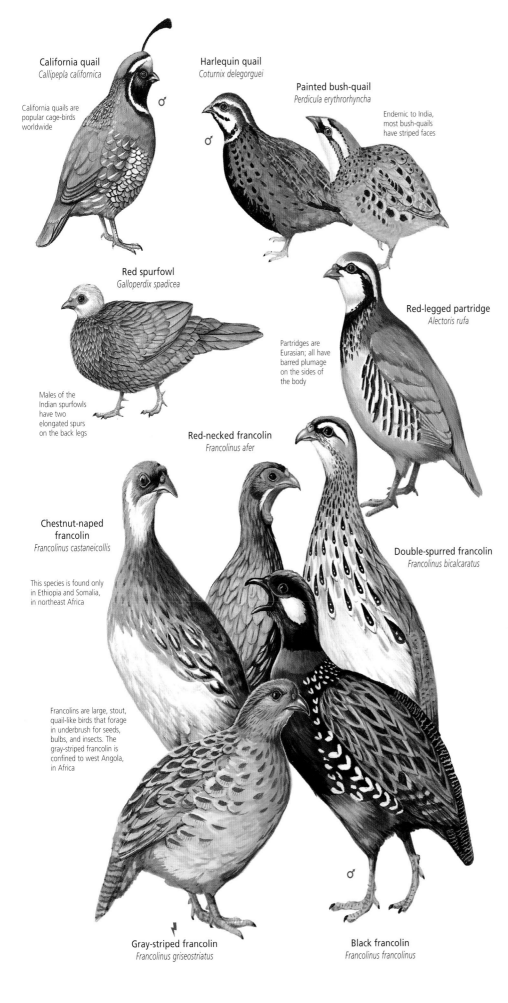

California quail
Callipepla californica

California quails are popular cage-birds worldwide

Harlequin quail
Coturnix delegorguei

Painted bush-quail
Perdicula erythrorhyncha

Endemic to India, most bush-quails have striped faces

Red spurfowl
Galloperdix spadicea

Males of the Indian spurfowls have two elongated spurs on the back legs

Partridges are Eurasian; all have barred plumage on the sides of the body

Red-legged partridge
Alectoris rufa

Chestnut-naped francolin
Francolinus castaneicollis

This species is found only in Ethiopia and Somalia, in northeast Africa

Red-necked francolin
Francolinus afer

Double-spurred francolin
Francolinus bicalcaratus

Francolins are large, stout, quail-like birds that forage in underbrush for seeds, bulbs, and insects. The gray-striped francolin is confined to west Angola, in Africa

Gray-striped francolin
Francolinus griseostriatus

Black francolin
Francolinus francolinus

FACT FILE

California quail Both sexes of this species have a head plume, as do many New World quails, and lack "leg" spurs. Although normally herbivorous, they do eat invertebrates. Young hatch with well-developed flight feathers and leave the nest at once to follow their mother.

⊥ Up to 11 in (28 cm)
● 13–17
⫽ Sexes differ
⊘ Sedentary
↟ Common

W. USA, N.W. Mexico, S.W. Canada

Red-legged partridge The female can lay two clutches in two different nests, leaving one clutch for the male to incubate. This species has been introduced to Britain as a gamebird.

⊥ Up to 15 in (38 cm)
● 11–13
⫽ Sexes alike
⊘ Sedentary
↟ Locally common

Iberia & France to N. Italy

Double-spurred francolin Often seen in small parties, this bird lives along the edges of wooded areas in coastal lowlands. It is usually shy but males call territorially from a mound or post.

⊥ Up to 13 in (33 cm)
● 5–7
⫽ Sexes alike
⊘ Sedentary
↟ Locally common

W. Morocco & S. Senegal to S. Chad & Cameroon

Black francolin The six subspecies of this bird differ slightly in size and plumage hue; these differences are most apparent in females. Black francolins have been introduced in many countries.

⊥ Up to 14 in (36 cm)
● 6–12
⫽ Sexes differ
⊘ Sedentary
↟ Locally common

Middle East & trans-Caucasia to N. India

⚡ CONSERVATION WATCH

Under threat Although gamebirds are widely hunted and trapped for trade, they can usually withstand such pressure because they rear large broods. When habitat destruction is added to hunting, however, serious declines follow. Pheasants have been the most affected: of the 50 species worldwide, 23 (almost half) are listed as threatened.

PEACOCK DISPLAY

Brilliance of plumage and ease of domestication have brought the peacock, or male peafowl, into the great parks and gardens of the world. The Indian peafowl (*Pavo cristatus*) is the most common; its males have a rich, glossy blue head and neck. The pride of a peacock's plumage is his great, eye-patterned tail-train. These feathers, not true tail feathers, actually arise from the lower rump. In display they are first thrown vertically up, then shimmered out sideways in a huge fan, as cock faces hen.

Flashy feathers The peacock's iridescent colors are produced by layers of clear structural keratin over dull, blackish pigment in feather barbules. The keratin reflects colors of the rainbow not absorbed by the underlying pigment to create the patterns and tones seen in peacock plumage.

White mutation White peacocks are albino mutants in which the genetic mechanism that creates pigments in the feather barbules has been shut off. Impinging light is then reflected as "white" light. Only males have the spectacular tail fan for which peacocks are famous; the females are drab.

SPURRED ON

In the red junglefowl (and many of its relatives), the male bird has sharp, one-inch spurs on the back of its legs, just above its hind toe. These are used as weapons when fighting other males for territory. The sport of cockfighting, using domesticated birds, has been practiced for millennia. It is illegal in most countries but still takes place in others. The spurs themselves do not kill, but when metal blades are attached to the legs as well, fighting can be lethal.

Blue eared pheasant
Crossoptilon auritum

Blue and white eared pheasants belong to a small group of round-tailed pheasants with projecting white ear tufts. They live only in China

White eared pheasant
Crossoptilon crossoptilon

The only member of its group with whitish plumage

♀ Female red junglefowl carry out all the brooding of eggs and chicks

♂

Red junglefowl
Gallus gallus

Males crow to advertise their territory

Koklass pheasant
Pucrasia macrolopha

♂

♀

Rock ptarmigan
Lagopus muta

Eurasian black grouse
Lyrurus tetrix

Winter plumage for camouflage

Summer breeding plumage

Ocellated turkey
Meleagris ocellata

Replaces the North American wild turkey in the American isthmus

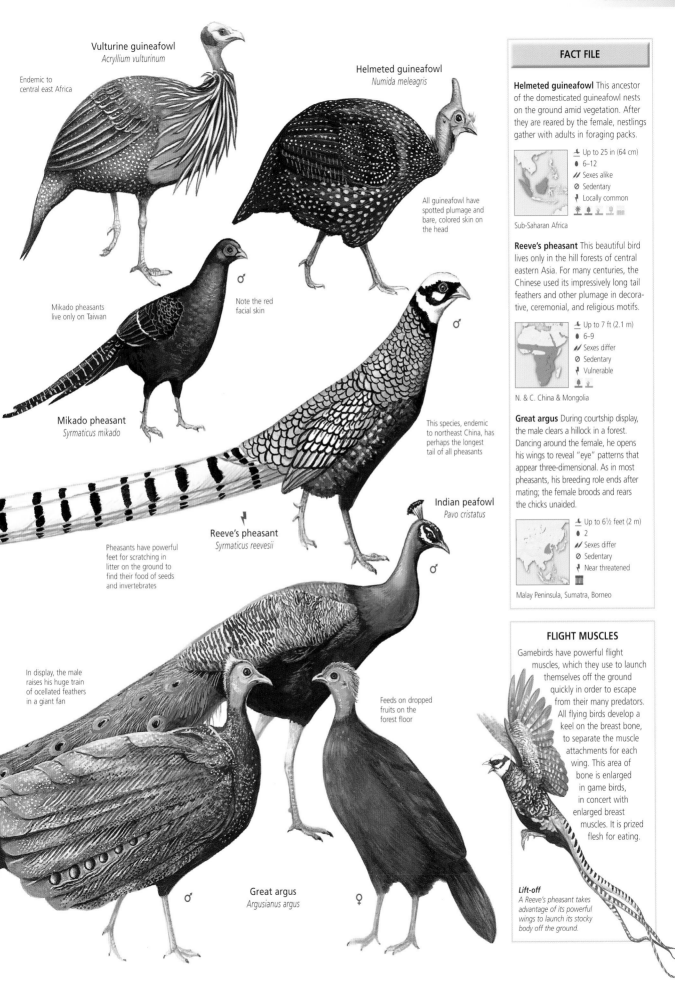

Vulturine guineafowl
Acryllium vulturinum

Endemic to central east Africa

Helmeted guineafowl
Numida meleagris

All guineafowl have spotted plumage and bare, colored skin on the head

Mikado pheasants live only on Taiwan

Note the red facial skin

♂

Mikado pheasant
Syrmaticus mikado

♂

This species, endemic to northeast China, has perhaps the longest tail of all pheasants

Reeve's pheasant
Syrmaticus reevesii

Pheasants have powerful feet for scratching in litter on the ground to find their food of seeds and invertebrates

Indian peafowl
Pavo cristatus

♂

In display, the male raises his huge train of ocellated feathers in a giant fan

Feeds on dropped fruits on the forest floor

♂

Great argus
Argusianus argus

♀

FACT FILE

Helmeted guineafowl This ancestor of the domesticated guineafowl nests on the ground amid vegetation. After they are reared by the female, nestlings gather with adults in foraging packs.

- ⬆ Up to 25 in (64 cm)
- ● 6–12
- ∥ Sexes alike
- ⊘ Sedentary
- ⸙ Locally common

Sub-Saharan Africa

Reeve's pheasant This beautiful bird lives only in the hill forests of central eastern Asia. For many centuries, the Chinese used its impressively long tail feathers and other plumage in decorative, ceremonial, and religious motifs.

- ⬆ Up to 7 ft (2.1 m)
- ● 6–9
- ∥ Sexes differ
- ⊘ Sedentary
- ⸙ Vulnerable

N. & C. China & Mongolia

Great argus During courtship display, the male clears a hillock in a forest. Dancing around the female, he opens his wings to reveal "eye" patterns that appear three-dimensional. As in most pheasants, his breeding role ends after mating; the female broods and rears the chicks unaided.

- ⬆ Up to 6½ feet (2 m)
- ● 2
- ∥ Sexes differ
- ⊘ Sedentary
- ⸙ Near threatened

Malay Peninsula, Sumatra, Borneo

FLIGHT MUSCLES

Gamebirds have powerful flight muscles, which they use to launch themselves off the ground quickly in order to escape from their many predators. All flying birds develop a keel on the breast bone, to separate the muscle attachments for each wing. This area of bone is enlarged in game birds, in concert with enlarged breast muscles. It is prized flesh for eating.

Lift-off
A Reeve's pheasant takes advantage of its powerful wings to launch its stocky body off the ground.

WATERFOWL

CLASS Aves
ORDERS 1
FAMILIES 3
GENERA 52
SPECIES 162

Among the first birds to be domesticated, ducks and geese were raised for food more than 4,500 years ago. Swans have also been kept in captivity, because of their beauty and grace. Several species are flightless, but the rest are powerful fliers; many northern species migrate in flocks over great distances. In the air, they flap their wings continuously and can attain top speeds of 70 miles per hour (125 km/h). Some have been observed flying at an altitude of 28,000 feet (8,500 m), near the summit of Mount Everest. Some doze on water; others come ashore to rest. Their calls range from quacks to barks, hisses, whistles and even trumpeting sounds.

Citizens of the world Waterfowl may predominate in the Northern Hemisphere (with the largest number of species in North America), but they are found worldwide, except in Antarctica. They occur in almost every type of wetland, from city ponds to Arctic sea inlets. Some species spend a great deal of time at sea.

AT HOME ON THE WATER

All species are remarkably similar in form, with short legs, webbed feet, relatively long necks, and flattened, broad bills. Most are excellent swimmers, although several species have adapted to life on land and have less webbing on their feet. The upper bill has scale-like lamellae along its edges which many species use to sift food by pumping water through them as they dabble.

To protect them from the cold water, waterfowl rely on their dense, waterproof feathers and a thick coat of insulating down. This down is also used to line their nests which may be scrapes on the ground, platforms of stems in swamps, or tree hollows.

Waterfowl have been domesticated worldwide, their breeds descended from mallards, muscovies, graylags, and swan geese. Many consume grass, seeds, grain, and other vegetation in water or on land, but some species eat aquatic insects, mollusks, and crustaceans.

The South American screamers bear little superficial resemblance to other waterfowl, but they share basic anatomical traits with ducks and so are grouped here.

Primed for take-off The largest and most majestic of waterfowl, swans (above) are almost 5 feet (1.5 m) tall. They must run on water and flap their wings vigorously to build up enough speed to launch their heavy bodies into the air.

Follow the leader Young common shelducks swim behind their mother (above, top). Ducklings can feed themselves, but they imprint on a parent, following the adult in order to learn various behaviors. The image of their mother also later influences what they look to when seeking a mate.

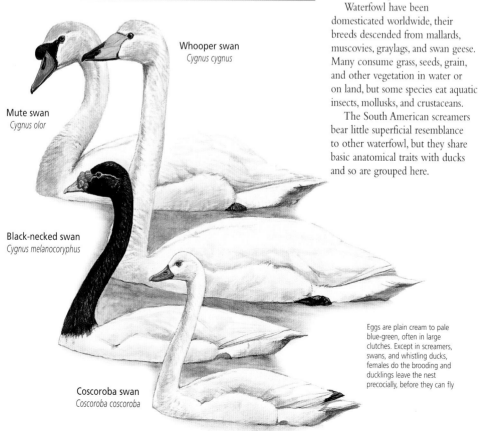

Whooper swan
Cygnus cygnus

Mute swan
Cygnus olor

Black-necked swan
Cygnus melanocoryphus

Coscoroba swan
Coscoroba coscoroba

Eggs are plain cream to pale blue-green, often in large clutches. Except in screamers, swans, and whistling ducks, females do the brooding and ducklings leave the nest precocially, before they can fly

Southern screamer
Chauna torquata

The three species of screamers all live in tropical and subtropical South America. They feed on succulent vegetation on stream sides

Vulturine bill is adapted for grasping and pulling

Magpie-goose
Anseranas semipalmata

Magpie-geese are found only in the swamps of northern Australia and New Guinea. They breed in huge colonies on floating vegetation

Although its feet are only part-webbed, this bird is a good swimmer

Snow geese are migratory, breeding in the north American tundra and wintering on the east and west coasts of the United States

Snow goose
Anser caerulescens

White-faced whistling-duck
Dendrocygna viduata

This species has an unusual distribution, with widespread populations in both Africa and South America. It forms huge flocks when not breeding

Red-breasted goose
Branta ruficollis

Canada goose
Branta canadensis

Bean goose
Anser fabalis

The only goose with a black head and neck ornamented with a white bib

Bean geese breed in the high arctic zone of Eurasia and fly south to winter in China and the Mediterranean

---

FACT FILE

Southern screamer This bird typically lives in groups along watercourses and in marshlands. It is a fine swimmer, despite the lack of webbing on its feet. Pairs nest alone, building a platform of plant matter in reedy swamps. Eggs are white and nestlings tawny.

➤ Up to 37 in (95 cm)
● 3–5
✂ Sexes alike
⊘ Sedentary
♩ Locally common

C. & E. South America

Magpie goose The sole member of its family, this "goose" has a semi-hooked bill for digging up food, mostly the corms of sedges. Breeding depends on monsoonal rains and fails if they do not come. One male and two females make up the breeding unit; all share incubation. Nests are bowls of reeds.

➤ Up to 35 in (89 cm)
● 5–12
✂ Sexes alike
∼ Nomad
♩ Locally common

Coastal N. Australia, S. New Guinea

White-faced whistling-duck Named for its squeaky whistles when it flushes en masse, this is the most brightly colored of whistling ducks. It feeds mainly at night, diving or dabbling in freshwater wetlands for weeds, seeds, and invertebrates, and nests in marshy ground, using minimal down.

➤ Up to 19 in (48 m)
● 4–13
✂ Sexes alike
∼ Partial nomad
♩ Common

N. & E. South America, C. & S. Africa, Madagascar

Canada goose There are about a dozen races of Canada goose, varying in size, color, and distribution. Native to North America, where it is a common sight grazing in city parks, this goose has been introduced worldwide.

➤ Up to 3¾ ft (1.15 m)
● 4–7 usually
✂ Sexes alike
↻ Migrant
♩ Common

North America, N. Europe, N.E. Asia

STRENGTH IN NUMBERS

Waterfowl commonly gather in flocks, both small and large. Whooper swans (right) congregate to feed at night, dabbling and pulling water weed along the edge of Lake Kuccharo on Hokkaido, Japan. Yet flocking confers more advantages than just the exploitation of flushes of food. It gives protection to the individual, its flight in V-formation breaks wind resistance on long migrations, and, for the smaller ducks, it facilitates random pairing each breeding season. Flocks also take advantage of often temporary water havens for molting, where all members replace their plumage safely at the same time over a period of several weeks. Like grebes, waterfowl become almost flightless then. For general protection, they commonly move and feed in the dark hours, particularly on exposed shallows from which there is no quick escape.

Paragons of fidelity Swans mate for life, which can span up to 35 years. Almost all waterfowl copulate in water and this, in swans, is important for maintaining the pair bond as well, judged by the high frequency of copulation. Unlike most other birds, males have a copulatory organ resembling a penis. In contrast to the glowing white of adults, young swans (cygnets) are clothed in dull gray down which is waterproof.

Eurasian giant The whooper swan (right) is one of the largest swans at up to 5 feet (1.6 m) tall. It breeds in lakes and pools across boreal Eurasia, from Scandinavia to Kamchatka, and before the winter freeze each year, it migrates to the coasts of Europe, eastern China, Korea, and Japan.

Freckled duck Without close relatives, this Australian duck feeds by dabbling and sieving microplankton from the shallow muddy waters of freshly flooded inland swamps. It nests in tussocks in inland swamps at times of flooding, where flood mitigation is depressing breeding.

- Up to 22 in (55 cm)
- 5–10
- Sexes alike
- Nomad
- Rare

Inland S. Australia

Egyptian goose The most widespread duck in Africa, the Egyptian goose is really related to shelducks. It inhabits a diversity of wetlands and feeds mainly by grazing on vegetable matter on the verges, sometimes invading crops and doing much damage. To breed, pairs detach from local flocks to nest on the ground among low vegetation or in hollow trees. Chicks take over two months to fly.

- Up to 29 in (74 cm)
- 5–12
- Sexes alike
- Sedentary
- Common

C. & S. Africa

Common shelduck This bright, pugnacious bird looks heavy in flight and beats its wings slowly. It often breeds in old rabbit burrows or in gaps under old buildings. The male shelduck whistles and the female growls.

- Up to 25 in (64 cm)
- 8–10
- Sexes differ
- Migrant
- Common

W. Europe, C. Asia, N.W. Africa

V-FORMATION

Canada geese are among the species of geese that migrate flying in wedge formation. The leader breaks the air and causes a streamlining effect, stirring up updrafts that reduce air resistance for the birds flying behind. Each bird takes its turn flying in the lead so that they all may conserve energy equally. They fly both day and night to reach summer or winter quarters. To build energy for such prolonged flights, the geese eat copiously and lay down much body fat in late summer and early fall.

Freckled duck
Stictonetta naevosa

The base of the bill in male freckled ducks becomes bright scarlet during breeding

♂

Cape Barren goose
Cereopsis novaehollandiae

Often called pig-goose because of its grunting call. It is endemic to southern Australia

Orinoco goose
Neochen jubata

Lives along the forested sides of rivers in tropical South America

Blue-winged goose
Cyanochen cyanoptera

Upland goose
Chloephaga picta

Egyptian goose
Alopochen aegyptiaca

Endemic to southern South America

Confined to the highlands of Ethiopia and Eritrea

Common shelduck
Tadorna tadorna

Recent sightings of this east Asian duck have been so sporadic and anecdotal that it is feared extinct

Crested shelduck
Tadorna cristata

Male has an orange knob above the base of the bill; the female's knob is smaller and white

♂

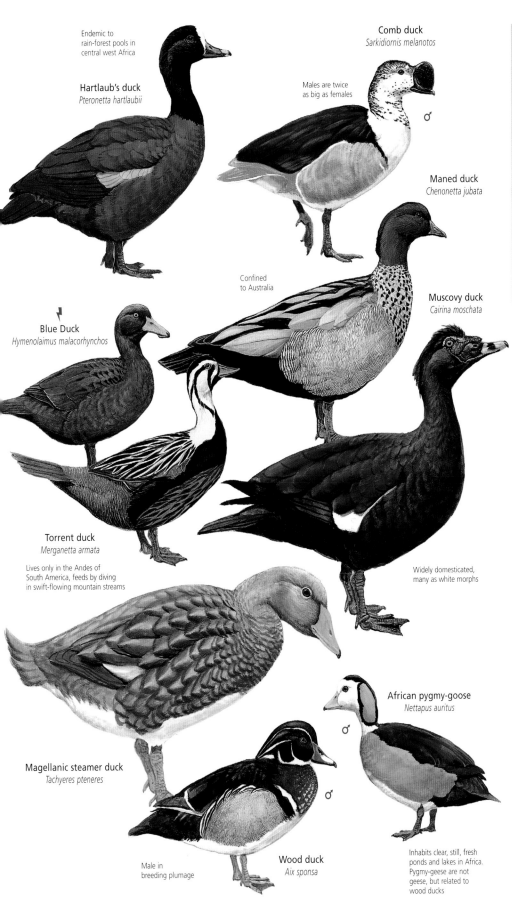

Endemic to
rain-forest pools in
central west Africa

Hartlaub's duck
Pteronetta hartlaubii

Comb duck
Sarkidiornis melanotos

Males are twice
as big as females

♂

Maned duck
Chenonetta jubata

Confined
to Australia

Blue Duck
Hymenolaimus malacorhynchos

Muscovy duck
Cairina moschata

Torrent duck
Merganetta armata

Lives only in the Andes of
South America, feeds by diving
in swift-flowing mountain streams

Widely domesticated,
many as white morphs

Magellanic steamer duck
Tachyeres pteneres

African pygmy-goose
Nettapus auritus

♂

♂

Male in
breeding plumage

Wood duck
Aix sponsa

Inhabits clear, still, fresh
ponds and lakes in Africa.
Pygmy-geese are not
geese, but related to
wood ducks

FACT FILE

Comb duck This bird is also known as the knob-billed duck, due to a prominent fatty comb atop the drake's bill which enlarges considerably prior to breeding. A vegetarian, it feeds by grazing and dabbling.

- Up to 30 in (76 cm) (male)
- 6–20
- Sexes differ
- Mainly sedentary
- Locally common

Sub-Saharan Africa, S. Asia, N. & E. South America

Magellanic steamer duck Goose-like birds, marine steamer ducks are partially flightless. The magellanic is one of four species, and it dives for its food—mostly mollusks and crustaceans—in kelp beds off rocky coasts, mostly at high tide. It breeds in dispersed pairs that conceal their nests in close ground vegetation.

- Up to 33 in (85 cm)
- 5–8
- Sexes alike
- Sedentary
- Locally common

Coastal S.W. South America

Wood duck This handsome duck nests in tree cavities. After nesting, the male changes into drab, female-like plumage, but retains a distinctive red bill. Wood ducks make a nasal squealing sound and feed on weed by dabbling and up-ending in freshwater.

- Up to 20 in (51 cm)
- 9–15
- Sexes differ
- Partial migrant
- Locally common

Temperate North America & W. Cuba

CONSERVATION WATCH

Ducks endangered Twenty six of the 162 species of waterfowl are threatened, 9 of them endangered and another 6 critically so. Habitat alienation, not hunting pressure, is the main cause. The New Zealand blue duck, for example, lives in fast-flowing mountain streams where it feeds on special invertebrates. It is sensitive to modifications of torrents of clear water and affected by hydroelectric schemes and mining, leading to serious decline.

FACT FILE

Eurasian wigeon This is a dabbling duck of shallow ponds and marshes that also grazes on plant matter on banks. It nests on the ground in dense, low growth across northern Eurasia and winters in flocks mainly in southern Europe and Asia.

- Up to 20 in (51 cm)
- 8–10
- Sexes differ
- Migrant
- Common

N. & S. Eurasia, N. Africa (Nile valley)

Pink-eared duck Adapted to the floods and droughts of inland Australia, this duck moves about in large flocks to temporary, often saline, floodwaters. It breeds in shrubbery, using much down in its nest. The pink-eared duck feeds by detecting and filtering planktonic food from mud with the help of specialized flaps on its bill.

- Up to 18 in (46 cm)
- 5–10
- Sexes alike
- Nomad
- Locally common

Inland Australia

Ferruginous duck Like other pochards, the ferruginous duck dives and up-ends to pick aquatic plants and invertebrates under water. It prefers shallow pools and marshes, where it nests in pairs under cover on the ground or in reed banks. When in flight, its wings beat faster than those of other ducks.

- Up to 17 in (42 cm)
- 8–12
- Sexes alike
- Migrant
- Common, declining

NC. Eurasia (breeding), SC. Eurasia, C. Africa (winter)

SPATULATE BEAK

The northern shoveler gets its name from its distinctive, heavy, shovel-like bill, which is longer than its head. It feeds in shallow water, extending its neck and dabbling its bill just below the water surface. Comb-like serrations along the sides of the bill help it strain food items from the water.

Feeding tool
This bird's long bill helps it feed on a variety of plants, mollusks, and crustaceans in the water.

Eurasian wigeon
Anas penelope

Northern shoveler
Anas clypeata

Widespread across the Northern Hemisphere where migratory

Chestnut teal
Anas castanea

Prefers coastal and saline wetlands in southern Australia

Named for the tiny magenta spot over the ear

Pink-eared duck
Malacorhynchus membranaceus

Green-winged teal
Anas crecca

Widespread across the Northern Hemisphere

Mallard
Anas platyrhynchos

A dabbling duck that has adapted to town parks and gardens. Widespread in the Northern Hemisphere; introduced to Australasia

Quacking calls differ between males and females

Ferruginous duck
Aythya nyroca

Common goldeneye
Bucephala clangula

Goldeneyes breed on freshwater boreal lakes but winter in coastal wetlands

Red-crested pochard
Netta rufina

Common pochard
Aythya ferina

Oldsquaw
(Long-tailed duck)
Clangula hyemalis

Despite their distinctively long tails, oldsquaws dive almost exclusively for their food of crustaceans and mollusks in the Arctic

Pochards feed mostly by diving and dabbling. They paddle to the floors of lakes and swamps for vegetable matter and seeds

Common merganser
Mergus merganser

Dives and chases for its food of fishes and aquatic invertebrates underwater, in the north temperate zone

Musk duck
Biziura lobata
♂

Males of this southern Australian species have a large lobe of skin under the bill. Dives for its food

Eiders are marine, living in often rough seas around rocky coasts and diving for mollusks and crustaceans

Common eider
Somateria mollissima
♀

♂

Male in full breeding plumage

White-headed duck
Oxyura leucocephala
♂

Males have an eclipse plumage, but are never as dull as the brown females

PENGUINS

CLASS	Aves
ORDERS	1
FAMILIES	1
GENERA	6
SPECIES	17

The most aquatic of all birds, penguins have remained unchanged in form for at least 45 million years. Although they evolved from flying birds, none of the 17 species can fly. Highly specialized, social seabirds, they take advantage of their streamlined bodies (which minimize drag) and small, flipper-like wings to travel underwater at speeds of up to 15 miles per hour (24 km/h). They spend up to three-quarters of their life in the sea, staying underwater for as long as 20 minutes or more at a time, and coming ashore only to breed and molt. Penguins eat fishes, krill, and other invertebrates, swallowing prey underwater.

South seas dwellers Penguins are widely distributed throughout the colder waters of the world's southern oceans. The greatest diversity of species is found in and around New Zealand and the Falkland Islands. The northernmost penguin lives right on the equator, in the Galápagos Islands.

Polar survivors Antarctica is home to some of the world's strongest blizzards. Wind speeds of up to 100 miles per hour (160 km/h) are frequent, usually accompanied by heavy, swirling snow. Penguins constantly shuffle about so that the shifting mass provides some shelter and relief from the extreme weather.

Warm spot Chicks depend on their parents for warmth and protection. Some penguins nest on mounds on the ground or in burrows, but emperor penguins incubate eggs on their feet under a protective flap of skin. Both sexes brood in turn. At six months, the chicks molt and can then go to sea.

A crowded life Penguins raise their young in crowded colonies. A lone adult king penguin stands out among a sea of chicks (left), which are covered in dull gray-brown down before growing adult plumage. Parents recognize their own chicks by voice and feed them by regurgitation.

GOING TO EXTREMES

Nesting penguins endure a remarkably wide range of temperatures, from -80°F (-63°C) in the southern polar regions to 100°F (38°C) in the tropics. Their dense, fur-like feathers protect them by trapping warm air in an insulating layer. Penguins also benefit from a layer of blubbery fat under the skin that provides warmth as well as neutral buoyancy.

Chicks are born with insulating down, but cannot enter the water until they have grown their first adult layer of waterproof feathers. As adults, they then lose this layer when they molt and must remain ashore for three to six weeks to regrow it; during this period, they may lose a third or more of their body weight.

Penguins are superb swimmers and divers, propelling themselves with their wings, which have evolved into stiff, flat, paddle-like flippers. They twist their flippers in such a way as to provide thrust on both the upstroke and downstroke. Their bodies also have numerous special physiological features that allow them to regulate their body temperatures and oxygen levels in cold waters.

⚑ CONSERVATION WATCH

Not out of danger Mass exploitation for their fat and eggs decimated many species of penguins; mining of guano also disturbed nesting. Such activities have slowed in recent times but breeding colonies remain vulnerable: 10 of the 17 species are threatened, 3 of them endangered.

EMPEROR PENGUIN ANATOMY

Arteries and veins in the feet and flippers are close together, so blood is kept warm as it returns from the extremities. These penguins have a dense cover of more than 77 feathers per square inch (12 feathers/cm²). The fluffy down at the base of each feather traps warm air, and the scaly, oily tips keep cold seawater out.

Feather layering

Long toenails to grip the ice

Flying through the water

Penguins are ungainly on land, but underwater they are efficient swimmers. They often enter the water by tobogganing down icy shores on their stomachs and plunging in. They have been known to reach depths of 2,000 feet (610 m) and can remain submerged for up to 20 minutes.

Emperor penguin chicks are grayish white with faces patterned in black-and-white

Chinstrap penguins can dive to depths of 230 feet (70 m) chasing prey

King penguin
Aptenodytes patagonicus

Adelie penguin
Pygoscelis adeliae

Chinstrap penguin
Pygoscelis antarctica

Emperor penguin
Aptenodytes forsteri

King penguins can dive to depths of over 650 feet (200 m) chasing their food of fish and some cephalopods

Emperor penguin The largest penguin, the emperor is unique in that it breeds in the middle of winter. These penguins usually do so on annual fast ice, making them the only birds to not normally set foot on solid ground.

Up to 4 ft (1.2 m)
1
Sexes alike
Sedentary
Locally common

Seas & coasts of Antarctica

King penguin The young of this second-largest (and most colorful) species spend the winter in large groups known as creches. They are fed sporadically and many perish. Breeding colonies can exceed 100,000 pairs.

Up to 3¼ ft (1 m)
1
Sexes alike
Local nomad
Locally common

Sub-Antarctic seas and islands

Chinstrap penguin Limited to pack-ice waters, this penguin feeds almost exclusively on krill captured by pursuit diving, and rests on pack ice between hunting. It breeds in massed colonies of thousands on ice-free rocky areas over summer. Nests are simple platforms of stones.

Up to 31 in (78 cm)
Usually 2
Sexes alike
Nomad
Common

Antarctica and its waters

GENTOO PENGUIN

These penguins, whose main colonies are on the Falkland Islands, nest on rocky shores and inland grasslands. They build skimpy nests of pebbles and molted feathers (in Antarctica) or vegetation (on sub-Antarctic islands), and can be aggressive—they will fight over their possessions. Eggs are round and dull white, as in all penguins.

FACT FILE

Fjordland penguin This colorful, crested penguin with startling red eyes breeds only on the southwest coast of New Zealand's South Island, in dispersed colonies under rain forest. It feeds by pursuit diving on small squid and crustaceans.

- Up to 28 in (71 cm)
- 2
- Sexes alike
- Regional nomad
- Vulnerable

New Zealand & S. Australian seas

Rockhopper penguin Named for its hopping over rocky ground at nesting sites, this species breeds in mass colonies on sub-Antarctic islands and builds simple nests of grass, stone, and bones. It has the greatest tolerance of water temperature and stays at sea for six months between breeding.

- Up to 24 in (61 cm)
- 2
- Sexes alike
- Regional nomad
- Vulnerable

Sub-Antarctic waters of the Southern Ocean

Magellanic penguin Like other jackass penguins, the magellanic feeds on small, pelagic school fish, but it breeds seasonally only over spring and summer. It nests in colonies, each pair using deep scrapes. Young do not become sexually mature until four to five years old.

- Up to 30 in (76 cm)
- 2
- Sexes alike
- Partial migrant
- Common

Coastal S. South America

Little penguin This tiny penguin feeds mainly on small fish, rounding up schools, then plunging into them. It is popular with tourists in southeast Australia and sleeps and nests in individual burrows on shore. It would take up to 30 of this species to equal the weight of the emperor penguin.

- Up to 18 in (46 cm)
- 2
- Sexes alike
- Sedentary
- Locally common

Coasts of S. Australia & New Zealand

Jackass penguin
Spheniscus demersus

Snares penguin
Eudyptes robustus

Fjordland penguin
Eudyptes pachyrhynchus

Wanders regularly to Australian waters

Magellanic penguin
Spheniscus magellanicus

Lives off the southern end of New Zealand and captures food (crustaceans and cephalopods) by pursuit-diving

Royal penguin
Eudyptes schlegeli

Differs from other jackass penguins by large size and double black breast stripe

Rockhopper penguin
Eudyptes chrysocome

Threatened by egg collecting on islands in the South Atlantic

Little penguin
Eudyptula minor

Yellow-eyed penguin
Megadyptes antipodes

This species breeds only around Macquarie Island, in the Southern Ocean

Confined to southwest New Zealand and considered endangered

DIVERS AND GREBES

Although both are aquatic birds that use their webbed or lobed feet for propulsion underwater, divers (known as loons in North America) and grebes are only distantly related to each other. Their similarities are the result of convergent evolutionary paths, over the course of which they both developed features suited to diving for fishes and aquatic invertebrates. Physically, loons resemble sleek ducks and cormorants that ride low in the water and have pointed bills. They are thought to be descended from wing-propelled swimming ancestors and therefore may be related to penguins and petrels. Some grebes are slim and elegant; smaller ones resemble ducklings.

CLASS	Aves
ORDERS	2
FAMILIES	2
GENERA	7
SPECIES	27

Watery world Loons and grebes spend most of their lives on water, coming ashore only to nest (grebes even nest on the water, on floating platforms of vegetation). Loons live on freshwater lakes in the boreal north; grebes inhabit both fresh and saline wetlands worldwide.

LOON CALL

A loon (above) gives an aggressive territorial call. The loud, yodelling notes—audible for a mile (1.6 km) or more—of returning migratory loons are a familiar sign of summer in boreal North America and Eurasia. These shy birds are most easily seen during migration.

Not just for flying Great crested grebes (right) and other grebe species eat large quantities of feathers. These form soft balls in their stomachs, perhaps protecting the alimentary tract from ingested fish bones.

SKILLED SWIMMERS

Loons are shy, rather solitary birds that cannot walk properly. They nest in a shallow heap of plant matter on the edges of lakes, to make it easier to slip into the water. They can swim rapidly and dive to depths of more than 200 feet (60 m) chasing fishes. They spend their winters at sea.

Grebes can also be elusive. They lack obvious tails, instead their bodies ending in a powder-puff of loose feathers. Their toes are not webbed but broadly lobed instead for swimming. They build floating nests of weed and lay cream eggs.

Loon and grebe chicks can swim and dive as soon as they hatch, but because they are sensitive to cold water, they prefer to hitch rides on their parents' backs or shelter under their parents' wings.

These birds do not fly much on a daily basis and usually avoid danger by diving underwater.

PROTECTIVE PARENTS

Chicks ride on the back of a parent pied-billed grebe, ready to hide under its wings at any hint of danger. By this means, parents are able to move new hatchlings around safely and efficiently. Like other grebes, a brooding pied-billed will cover its eggs with water-weed whenever it leaves its exposed, floating nest. This custom hides the eggs from predators and protects them from the elements. Although parents swallow most of their own prey underwater, they bring food to the surface for chicks.

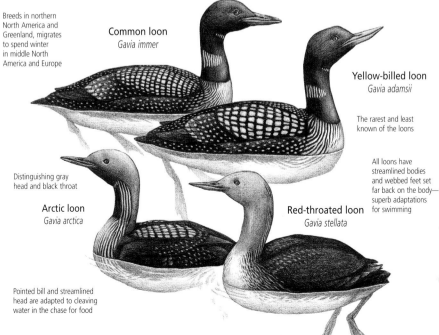

Breeds in northern North America and Greenland, migrates to spend winter in middle North America and Europe

Common loon
Gavia immer

Yellow-billed loon
Gavia adamsii

The rarest and least known of the loons

All loons have streamlined bodies and webbed feet set far back on the body—superb adaptations for swimming

Distinguishing gray head and black throat

Arctic loon
Gavia arctica

Red-throated loon
Gavia stellata

Pointed bill and streamlined head are adapted to cleaving water in the chase for food

FACT FILE

Atitlan grebe This giant, pied-billed grebe is probably extinct. It was found only on Lake Atitlán in Guatemala, and has been declining since the 1920s due to the introduction of bass, pollution, earthquakes, and competition from another grebe. It has not been seen since the mid 1980s.

- Up to 21 in (53 cm)
- 2–5
- Sexes alike
- Sedentary
- Probably extinct

Lake Atitlán, Guatemala

Madagascan grebe This bird is one of the dabchicks, a group of five species of small grebes with red washes on the neck but no head plumes. It prefers ponds of freshwater to other wetlands and lives alone, in pairs, or loose groups.

- Up to 10 in (25 cm)
- 3–4
- Sexes alike
- Mainly sedentary
- Vulnerable

Madagascar

Red-necked grebe This boreal species lives on small, shallow, freshwater bodies surrounded by forest and tundra. Despite its size and dagger-shaped bill, it eats aquatic insects rather than fish, capturing them both underwater and on the surface. It disperses in pairs to breed but congregates in large flocks in coastal regions during winter.

- Up to 20 in (51 cm)
- 4–5
- Sexes alike
- Migrant
- Uncommon

Boreal N. America, E. Asia & C. Europe to Russia

GREBE SISTERS

The western grebe (above) and Clark's grebe (below) are sister species that live on freshwater ponds in western North America. They hunt in the same way for similar foods. Clark's has a brighter, almost orange bill.

ELABORATE COURTSHIP

Courtship in western grebes (below) is highly ritualized. The birds initially perform a "weed dance," where both birds face one another holding strands of vegetation in their bills and make a number of ritualistic displays. Then they rise and run across the water surface together. This is called "rushing." Either sex can initiate courtship and pair bonds are usually seasonal. Both male and female grebes participate in nest building and egg incubation. Rival males also dance to defend their territories.

Dancing duo *Grebes are seasonally monogamous. At the height of courtship, western grebes rise in a graceful pose and, necks arched, run across the water's surface for some distance before diving below.*

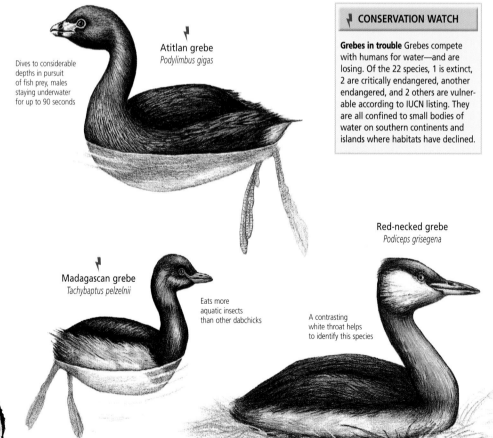

Dives to considerable depths in pursuit of fish prey, males staying underwater for up to 90 seconds

Atitlan grebe
Podylimbus gigas

Madagascan grebe
Tachybaptus pelzelnii

Eats more aquatic insects than other dabchicks

Red-necked grebe
Podiceps grisegena

A contrasting white throat helps to identify this species

⚡ CONSERVATION WATCH

Grebes in trouble Grebes compete with humans for water—and are losing. Of the 22 species, 1 is extinct, 2 are critically endangered, another endangered, and 2 others are vulnerable according to IUCN listing. They are all confined to small bodies of water on southern continents and islands where habitats have declined.

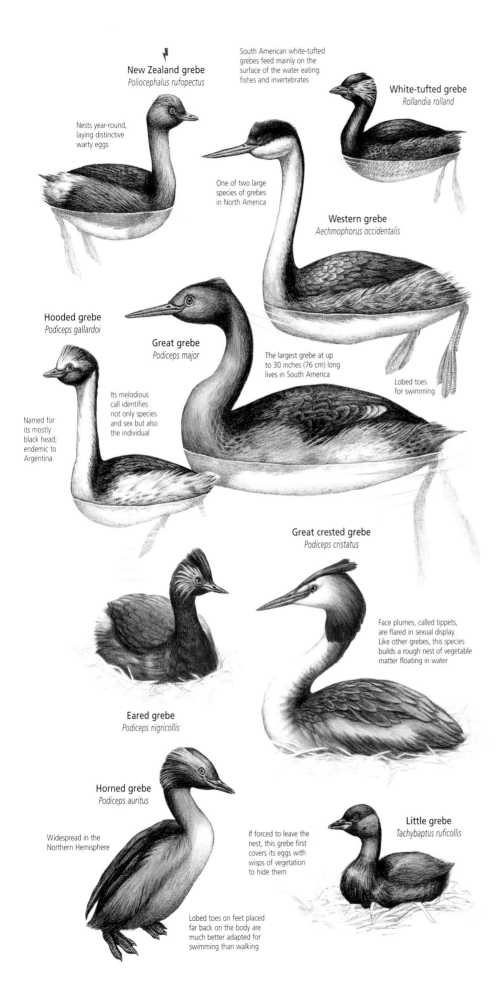

New Zealand grebe
Poliocephalus rufopectus

Nests year-round, laying distinctive warty eggs

South American white-tufted grebes feed mainly on the surface of the water eating fishes and invertebrates

White-tufted grebe
Rollandia rolland

One of two large species of grebes in North America

Western grebe
Aechmophorus occidentalis

Hooded grebe
Podiceps gallardoi

Great grebe
Podiceps major

The largest grebe at up to 30 inches (76 cm) long lives in South America

Lobed toes for swimming

Its melodious call identifies not only species and sex but also the individual

Named for its mostly black head; endemic to Argentina

Great crested grebe
Podiceps cristatus

Face plumes, called tippets, are flared in sexual display. Like other grebes, this species builds a rough nest of vegetable matter floating in water

Eared grebe
Podiceps nigricollis

Horned grebe
Podiceps auritus

Widespread in the Northern Hemisphere

If forced to leave the nest, this grebe first covers its eggs with wisps of vegetation to hide them

Little grebe
Tachybaptus ruficollis

Lobed toes on feet placed far back on the body are much better adapted for swimming than walking

FACT FILE

Western grebe This elegant bird is famous for its spectacular courtship displays. It nests in colonies on lakes and migrates to the coast. A nocturnal feeder, it belongs to the only group of grebes that spear fish with the bill.

- Up to 29 in (74 cm)
- 3–4
- Sexes alike
- Migrant
- Locally common

W. & C. North America

Great crested grebe The best-known grebe, it was almost hunted to extinction in some countries for its ornate head feathers. Its crests flare in display but are lost out of breeding. It catches fishes by pursuit-diving but will also pick up aquatic invertebrates from near or on the surface.

- Up to 25 in (64 cm)
- 3–5
- Sexes alike
- Partial migrant
- Locally common

Eurasia, S. Africa, S. Australia, New Zealand

Eared grebe This grebe inhabits mostly marshes, ponds, and lakes. Its feathers were once popular adornments for clothing, and its eggs, plain cream and nest-stained like those of other grebes, were collected for food. Like all grebes, pairs perform ritual courtship and bonding dances.

- Up to 13 in (33 cm)
- 3–5
- Sexes alike
- Migrant
- Common

North America, W. & E. Eurasia, S. Africa

Little grebe This small, dumpy bird appears to have a fluffy rear end. If disturbed it submerges, reappearing some distance away. It makes loud, distinctive rattling trills. When not breeding, its rufous neck molts into fawn and its cream gape spot dulls.

- Up to 11 in (28 cm)
- 3–7
- Sexes alike
- Partial migrant
- Common

Sub-Saharan Africa, W. & S. Eurasia to N. Melanesia

ALBATROSSES AND PETRELS

CLASS	Aves
ORDERS	1
FAMILIES	4
GENERA	26
SPECIES	112

These seabirds, collectively known as tubenoses, are highly adapted to life at sea. They can glide for hours without beating their wings, and it is not uncommon for them to fly hundreds of miles in search of squids, fishes, and the large zooplankton that comprise their diets. They seldom come within sight of land, except to breed. The biggest tubenose is the wandering albatross, which has the largest wingspan—up to 11 feet (3.3 m)—of any bird. Giant petrels are the size of some albatrosses, but the smallest storm petrels have an average wingspan of only about 12 inches (30 cm). Diving petrels have small, rigid wings as much suited for underwater propulsion as for flying.

Ocean-going birds Albatrosses are signature birds of the windswept expanses of southern oceans; but one group lives in the north Pacific.

Nesting instinct Two laysan albatross (*Phoebastria immutabilis*) parents tend their week-old chick (above). Adults regurgitate a fattening mixture of half-digested food and stored oil to feed their young, which take many months to fledge.

Courtship display Wandering albatrosses (*D. exulans*) (left) greet each other with outstretched wings in an "ecstatic" display, climaxing in braying whistles with bills pointed skyward. Albatrosses mate for life.

EXPRESSING THEMSELVES

Tubenoses are found throughout the world's oceans. They have large, external, tubular nostrils and a well-developed sense of smell that they may use to locate food, breeding sites, and each other. All species have webbed feet for swimming and a musty body odor that persists for decades in museum exhibits.

Most tubenoses store large quantities of oil in their stomachs, which they regurgitate for their young or eject to deter predators.

Albatrosses court spectacularly when they return to their nest sites, renewing bonds with rituals that can last for days. Many petrels perform elaborate courtship flights, as do little storm-petrels. Displays in diving-petrels are less showy.

All species nest in colonies, to help mate-finding after months at sea, and usually on islands remote from predators. Albatrosses are long-lived birds but do not begin breeding until they are around 10 years old. All lay dull, oblong, white eggs.

Northern fulmar
Fulmarus glacialis

Feeds on krill, offal, and refuse mostly while surface-swimming and picking busily like a pigeon

Cape petrel
Daption capense

Huge, slender wings enable albatrosses to wander the oceans by gliding effortlessly on wind currents

Yellow-nosed albatross
Thalassarche chlororhynchos

Royal albatross
Diomedea epomophora

⚡ CONSERVATION WATCH

Albatrosses and other large tubenoses are seriously threatened by long-line fishing. The birds follow fishing ships, dive for bait on lines thrown overboard, get hooked, and drown. One albatross, the Short-tailed albatross (*Phoebastria albatrus*), was hunted almost to extinction for the feather trade in the early 20th century. The 49 acceptable species of tubenoses on the IUCN threatened list are categorized as follows:

3	Extinct
10	Critically endangered
13	Endangered
23	Vulnerable

Gray petrel
Procellaria cinerea

Rides around the world on Southern Ocean air currents

Fiji petrel
Pseudobulweria macgillivrayi

A rare species known only from around Fiji

Jouanin's petrel
Bulweria fallax

Confined to the northwest Indian Ocean. Its breeding grounds have yet to be found

Found in both North Atlantic and Pacific oceans

Bulwer's petrel
Bulweria bulwerii

Manx shearwater
Puffinus puffinus

Breeds on islands around England and in the North Atlantic and winters in the south

Longer, more pointed wings, forked tails, and short feet distinguish northern storm petrels from those in Southern Hemisphere waters

Band-rumped storm petrel
Oceanodroma castro

Diving-petrels have small, chunky, bullet-shaped bodies adapted to plunge-diving for food

Long, wedge-shaped tail is diagnostic

Lives in tropical and subtropical Pacific and Indian oceans

Common diving petrel
Pelecanoides urinatrix

This transequatorial migrant is the most widespread petrel in the world

Wedge-tailed shearwater
Puffinus pacificus

Wilson's storm petrel
Oceanites oceanicus

FACT FILE

Common diving petrel This bird dives for its food, traveling through water and air with equal ease. Planktonic crusteans are its main prey. Its tubular nostrils open upward to prevent water entering.

⬆ Up to 10 in (25 cm)
🥚 1
// Sexes alike
⊘ Sedentary to local nomad
🐾 Common

Southern Ocean off S.E. Australia & New Zealand, S.W. Africa & S.W. South America

Wilson's storm petrel Like other storm petrels, this bird is colonial and nests in rock crevices or underground, mostly on isolated islands. It migrates between the Antarctic and the subarctic and feeds by pattering over the sea surface to pick krill and fishes.

⬆ Up to 7½ in (19 cm)
🥚 1
// Sexes alike
↻ Migrant
🐾 Common

Antarctica, all oceans to north of equator

THE LONG WAY HOME

Short-tailed shearwaters exemplify migration in a loop pattern. These birds skirt the coastline of one continent in the spring and a different one in the fall. Loop migrations may be undertaken due to food availability, ocean currents, prevailing winds, and changing temperature.

Migratory path between breeding and winter seas

Long flight
A shearwater's long wings help it migrate over large distances across open oceans.

RULER OF THE SKY

No other birds dominate the skies of the world's southern oceans like the great albatrosses, led by the wandering albatross with its enormous 11 foot (3.3 m) wing span. Their flight is effortless. Gliding on stiff wings, they rise and fall with majestic ease. To rise, they turn into the wind, picking up gusts which lift them over 50 feet (15 m) up, then they pull out and soar down-wind along troughs in waves, falling gradually away until they turn again to rise. This cycle continues day and night when albatrosses are on the move. Tubular nostrils help as well. Not only do they have a strong sense of smell for finding food, but they can also monitor air pressures to pick the right wind gusts at the right moment.

The long, strong, slightly hooked bill is adapted for snatching squid, fishes, and crustacea on or near the sea surface while albatrosses are swimming. Much fishing is done at night when squid migrate to the surface.

Limitations on land Albatrosses are not at home on land. Their wings are so huge that to take off they need a runway with wind assistance; they cannot maneuver easily, and often land awkwardly. So they only come to land to breed. Nestling black-browed albatrosses (above) wait on the nest, a mound of accumulated dry mud, for the arrival of parents with food. Parents stay at sea for days at a time, traveling great distances and returning only briefly to feed the chick by regurgitation. Chicks fledge in about four months which, added to over two months of shared incubation, ties breeding birds to their nesting islands for over six months at a time. Because of this, they breed only every second year.

transit path of a
wandering albatross

temporary diversion to
avoid particularly stormy
weather close to Cape Horn

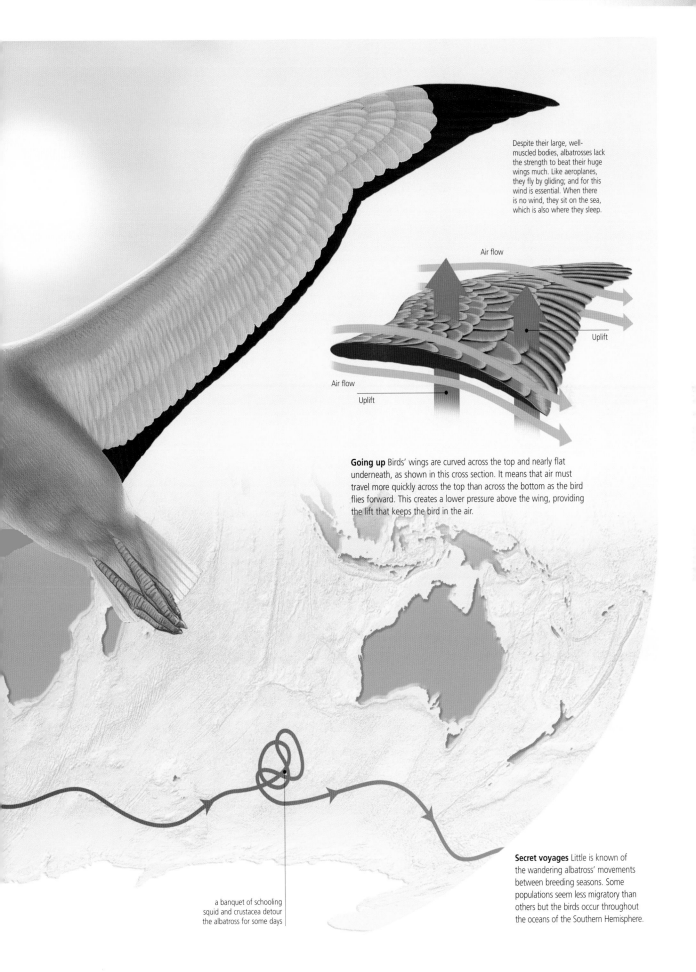

Despite their large, well-muscled bodies, albatrosses lack the strength to beat their huge wings much. Like aeroplanes, they fly by gliding; and for this wind is essential. When there is no wind, they sit on the sea, which is also where they sleep.

Air flow

Uplift

Air flow

Uplift

Going up Birds' wings are curved across the top and nearly flat underneath, as shown in this cross section. It means that air must travel more quickly across the top than across the bottom as the bird flies forward. This creates a lower pressure above the wing, providing the lift that keeps the bird in the air.

a banquet of schooling squid and crustacea detour the albatross for some days

Secret voyages Little is known of the wandering albatross' movements between breeding seasons. Some populations seem less migratory than others but the birds occur throughout the oceans of the Southern Hemisphere.

MIGRATIONS

Nearly half of the world's birds divide their time between summer and winter quarters because of seasonal fluctuations in the availability of food. Many species travel alone, but others migrate in flocks comprising one or more species. They travel either by day or night, and either overland or across oceans. Most break the journey into short hops of a couple of hundred miles. But terrestrial birds that cross oceans and cannot land on water must complete the entire journey in one epic flight. One such bird is the American golden plover, which flies between Alaska and Hawaii twice a year. To prepare for such energy-intensive journeys, birds load up on food to deposit fat reserves almost equal to their regular weight before they leave.

Travelers Garden warblers (*Sylvia borin*) (above) spend their summers in Europe and their winters in Africa.

Epic journey The Arctic tern (*Sterna paradisaea*) (below) migrates over a greater distance than any other bird. Twice a year it flies between the two polar regions.

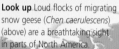

Look up Loud flocks of migrating snow geese (*Chen caerulescens*) (above) are a breathtaking sight in parts of North America.

Breeding range
Arctic terns spend their summers in the world's far northern latitudes. The birds nest there in colonies on the ground.

On the wing
An Arctic tern's migration route depends on which part of the Arctic its particular population is starting from. It can even take them over land.

A record
The Arctic tern's biannual journey eclipses that of any other bird species, covering 12,400 miles (20,000 km) each way.

Meals en route
Arctic terns can eat fish along their migration routes. They hover, then plunge into the water to catch their quarry.

SUN AND MIGRATION

Environmental cues such as day length and temperature shifts tell birds when it is time to migrate. They also navigate by other cues, including landmarks, the position of the sun and stars, and Earth's magnetic field. Birds have a keen time sense as well that helps them judge journey lengths.

A bird innately knows it should fly at a certain angle to the sun.

In a cage where mirrors deflect the sun's angle, the bird reorients.

No matter how the sun's angle is altered, the bird flies relative to it.

FLAMINGOS

CLASS Aves

ORDERS 1

FAMILIES 1

GENERA 3

SPECIES 5

These elegnt and graceful birds are easily recognized by their rich pink or red and white plumage, their long legs and neck (proportionately longer than on any other bird), and their oddly depressed bills. There are five living species of flamingo; the largest is the greater flamingo, almost 5 feet (1.5 m) tall. Vast flamingo flocks that congregate on the lakes of the Great Rift Valley are one of the famous natural spectacles of Africa. The reddish color of flamingo plumage comes from carotenoid proteins in the birds' diet of plant and animal microplankton. Liver enzymes break down these proteins into usable pigments that are deposited in both skin and feathers.

Old salts Flamingos were once found on every continent, but have disappeared from Australasia. These mainly tropical birds live in shallow lakes and coastal regions, preferring salty or brackish water. They inhabit some isolated islands and can also be seen at high altitudes in the Andes.

All together now Like other flamingos, greater flamingos (right) are gregarious birds that build conical nests out of mud and sand that they scrape together in shallow waters where they breed in Africa and the Caribbean.

Unusual angle
The long neck and downturned bill are adapted to feeding by immersing the head upside-down, well underwater for long periods.

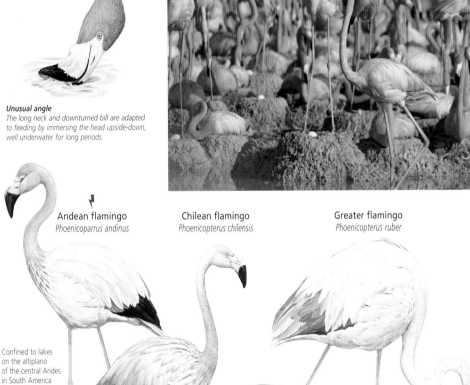

SPECIALIZED FEEDERS

The evolutionary lineage of flamingos is still something of a mystery, though they may represent the link between herons and their allies, and waterfowl.

The flamingo's strongly hooked bill is well designed for filter feeding on small shellfish, insects, single-celled animals, and algae. To feed, the bird bends forward, turns its head upside down (looking back-ward between its legs) and drags its opened bill through the water. After closing its bill, it uses its lower jaw and tongue (which has tooth-like projections) to pump water and mud out through the slits lining the upper jaw. The bird then swallows the food that remains.

The shallow waters where flamingos live sometimes drain away, forcing them to travel great distances to other feeding grounds. The flocks travel at night, honking as they fly.

Flamingos nest in dense colonies on lakes and in coastal wetlands, laying one or two chalky white eggs per breeding season. The young can run and swim well at an early age, leaving the nest to follow their parents within days of hatching, and flying by the age of 70–80 days.

Adults sometimes swim rather than walk while they feed in deep waters, often at night.

Andean flamingo
Phoenicoparrus andinus

Chilean flamingo
Phoenicopterus chilensis

Greater flamingo
Phoenicopterus ruber

Confined to lakes on the altiplano of the central Andes in South America

Lesser flamingo
Phoeniconaias minor

Feet have a short but distinct hind toe missing from other species

Long, slender, bare-legged feet adapted for wading in water 3¼ feet (1 m) or more deep

CONSERVATION WATCH

Salty habitats As flamingos live in saline waters, their wetland habitats have not been as affected as those of other water birds. Even so, one species found only in the South American Andes, the Andean flamingo (*Phoenicoparrus andinus*), is considered threatened.

HERONS AND ALLIES

CLASS	Aves
ORDERS	1
FAMILIES	3 or 5
GENERA	41
SPECIES	118

Long-legged and dagger-billed, herons wade stealthily in water to stalk their prey: amphibians, fishes, and insects. So do their allies the storks, ibises, and spoonbills, which probe and paddle for food. White herons are known as egrets, named for their special, filamentous breeding plumage, which was much sought after by 19th-century hat-makers. Many species are gregarious, and large gatherings of several species sometimes feed, roost, and even nest together. The white stork, a migratory bird that often nests in pairs on chimneys in Europe, has long been associated with human births in folk tales.

Freshwater dwellers Herons and their allies range worldwide, except near the poles. They are typically found in or near freshwater habitats, including swamps, marshes, rivers, streams, lakes, and ponds. However, several herons and ibises have adapted their feeding to dry fields.

A safe perch Although they spend most of their waking time down on the ground, scarlet ibises (*Eudocimus ruber*) (above) roost in large groups in trees, out of harm's way. Some other species in this group nest on the ground.

A catch A young great blue heron (above, right) holds a fish it has just caught. Most herons have long bills with which to stab at fishes. The bills of other birds in this group vary, depending on their diets and feeding styles.

WADING IN

All birds in this group have long bills, necks, and heads, but vary much in size, coloring, and feeding behavior. Many herons have specialized to fill very specific niches. The cattle egret, for example, follows grazing animals such as buffalo, eating the insects disturbed. Other herons, known as bitterns, camouflage themselves in marshes; if approached, they try to blend in with the reeds by freezing, bills pointed skyward and bodies compressed. All herons lay plae blue eggs.

Unlike storks and ibises, herons fly with their heads folded back on their shoulders, making them easy to recognize. They also have specialized patches of feathers, called powder-down, on the breast and lower back. These feathers are never molted, but grow continually. As the tips fray, they turn into a fine powder that the bird picks up in its bill and uses to remove slime and oil when grooming.

Some storks and ibises have bare necks, perhaps to prevent fouling plumage while feeding in mud or on carrion. When moving between feeding grounds, these birds often circle-soar on thermals to gain height, spy new sites, and save energy for the journey. Northern storks often migrate to warmer regions to escape poor feeding in winter.

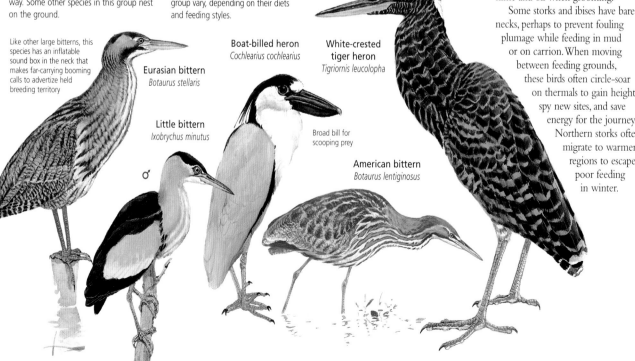

Like other large bitterns, this species has an inflatable sound box in the neck that makes far-carrying booming calls to advertize held breeding territory

Eurasian bittern
Botaurus stellaris

Little bittern
Ixobrychus minutus

♂

Boat-billed heron
Cochlearius cochlearius

Broad bill for scooping prey

White-crested tiger heron
Tigriornis leucolopha

American bittern
Botaurus lentiginosus

Rufous-bellied heron
Ardeola rufiventris

Black-crowned night heron
Nycticorax nycticorax

Carriers of the
encephalitis virus

Nankeen night heron
Nycticorax caledonicus

This species
replaces the
black-crowned
heron in
Australasia. Its
ecology is similar

Agami heron
Agamia agami

Breeds in
south Japan
and winters in
east China and
the Philippines

Japanese
night heron
Gorsachius goisagi

Bright rufous
and white
breeding
plumage

Striated heron
Butorides striatus

Squacco heron
Ardeola ralloides

Javan
pond heron
Ardeola speciosa

FACT FILE

Black-crowned night heron As its
name says, this heron hunts by night,
not only stalking amphibians, fishes,
and large invertebrates but also diving
after them from vantage perches. By
day, it roosts in small groups on
branches under the shade of leafy trees.
Of the eight species of night herons
worldwide, this is the most widespread.

⬧↕ 25 in (64 cm)
● 3-5
// Sexes alike
~ Nomad to migrant
♟ Common

N. & S. America, Africa, S. Eurasia to Sundra Is.

Agami heron This large, richly colored
heron lives on lakes and stream-margins
in tropical forest. A solitary bird, it stalks
the waters edge hunting fish. It may mix
with other species of herons when
nesting, building rough stick nests in low,
waterside trees and lays pale blue eggs.
Chicks are black-downed. Non-breeding
adults lack crest and back plumes.

⬧↕ 30 in (76 cm)
● 2-4
// Sexes alike
~ Local nomad
♟ Rare

Tropical America, including Amazon basin

Striated heron One of the most widespread herons, this species has evolved
at least 20 subspecies on different
continents and islands. At home in both
fresh and saltwater, it favors mud-flats
between water and woods or mangroves.
There it skulks along, hunting, body
hunched and alert, ready to dash back
to cover at any hint of danger. It usually
breeds in solitary pairs, building rough
stick nests in low, waterside foliage.

⬧↕ Up to 19 in (48 cm)
● 2-5
// Sexes alike
⊘ Sedentary (nothern subspecies migratory)
♟ Common

N. & S. America, sub-Saharan Africa,
Madagascar, S. & E. Asia to coastal Australasia

FACT FILE

Gray heron This colonial bird generally nests high up in trees, often with other species. Both parents look after the young, which remain in the nest for almost two months. Eating mainly fishes, it is a passive watch-and-wait hunter.

⬥ Up to 3¼ feet (1 m)
● 3–5
// Sexes alike
ᘓ Partial migrant
⧈ Common

Sub-Saharan Africa, Eurasia to Indonesia

Great blue heron The most familiar large wading bird in North America, it is often seen stalking the shallows of lakes or marshes. This heron has both white and gray phases in different regions.

⬥ Up to 4½ ft (1.4 m)
● 3–7
// Sexes alike
ᘓ Partial migrant
⧈ Common

Mid-North to Central America, Galápagos Is.

Purple heron Less sociable than the larger gray heron, the purple heron nests alone or in small colonies among reeds. A common bird, it sometimes eats small birds and small mammals, in addition to its staple diet of amphibians, fishes, and invertebrates.

⬥ Up to 35 in (89 cm)
● 2–5
// Sexes alike
ᘓ Partial migrant
⧈ Locally common

S. & C. Europe to Middle East, sub-Saharan Africa, Madagascar, S. & E. Asia to Sunda Is.

SHADOW HUNTING

The black heron (*Egretta ardesiaca*) spreads its wings to create a cowl over the water. This reduces reflections on the surface, improving the bird's vision, and may also attract fishes into the shade. Some species of heron stand still, then grab any prey that comes near. Other species actively pursue their quarry.

Black-headed heron
Ardea melanocephala

Long, articulated neck for stabbing strikes at prey

Lives in Sub-Saharan Africa

Gray heron
Ardea cinerea

Whistling heron
Syrigma sibilatrix

Lives in grasslands in South America

Long, bare legs and feet for wading

Dagger-shaped bill for grasping prey from strikes

Great blue heron
Ardea herodias

Goliath heron
Ardea goliath
A huge African heron

Purple heron
Ardea purpurea

Cattle egret
Bubulcus ibis

Lives in forested swamps in Amazonia

Chinese egret
Egretta eulophotes

Capped heron
Pilherodius pileatus

Local in east China and the Malesian archipelagos

Cattle egret populations erupted around the world in the 20th century. This species associates in small flocks with domestic and wild stock, often perching on the backs of cattle

Jabiru
Jabiru mycteria

Lives in both
fresh and saline
wetlands in
Central America

Saddle-bill stork
Ephippiorhynchus senegalensis

Lesser adjutant
Leptoptilos javanicus

Marabou
Leptoptilos crumeniferus

European
white stork
Ciconia ciconia

Glossy ibis
Plegadis falcinellus

Abdim's stork
Ciconia abdimii

Breeds in north
tropical Africa and
winters in the south

Scarlet ibis
Eudocimus ruber

Bare-faced ibis
Phimosus infuscatus

White ibis
Eudocimus albus

Found in wet
savannas, pastures,
and swamps in
tropical South America

FACT FILE

Saddle-bill stork This great stork is
named for the basal flange on its bill.
It is a solitary wader, preferring large,
freshwater marshes and river banks
where it snaps up fishes and other
animals. Pairs nest alone, building large
platforms of sticks in tree tops that they
may reuse year after year. Eyes are
brown in males and yellow in females.

- Up to 5 ft (1.5 m)
- 2-4
- Sexes alike
- Sedentary
- Uncommon

Sub-Saharan Africa except extreme south

Lesser adjutant Like the greater
adjutant and African marabou, this
bird resembles an undertaker in its
drab garb, bent bald head, and
solemn walk. Unlike them, it does not
eat much carrion, and frequents tidal
shores, swamps, and mangroves. It
stalks about thrusting out its bill after
mudskippers, other fishes, and herptiles.

- Up to 4 ft (1.2 m)
- 2-4
- Sexes alike
- Sedentary
- Vulnerable

Coastal S.E. Asia & Greater Sundas

European white stork Nesting
white storks on roofs of buildings are
a familiar sight in central Europe. This
bird breeds in dispersed colonies and
builds large stick nests. It wades in
nearby marshlands where it snaps up
diverse vertebrates and invertebrates.
During winter it feeds in dry fields of
Africa and India.

- Up to 3¼ ft (1 m)
- 2-6
- Sexes alike
- Migrant
- Uncommon; declined

Iberian Peninsula & C. Europe to C. Asia
(breeding), C. & E. sub-Saharan Africa &
C. India (winter)

Scarlet ibis Spectacular red plumage
sets this ibis apart from all others. It
forages along muddy estuaries and
tidal flats in flocks, probing about for
crustacea. Like other ibises, it breeds
in colonies, building nests of large,
rough platforms of sticks low in trees.
Chicks fledge in five to six weeks, after
hatching from chalky white eggs.

- Up to 28 in (71 cm)
- 2 (1-3)
- Sexes alike
- Sedentary, local nomad
- Locally common

Coastal N. & N.W. South America

FACT FILE

Hamerkop Named for its hammer-shaped head, the hamerkop lives alone or in pairs. It flies in slow undulations and has a raucous call. It feeds on aquatic animals at twilight or at night and is the only member of its family.

- Up to 22 in (55 cm)
- 3–6
- Sexes alike
- Sedentary
- Locally common

Sub-Saharan Africa & Madagascar

Shoebill This large, odd-looking bird is thus named because it appears to be wearing a clog on its face. Its massive bill, which it usually rests on its breast, is well adapted for catching the slippery lungfish found in its wetland habitats.

- Up to 4 ft (1.2 m)
- 1–3
- Sexes alike
- Sedentary
- Vulnerable

C. Africa

Sacred ibis This snowy bird was very prominent in ancient Egyptian mythology. Sacred ibises eventually became extinct in Egypt but still thrive elsewhere. They feed in flocks by probing for insects in marshland and also scavenge around human habitation.

- Up to 35 in (89 cm)
- 2–3
- Sexes alike
- Partial migrant
- Common

Sub-Saharan Africa & W. Madagascar

Madagascan crested ibis This terrestrial ibis feeds on moist ground in forests and scrubs. When disturbed, it prefers to run away rather than fly. It breeds in solitary pairs.

- Up to 20 in (51 cm)
- 2–3
- Sexes alike
- Sedentary
- Near threatened

E. & W. Madagascar

CONSERVATION WATCH

Waning wetlands The draining and pollution of wetlands worldwide have caused marked contractions in many species of herons and allies. Several Asian storks, known as the Asian adjutants, have collapsed from loss of food and poisoning. The IUCN lists 8 herons, 6 storks, and 6 ibises and spoonbills as threatened.

Madagascan crested ibis
Lophotibis cristata

Color pattern of rusty brown body with white wings is unique to this species

Crested ibis
Nipponia nippon

Survives only in central China

Eurasian spoonbill
Platalea leucorodia

Shoebill
Balaeniceps rex

Hamerkop
Scopus umbretta

Roseate spoonbill
Ajaia ajaja

Spoonbills capture food in mud by sensing it with side-to-side sweeps of the bill. Nostrils are at the base of the bill so the bird can still breathe while the bill is deeply immersed

Sacred ibis
Threskiornis aethiopicus

Black stork
Ciconia nigra

Breeds across temperate Eurasia and winters from sub-Saharan Africa to north India and south China

Long, bare legs and feet are adapted for wading in shallow waters

Wood stork
Mycteria americana

These South American birds use their open bills to detect fish in muddy water

PELICANS AND ALLIES

The pouch-billed pelicans (which have been in existence since mid-Tertiary times, up to 30 million years ago) are related to five other families of water birds: tropicbirds; gannets and boobies; cormorants; anhingas; and frigatebirds. They all have webbed feet that allow them to move easily through water, and the webbing extends uniquely across all four toes. Many have large, naked throat sacs that are used to trap fishes or as a sexual attractant in courtship displays. Unusually extensive air-sac systems in their chests and lower necks make those areas well-cushioned (hence protective) in diving and buoyant. Fishes, as well as squid and other invertebrates, are primary food.

| CLASS Aves |
| ORDERS 1 |
| FAMILIES 6 |
| GENERA 8 |
| SPECIES 63 |

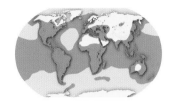

A varied range Pelicans and their relatives are found in all types of water environments, from open oceans and sea coasts to lakes, swamps, and rivers. Most species live in tropical or temperate areas.

EXPERT FISHERS

These birds are adapted to life on water. Tropicbirds cannot even walk because their legs are too far back on their bodies. One species of cormorant in the Galápagos Islands cannot fly. But pelicans are graceful in the air, despite being among the heaviest of flying birds. On the other hand, frigatebirds are lightweight and can remain in the air for days, buoyed by their massive wings.

Pelicans and their allies are skilled at catching fishes. Gannets and boobies dive from great heights. For centuries, Chinese fishermen have attached roped collars to cormorants, letting them out to catch fishes underwater, then pulling them back to the boats and taking their prey.

Cormorants and darters lack waterproofing in their feathers. This allows them to dive deeper and to move through water more efficiently. Eventually, their plumage becomes waterlogged, forcing them to spend considerable time ashore, wings spread, waiting for plumage to dry.

All, except tropicbirds, breed in large colonies. The stages of the breeding cycle may be synchronized within a colony. Many birds reuse the same nest sites year after year. All lay small clutches of chalky-white eggs in nests that are either mere scrapes in the ground or untidy platforms of twigs in trees or shrubbery. Both sexes brood.

Males have inflatable scarlet throat sacs which they blow up into balloons to attract females when courting

Lesser frigatebird
Fregata ariel

♂

Pelican party Most pelicans (above) feed as they sit on the surface of the water, dipping down to capture fishes in their pouches. Groups sometimes work as a team, herding fishes into shallow water where they can be more easily caught. Pelicans can often be seen scavenging near fishing boats and piers.

Darter
Anhinga melanogaster

♂

Darters and anhingas may look like cormorants, but instead of diving underwater to chase their prey, they submerge like a submarine

♀

Frigate birds are masters of the air in tropical seas. They hang-glide for hours, waiting to chase and steal food from other seabirds by forcing them to cough up their day's catch

Anhinga
Anhinga anhinga

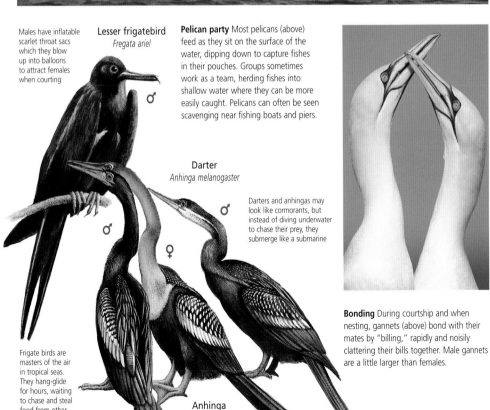

Bonding During courtship and when nesting, gannets (above) bond with their mates by "billing," rapidly and noisily clattering their bills together. Male gannets are a little larger than females.

⚡ CONSERVATION WATCH

Under threat Although many species of pelicans and their allies live at sea and nest on remote islands, they have still been vulnerable to massed killing at breeding colonies and to disturbance from guano extraction. Of the 16 threatened species listed, two breed only on Christmas Island.

FACT FILE

Great white pelican Because of its size (it is one of the heaviest flying birds in the world), the Great white pelican relies as much as possible on thermals. For reasons of balance, it cannot fly with a full pouch.

- ⚖ Up to 5¾ feet (1.75 m)
- ● 1–3
- ⚥ Sexes alike
- ⛟ Partial migrant
- ⚑ Locally common

S.E. Europe, Africa, S. & S.C. Asia

Northern gannet Spectacular in flight, this gannet quarters the sea on long, pointed wings to search for fish, then drops vertically onto it in towering plunge-dives. It nests on rocky coasts.

- ⚖ Up to 36 in (92 cm)
- ● 1
- ⚥ Sexes alike
- ⛟ Partial migrant
- ⚑ Locally common

N. Atlantic, Mediterranean Sea

Red-tailed tropicbird This tropicbird has tail-streamers and plunge-dives for fish in tropical seas. Pairs perform acrobatic and noisy display flights and breed in dispersed groups.

- ⚖ Up to 32 in (81 cm)
- ● 1
- ⚥ Sexes alike
- ～ Nomad; returns to nest sites
- ⚑ Locally common

Tropical Indian & Pacific oceans

BOOBY BOUNTY

Boobies are gannets of tropical seas, fish in the same way, and roost and nest colonially. The Peruvian and Blue-footed boobies are particularly great guano (excrement) producers, and responsible for driving Peru's early economic development.

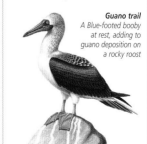

Guano trail
A Blue-footed booby at rest, adding to guano deposition on a rocky roost

Great white pelican
Pelecanus onocrotalus

Its eggs take 1½ months to hatch

Red-tailed tropicbird
Phaethon rubricauda

Dalmatian pelican
Pelecanus crispus

Northern gannet
Morus bassanus

Builds a low mound nest of cemented earth and fibre in dense colonies

Broad wings allow Dalmatian pelican to glide long distances, conserving energy during migrations across Eurasia

Brown pelican
Pelecanus occidentalis

Found in the east Pacific and Atlantic oceans

Unlike most pelicans, which fish by swimming, this species plunge-dives out of the air into the water for its food. It lives on west and east coasts of the Americas

Red-billed tropicbird
Phaethon aethereus

Blue-footed booby
Sula nebouxii

Distinctive black bill

Nests of the blue-footed booby are nothing more than a circle of excreta on the ground or among vegetation there

Peruvian booby
Sula variegata

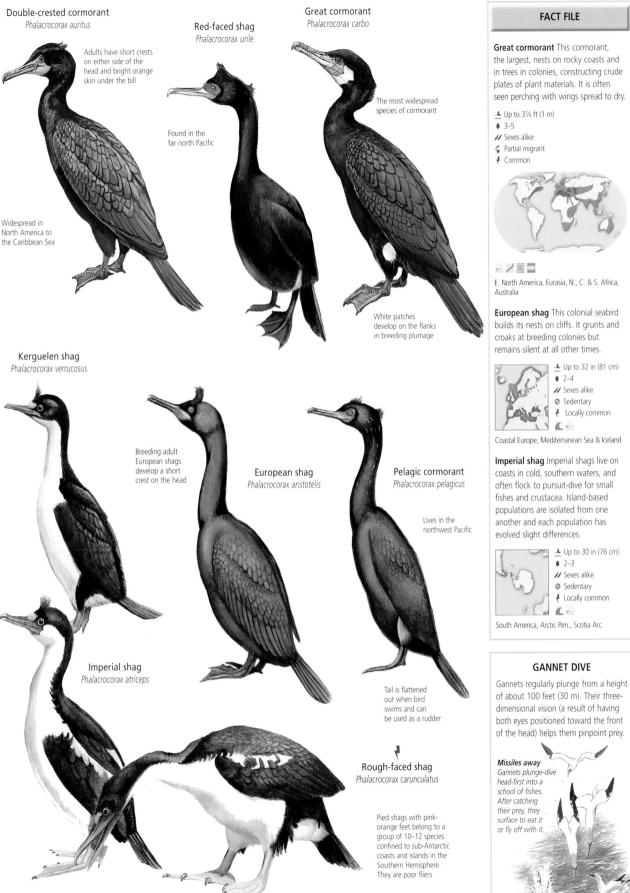

Double-crested cormorant
Phalacrocorax auritus

Adults have short crests on either side of the head and bright orange skin under the bill

Widespread in North America to the Caribbean Sea

Red-faced shag
Phalacrocorax urile

Found in the far north Pacific

Great cormorant
Phalacrocorax carbo

The most widespread species of cormorant

White patches develop on the flanks in breeding plumage

Kerguelen shag
Phalacrocorax verrucosus

Breeding adult European shags develop a short crest on the head

European shag
Phalacrocorax aristotelis

Pelagic cormorant
Phalacrocorax pelagicus

Lives in the northwest Pacific

Tail is flattened out when bird swims and can be used as a rudder

Imperial shag
Phalacrocorax atriceps

Rough-faced shag
Phalacrocorax carunculatus

Pied shags with pink-orange feet belong to a group of 10–12 species confined to sub-Antarctic coasts and islands in the Southern Hemisphere. They are poor fliers

FACT FILE

Great cormorant This cormorant, the largest, nests on rocky coasts and in trees in colonies, constructing crude plates of plant materials. It is often seen perching with wings spread to dry.

⬧ Up to 3¼ ft (1 m)
● 3–5
⫽ Sexes alike
ᘓ Partial migrant
⨙ Common

E. North America, Eurasia, N., C. & S. Africa, Australia

European shag This colonial seabird builds its nests on cliffs. It grunts and croaks at breeding colonies but remains silent at all other times.

⬧ Up to 32 in (81 cm)
● 2–4
⫽ Sexes alike
⊘ Sedentary
⨙ Locally common

Coastal Europe, Mediterranean Sea & Iceland

Imperial shag Imperial shags live on coasts in cold, southern waters, and often flock to pursuit-dive for small fishes and crustacea. Island-based populations are isolated from one another and each population has evolved slight differences.

⬧ Up to 30 in (76 cm)
● 2–3
⫽ Sexes alike
⊘ Sedentary
⨙ Locally common

South America, Arctic Pen., Scotia Arc

GANNET DIVE

Gannets regularly plunge from a height of about 100 feet (30 m). Their three-dimensional vision (a result of having both eyes positioned toward the front of the head) helps them pinpoint prey.

Missiles away
Gannets plunge-dive head-first into a school of fishes. After catching their prey, they surface to eat it or fly off with it.

THE ULTIMATE FISHER

A pelican's bill is designed above all to catch fishes, their staple diet. The upper mandible is firm and narrow, and ends in a sharp, hooked nail for gripping awkward fishes. The lower bill is the more specialized, with a flexible bow-like outer frame from which hangs an enormous, extensible pouch of leathery skin. The tongue is tiny, but the tongue muscles control the pouch, opening it by bowing the frame and contracting it to expel as much as 4 gallons (14 liters) of water at a time. Most fishes are caught by swimming pelicans which, when sighting fishes, lunge forward and open the bill underwater to engulf prey. The upper bill then acts as a lid and snaps shut as water is expelled. To keep the pouch in top working order, pelicans do exercises to stretch it length-wise and sideways. They eat up to 4 pounds (2 kg) of fish daily.

Lunch box Before pelican chicks are old enough to hunt for themselves, they stick their bills down their parents' throats, prompting them to regurgitate a half-digested fish meal. Unlike adult pelicans, which are essentially voiceless, chicks beg loudly for food.

Snaring fishes The brown pelican (right) is the only pelican that dives from varying heights to catch a meal. Other species all feed as they sit on the surface, dipping down into the water with their bill and pouch. Groups herd fishes into shallow water where they are more easily caught.

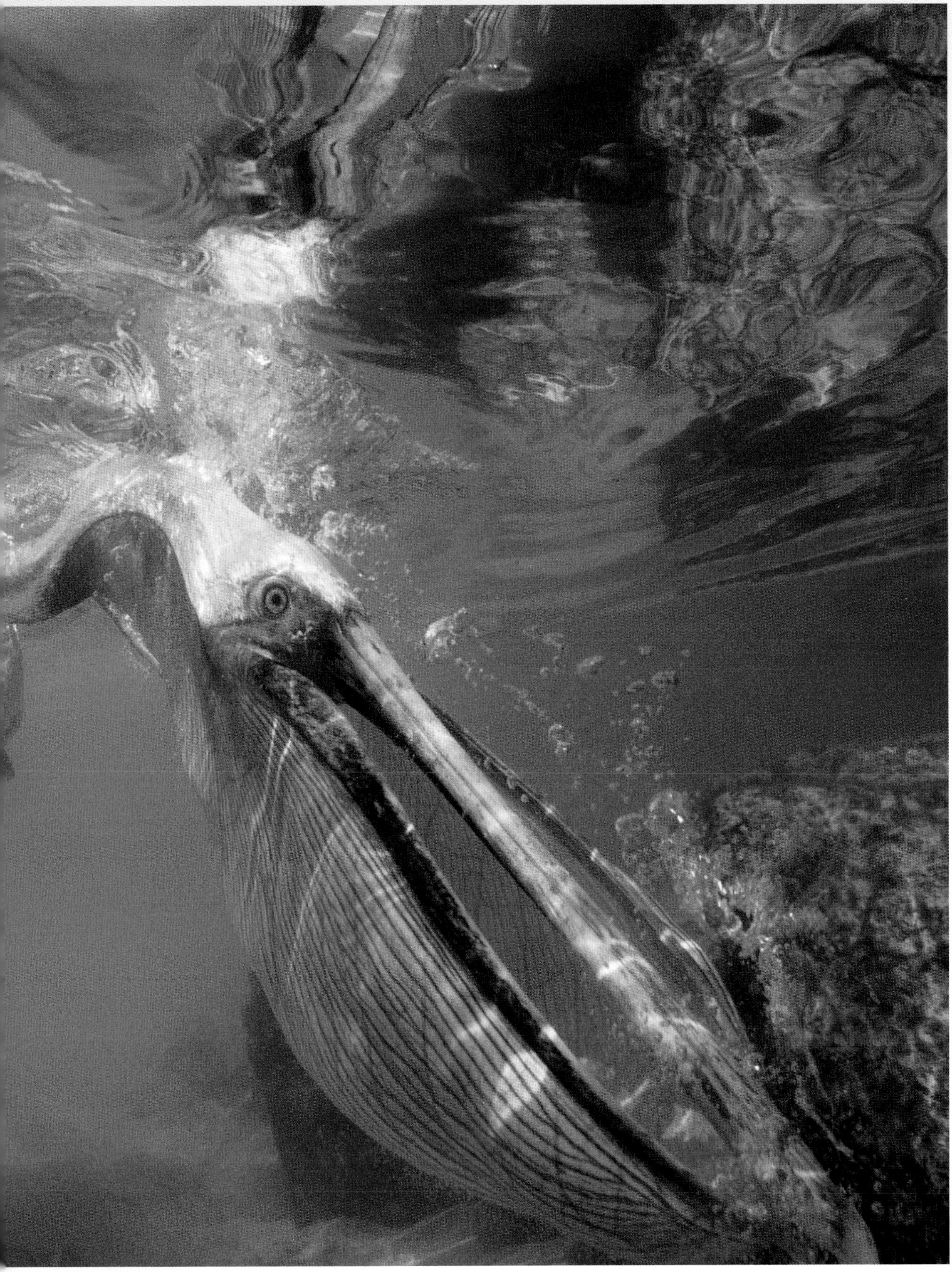

BIRDS OF PREY

CLASS Aves
ORDERS 1
FAMILIES 3
GENERA 83
SPECIES 304

These skilled hunters are collectively known as raptors, from the Latin word meaning "one who seizes and carries away." They comprise one of the bird world's larger orders, with members ranging from the world's fastest birds to its ugliest scavengers, and varying in standing height from 6 inches (15 cm) to over 4 feet (1.2 m). The group includes eagles, kites, falcons, buzzards, vultures, and hawks. The raptors' hunting prowess has awed humans throughout history, making them common features on military insignia and national crests. They all have sharp, hooded eyes, hooked beaks, and great claws. Their nests are rough platforms of sticks and chicks are white-downed.

Widespread predators Raptors are found worldwide in most habitats, from Arctic tundra to tropical rain forests, deserts, marshes, fields, and cities. Because they need space for their hunting, their presence is determined by physical environment rather than by type of vegetation.

WINGING IT

Some raptors have broad wings suited for soaring while looking for carrion or live prey on the ground. Others have pointed wings that allow them to fly quickly and change direction rapidly when chasing prey.

Andean condor – 10 feet (3 m)

Bearded vulture – 8½ feet (2.7 m)

Secretarybird – 7 feet (2.2 m)

White-bellied sea eagle – 6½ feet (2 m)

Rough-legged buzzard – 5 feet (1.5 m)

Peregrine falcon – 3½ feet (1.1 m)

Lesser kestrel – 2¼ feet (0.7 m)

Little sparrowhawk – 1¼ feet (0.4 m)

Got it Some raptors such as this osprey (above, top) specialize in swooping upon prey, which they grab and carry off with their talons. Many species can fly far and fast in search of prey. Scavengers do not need to be as agile and instead may soar for long periods on thermals looking for a kill.

A meaty treat Like this red kite (above), most raptors nest in trees, although some build among undergrowth or lay eggs in small hollows scraped on cliff edges. There is usually a clear division of labor, males doing most of the hunting and females feeding torn-up prey to the young.

Sizing up Female raptors are typically larger than their male counterparts, as in this pair of African fish eagles (*Haliaeetus vocifer*) (above). Such dimorphism is less pronounced among species that eat slower-moving or immobile prey. Raptors are monogamous.

SUPREME HUNTERS

Raptors have sharp, hooked bills adapted for tearing flesh; powerful feet and talons for grabbing prey; and long-sighted eyes for spotting their quarry in daylight. Their diets vary from species to species and include insects, birds, mammals, fishes, and reptiles. Anatomical features vary accordingly. Long toes help falcons grab airborne prey. Their sturdy legs allow them to hit birds hard enough to incapacitate them. Large legs and talons help forest eagles capture monkeys, sloths, and other tree-dwelling mammals in foliage.

Raptors are renowned for their keen eyesight and aerial prowess. Eagles dive on prey from great heights and can pick out a rabbit at more than a mile (1.6 km) away. Many scavenging raptors have bare skin on their heads and necks, to prevent clotting feathers when they stick their heads into carcasses and perhaps regulate body temperature.

At the top of the food chain, raptors are rarely abundant and usually forage alone on the wing over wide areas. Their eggs are dull white, often freckled in browns.

Andean condor
Vultur gryphus

World's largest
bird of prey

Californian condor
Gymnogyps californianus

Like all American
vultures, this condor
soars on thermals
looking for carrion

Black vulture
Coragyps atratus

Widespread from
southern North
America to most
of South America

Like most vultures,
these birds are
scavengers and
have weak talons

Turkey-vulture
Cathartes aura

One of the
most common
American raptors,
both in the north
and south continents

Osprey
Pandion haliaetus

The ultimate fish-
catching raptor,
the osprey will
even plunge
underwater
to seize prey

King vulture
Sarcoramphus papa

Black baza
*Aviceda
leuphotes*

African cuckoo-hawk
Aviceda cuculoides

♂

♀

Apart from sexual
differences, this
American kite has
dark and light morphs

Cuckoo-hawks hunt
low over tree tops in
search of large insects,
or dive on small reptiles
from set perches

Hook-billed kite
Chondrohierax uncinatus

FACT FILE

Californian condor One of the
American vultures, this huge scavenger
has the longest nestling period—
six months—of any raptor. It is now
being bred in captivity and released into
the wild in efforts to save the species.

⬇ Up to 4⅓ ft (1.3 m)
⬆ Up to 9 ft (2.8 m)
● 1
∅ Sedentary
⚡ Critically endangered

S.W. USA

King vulture This powerful raptor
typically nests high up in trees and
feeds on carrion. It uses its strong
beak to tear apart and eat the flesh
of carcasses ahead of its rivals.

⬇ Up to 32 in (81 cm)
⬆ Up to 6½ ft (2 m)
● 1
∅ Sedentary
⚡ Locally common

Central & N. & C.E. South America

Osprey This fish hawk lives on lakes,
rivers, and seashores and soars over
water to hunt. It builds huge, crude
nests of dry branches and other plant
matter that it accumulates over years.
It feeds almost exclusively on fishes.

⬇ Up to 23 in (58 cm)
⬆ Up to 5½ ft (1.7 m)
● 2–4
⚡ Partial migrant
⚡ Common

N. & S. America, Eurasia, Africa, Australia

POWERFUL TOOLS

Ospreys drop feet first into the water
to catch fishes. Their reversible
outer toe, long curved talons,
and rough, spiny soles
(with thorny
growths called
"spicules") help
them grab and
carry
prey. Like all raptors,
they have strong,
curved beaks
to tear flesh.

FACT FILE

Snail kite This raptor eats mainly water snails in freshwater marshes. Diving from perches, it snatches them with its talons. Snail kites sometimes gather in large flocks. Nests are built among grasses and aquatic bushes.

- ⟵ Up to 17 in (43 cm)
- ⟸ Up to 3½ ft (1.1 m)
- ● 2–3
- ⟲ Partial migrant
- ⌇ Locally common

Central America, N. South America

Short-toed eagle This eagle prefers to nest in evergreen trees. Its habitat includes terrain with scrubby vegetation and woods with large clearings. It eats mainly reptiles, especially snakes and lizards.

- ⟵ Up to 26½ in (67 cm)
- ⟸ Up to 6 ft (1.8 m)
- ● 1
- ⟲ Partial migrant
- ⌇ Locally common

N.W. Africa, W. to C. Eurasia, W. China & India

White-bellied sea eagle Soaring on upswept wings, this white eagle is a majestic sight. It hunts fishes, turtles, and waterfowl around coasts and estuaries. Pairs hold permanent territory, building imposing nests with alerting views in all directions.

- ⟵ Up to 34 in (86 cm)
- ⟸ Up to 6½ ft (2.2 m)
- ● 2–3
- ⊘ Sedentary
- ⌇ Locally common

Coastal India & S.E. Asia to Australasia

PAIR BONDS

Like most raptors, bald eagles are monogamous. Pairs renew their bonds with spectacular acrobatic displays. The male usually dives toward the female, which flies below. She then rolls and raises her legs, grasping his feet as the two of them tumble together.

Flying united A pair of bald eagles clasp talons in midair during an aerial display fight. Their bare lower "legs" identify them as fish eagles.

Mississippi kite
Ictinia mississippiensis

Hunts on the wing, stooping to feed mainly on insects flushed by grazing animals or fires

Scissor-tailed kite
Chelictinia riocourii

Bald eagle A bald eagle (right) flies off with its catch. Fishes are its main prey, but it also takes waterfowl and carrion. Because of its imposing size and character, this bird is the national symbol of the United States.

European honey buzzard
Pernis apivorus

Honey buzzards feed on wasps and bees, attacking their nests and combs. They breed across Europe and winter in sub-Saharan Africa

Distinguished by its deeply forked tail and elegant gray form. Ranges across northern tropical Africa

Congregate to roost in flocks of up to 1,000

Snail kite
Rostrhamus sociabilis

Distinctive red feet and facial skin. Slender bill adapted to cut a snail's retractor muscle and extract it

An adept scavenger around human habitation. Widespread through Africa and Eurasia to Australia

Black kite
Milvus migrans

Specializes in preying on small reptiles, plunging from the sky, seizing them, and then swallowing them whole

Short-toed eagle
Circaetus gallicus

White-bellied sea eagle
Haliaeetus leucogaster

Both these raptors are fish eagles, with huge talons and feet bare of feathers that could otherwise become water-logged when seizing fishes

White-tailed eagle
Haliaeetus albicilla

FACT FILE

Eurasian griffon The largest vulture in Europe, this bird prefers to nest, roost, and soar in mountainous terrain. It moves to open plains to feed on carrion, mainly from mammals such as sheep.

- ⤒ Up to 3½ ft (1.1 m)
- ✥ Up to 9 ft (2.8 m)
- ● 1
- ⊘ Sedentary
- ↯ Locally common

N. & S. Africa, S. Europe to Middle East & Caucasia

Egyptian vulture This scavenger builds crude nests using small branches and rubbish, which it typically places in holes and nooks in rocks. Its diet includes rotten fruit, rubbish, carrion, and dung. It is a small vulture.

- ⤒ Up to 27 in (69 cm)
- ✥ Up to 5½ ft (1.7 m)
- ● 2
- ↺ Partial migrant
- ↯ Locally common

🌼 ⤓ ▬ ▭

S. Europe, N. & E. Africa, S.W. Asia to India

Hooded vulture This vulture cannot compete with larger scavengers at carcass sites, so it circles around the periphery, picking up the scraps. It is the only vulture that can live in areas of high rainfall.

- ⤒ Up to 27 in (69 cm)
- ✥ Up to 6 ft (1.8 m)
- ● 1
- ⊘ Sedentary
- ↯ Common

🌼 ⤓ ▭

Sub-Saharan Africa excl. Congo Basin & South Africa

SCAVENGING

Like other griffon vultures, Ruppell's griffons are gregarious birds. Several hundred may descend to feed on a carcass that one of them has spotted.

⚡ CONSERVATION WATCH

Vulture populations collapse Across southern Asia, vulture populations collapsed at the close of the 20th century. The reason was found to be poisons concentrated in carrion that caused the vulture's kidneys to fail. Five are now listed as threatened.

Bearded vulture
Gypaetus barbatus

Lappet-faced vulture
Torgos tracheliotus

Cinereous vulture
Aegypius monachus

These huge vultures feed mainly on the large bones of animal carcasses which they break open on rocks

An aggressive African scavenger, often wasting energy in competitive interaction instead of feeding

Found in mountains through southern Europe and central Africa

Eurasian griffon
Gyps fulvus

Egyptian vulture
Neophron percnopterus

Hooded vulture
Necrosyrtes monachus

The flesh of palm fruits are the staple diet of this central-African vulture

African white-backed vulture
Gyps africanus

Widespread in sub-Saharan Africa

Palm-nut vulture
Gypohierax angolensis

Gabar goshawk
Micronisus gabar

Lizard buzzard
Kaupifalco monogrammicus

Congo serpent eagle
Dryotriorchis spectabilis

Crested serpent eagle
Spilornis cheela

Lives in India and
Southeast Asia to
Borneo and Japan

Chants territorially
from treetops
before nesting

Hunts from exposed
perches, diving to
pounce on tree snakes
and other reptiles

Dark chanting
goshawk
Melierax metabates

Black harrier
Circus maurus

Flies low over open areas and
grasslands, gliding on upraised
wings as it hunts for prey.
Endemic to southern Africa

♂

Northern harrier
Circus cyaneus

Long, slender feet and
talons adapted for reaching
into vegetation and grasping
animal prey from shallow
dives or drops

Western marsh harrier
Circus aeruginosus

FACT FILE

Gabar goshawk This bird has two
color forms, one gray and one mostly
black. It ambushes birds, mammals,
lizards, and insects by flying swiftly
out from tree cover to snatch them.

- ⤒ Up to 14 in (36 cm)
- ↥ Up to 23½ in (60 cm)
- 2–4
- ♀ Partial migrant
- Common

Sub-Saharan Africa excl. Congo, S. Yemen

Congo serpent eagle A long tail
facilitates maneuvering in flight; and
large eyes help this eagle see in the
dimly lit forest understory where it
hunts chameleons, lizards, and other
animals including snakes.

- ⤒ Up to 20 in (51 cm)
- ↥ Up to 3½ ft (1.1 m)
- Unknown
- ⊘ Sedentary
- Locally common

Liberia to Congo basin

Northern harrier Formerly called a
marsh hawk, the northern harrier is
widespread in grasslands and open
fields, especially in marshy areas.
Unlike other hawks, it rarely perches
on anything higher than a fence post.

- ⤒ Up to 20 in (51 cm)
- ↥ Up to 4 ft (1.2 m)
- 3–6
- ♻ Migrant
- Common

North & Central America, N. & C. Eurasia

FLEDGLINGS

Most raptors breed in trees, but
harriers nest on the ground among tall
grass and shrubbery. The female feeds
the young with food brought by the
male until they are ready to fly and
hunt for themselves, about a month
after hatching.

FACT FILE

Rough-legged hawk This bird is one of the few raptors that breed in the Arctic. After raising its young on open tundra, it migrates to winter quarters: marshes and farmlands in North America, Europe, and Asia. It captures its prey on the ground.

⬇ Up to 24 in (61 cm)
⬆ Up to 5 ft (1.5 m)
● 3–5
↻ Migrant
🏵 Common

North America, N. & C. Eurasia

Eurasian sparrowhawk This raptor lives in forested areas interspersed with open spaces. It hunts its prey by flying low along the edge of woods, catching mostly birds, as well as small mammals and insects.

⬇ Up to 15 in (38 cm)
⬆ Up to 27½ in (70 cm)
● 3–6
↺ Partial migrant
🏵 Uncommon

Europe, far N. Africa, N. to S. Asia

FIGHTING BIRDS

Raptors sometimes squabble over prey. Eurasian buzzards attack each other with their powerful feet and sharp talons. Beaks, no matter how dangerous looking, are never used.

Foot fighting
*Two competing hawks
try to get the upper hand
the only way they know.*

Martial eagle
Polemaetus bellicosus

Lives in open habitats
in sub-Saharan Africa,
and hunts on the wing

Rough-legged hawk
Buteo lagopus

Hunts from vantage
perches; favored prey
includes lemmings, voles,
and other small mammals

Eurasian buzzard
Buteo buteo

White hawk
Leucopternis albicollis

Lives in open country
in central South America

Common
black hawk
*Buteogallus
anthracinus*

Crowned eagle
*Harpyhaliaetus
coronatus*

Black hawks
and white hawks
hunt from open
vantage perches
to spy prey. Both
species live in
tropical America

Mangrove
black hawk
Buteogallus subtilis

Harris's
hawk
*Parabuteo
unicinctus*

Ferruginous
hawk
Buteo regalis

Variable goshawk
Accipiter novaehollandiae

White phase; there are also
dusky phases. Even in the
normal phase, this Australasian
species varies from gray-and-
white to rufous-and-brown

Eurasian sparrowhawk
Accipiter nisus

Ornate hawk-eagle
Spizaetus ornatus

A powerful raptor. Hunts by stealth from perches within the crown of rain forests in tropical America

Javan hawk-eagle
Spizaetus bartelsi

Lives in rain forests and preys on large birds and smaller mammals

Crowned hawk-eagle
Stephanoaetus coronatus

Black-and-white hawk-eagle
Spizastur melanoleucus

Secretary bird
Sagittarius serpentarius

Small, south Eurasian eagle

Bonelli's eagle
Hieraaetus fasciatus

Long legs enable secretary birds to cover 6–12 miles (10–20 km) or more of ground daily. Toes are short with nail-like claws

Mated pairs often combine aerial hunting strategies and share prey

Golden eagle
Aquila chrysaetos

A true land eagle; fully feathered "legs"

Long-crested eagle
Lophaetus occipitalis

Tawny eagle
Aquila rapax

HUNTING METHODS

Raptors hunt and kill their prey in a variety of ways, although their powerful feet and sharp talons are their main weapons. Some pursue airborne prey; others capture reptiles and mammals on the ground. Hawks kill with their strong grips, squeezing their victims to death. Some vultures drop tortoises until they break, then swoop down to eat the flesh inside. Fish eagles and ospreys snatch fishes out of the water. The unusual secretary birds subdue their prey by kicking it. And the African harrier-hawk has extraordinarily flexible legs which it can bend at extreme angles to grope inside tree hollows for nestling birds and other small animals.

CRACKING UP

Egyptian vultures sometimes use tools such as twigs to open ostrich eggs. They may also drop eggs from the air, or hurl stones at eggs that are too large to drop. Bearded vultures also drop large bones on to favored rocks ("ossuaries") to break them up for eating.

Stages in prey capture Falcons strike and take their prey in midair. Here we see the sequence of attack by a peregrine falcon: circling to scout prey (top left); the attacking dive (left); the hit, a Eurasian oystercatcher (below). Raptors partially pluck bird and mammal prey before eating it.

Outfoxing prey Eagles (above) use their powerful legs and sharp talons to catch and kill mammals such as foxes. Fishes can be slippery prey, but fish eagles have particularly large talons with spiny soles to cope with this problem.

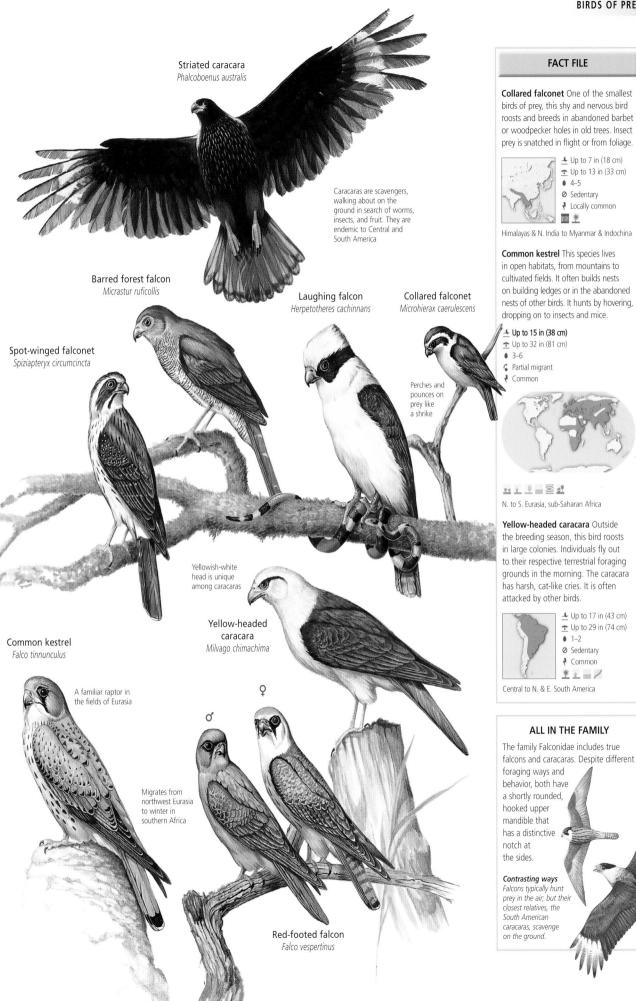

Striated caracara
Phalcoboenus australis

Caracaras are scavengers, walking about on the ground in search of worms, insects, and fruit. They are endemic to Central and South America

Barred forest falcon
Micrastur ruficollis

Laughing falcon
Herpetotheres cachinnans

Collared falconet
Microhierax caerulescens

Spot-winged falconet
Spiziapteryx circumcincta

Perches and pounces on prey like a shrike

Yellowish-white head is unique among caracaras

Yellow-headed caracara
Milvago chimachima

Common kestrel
Falco tinnunculus

A familiar raptor in the fields of Eurasia

♀

♂

Migrates from northwest Eurasia to winter in southern Africa

Red-footed falcon
Falco vespertinus

FACT FILE

Collared falconet One of the smallest birds of prey, this shy and nervous bird roosts and breeds in abandoned barbet or woodpecker holes in old trees. Insect prey is snatched in flight or from foliage.

⟘ Up to 7 in (18 cm)
⟙ Up to 13 in (33 cm)
🥚 4–5
⊘ Sedentary
🗲 Locally common

Himalayas & N. India to Myanmar & Indochina

Common kestrel This species lives in open habitats, from mountains to cultivated fields. It often builds nests on building ledges or in the abandoned nests of other birds. It hunts by hovering, dropping on to insects and mice.

⟘ Up to 15 in (38 cm)
⟙ Up to 32 in (81 cm)
🥚 3–6
↳ Partial migrant
🗲 Common

N. to S. Eurasia, sub-Saharan Africa

Yellow-headed caracara Outside the breeding season, this bird roosts in large colonies. Individuals fly out to their respective terrestrial foraging grounds in the morning. The caracara has harsh, cat-like cries. It is often attacked by other birds.

⟘ Up to 17 in (43 cm)
⟙ Up to 29 in (74 cm)
🥚 1–2
⊘ Sedentary
🗲 Common

Central to N. & E. South America

ALL IN THE FAMILY

The family Falconidae includes true falcons and caracaras. Despite different foraging ways and behavior, both have a shortly rounded, hooked upper mandible that has a distinctive notch at the sides.

Contrasting ways
Falcons typically hunt prey in the air; but their closest relatives, the South American caracaras, scavenge on the ground.

FACT FILE

New Zealand falcon New Zealand's only resident falcon swoops on small birds, picking them out from soaring watches or vantage perches. It hunts alone and roosts and breeds in high rock crevices, nesting in a bare scrape.

⬆ Up to 19 in (48 cm)
↔ Up to 35 in (89 cm)
● 2–4
∼ Local nomad
⚡ Rare

New Zealand

Gyrfalcon Adapted to cold, this massive falcon breeds north to the Arctic and winters in temperate zones nearby. It hunts low on swift wings, stooping suddenly on surprised lemmings, grouse, and other animals.

⬆ Up to 24 in (61 cm)
↔ Up to 4⅓ ft (1.3 m)
● 2–6
↻ Migrant
⚡ Locally common to rare

Arctic to n. temperate N. America & Eurasia

Eleonora's falcon Few falcons match Eleonora's for tactical maneuvering. It beats rapidly up from its perches on cliffs to gain height over sea, then stoops on flying prey at enormous speeds.

⬆ Up to 16 in (40 cm)
↔ Up to 3¼ ft (1 m)
● 2–6
↻ Migrant
⚡ Locally common

Mediterranean Sea, C. Africa, Madagascar

Merlin A swift hunter, the merlin catches small birds in midair. It ranges from seashore to mountains and forest to tundra. No nests are built, instead this species breeds on rock ledges or in the discarded nests of other birds.

⬆ Up to 13 in (33 cm)
↔ Up to 26 in (66 cm)
● 3–6
↻ Migrant
⚡ Common

N. & C. America, N. & S. Eurasia, N. W. Africa

New Zealand falcon
Falco novaezeelandiae

Like most falcons, this species is solitary and frequents open habitats, mountains, and forests away from human habitation

Lanner falcon
Falco biarmicus

Widespread in Africa and the Middle East

Prairie falcon
Falco mexicanus

Found widely in southwest North America

Eurasian hobby
Falco subbuteo

Gyrfalcon
Falco rusticolus

Catches small birds and bats by hunting at dusk. Migrates to southern Africa and Asia for winter

Eleonora's falcon
Falco eleonorae

Merlin
Falco columbarius

Nankeen kestrel
Falco cenchroides

♂

Confined to Australasia, this species hunts by hovering over fields, searching for insects and small rodents

Mauritius kestrel
Falco punctatus

CRANES AND ALLIES

This ancient bird group, so diverse as to seem a bunch of misfits, comprises a variety of predominantly ground-living birds that prefer walking and swimming to flying. Some species have, in fact, altogether lost the ability to fly. Probably descended from ground-dwelling shorebirds, cranes and their relatives have filled a variety of ecological niches around the world. They typically nest on the ground or on platform nests in shallow water; eggs are varicolored. Most have loud calls, and in some species the male and female perform duets. In parts of Asia, cranes are symbols of good luck and long life; one captive crane is known to have lived to the age of 83.

CLASS Aves
ORDERS 2 or 3
FAMILIES 12
GENERA 62
SPECIES 213

Worldwide This group lives in wetlands, forests, and deserts on every ice-free continent, and many islands too. Seriemas, sunbitterns, trumpeters, and limpkins occur in tropical America; bustards mostly in Africa; and ground-feeding mesites in Madagascan scrubs. Cranes, rails, finfoots, and buttonquails are more widespread.

Pick me Two gray crowned cranes (*Balearica regulorum*) (left) perform an elaborate courtship dance involving bowing and head shaking. Other cranes have even more bizarre dancing rituals to attract and strengthen pair bonds, including inflation of throat sacs and bugling.

Surprise discovery The once-abundant takahe (above) was rediscovered in an inaccessible valley in New Zealand in the 1940s, after not having been sighted for 50 years. This secretive, flightless rail is one of many unusual species in this group.

White-naped crane
Grus vipio

Siberian crane
Grus leucogeranus

Migratory, like most Northern Hemisphere cranes; it breeds across central Asia and winters in north sub-Saharan Africa and India

All crowned cranes have a distinct tuft of straw-like plumes on the head. They are endemic to Africa.

Black crowned crane
Balearica pavonina

Demoiselle crane
Anthropoides virgo

Red-crowned crane
Grus japonensis

FACT FILE

White-naped crane This crane, which stands out with its colorful head, builds flat nests of dry grass that it places on slightly elevated ground among marshes. A herbivore, it often forages in cultivated rice fields for food.

- Up to 5 ft (1.5 m)
- 2–3
- Sexes alike
- Migrant
- Vulnerable

N.E. Asia

Siberian crane Unlike most cranes, the Siberian crane has a flute-like voice and often wades in shallow waters. It does not breed until it is five to seven years old. It is very wary and difficult to approach. Nests are built near water.

- Up to 4½ ft (1.4 m)
- 2
- Sexes alike
- Migrant
- Critically endangered

N.E. Siberia to Iran, N.W. India & China

Demoiselle crane This bird often forages and nests close to human settlements, eating vegetable matter and invertebrates and nesting on bare ground. As in other cranes, the young remain with both parents until they are fully independent.

- Up to 35 in (89 cm)
- 1–2
- Sexes alike
- Migrant
- Rare to locally common

C. Eurasia to N.E. Africa & N. India

FACT FILE

Horned coot This aquatic rail builds a huge, cone-shaped nest that rises above the water on a base of pebbles or sticks over 3 feet (0.9 m) high. It can swim and dive well with its lobed toes.

⚊ Up to 21 in (53 cm)
◗ 3–5
∥ Sexes alike
⊘ Sedentary
⚡ Rare

High Andes of C.W. South America

Corncrake Active at twilight, this rail spends most of its time in tall grasses. It lays up to two clutches in a nest on the ground amid vegetation. It eats invertebrates, plants, seeds, and grain.

⚊ Up to 12 in (30 cm)
◗ 8–12
∥ Sexes alike
↻ Migrant
⚡ Vulnerable

W. & C. Eurasia, S.E. Africa

Takahe The largest rail, the flightless takahe uses its wings only in displays of courtship or aggression. It eats shoots and seeds. Usually only one chick per clutch survives its first winter. Adults mate permanently.

⚊ Up to 25 in (64 cm)
◗ 1–3
∥ Sexes alike
⊘ Sedentary
⚡ Endangered

S.W. South I. (New Zealand)

RAILS AND PREDATORS

A high proportion of island-based rail species cannot fly and are therefore vulnerable to over-predation by introduced animals such as rats. Reintroduction programs have helped some species to recover.

Back from the brink
The Lord Howe rail had fallen to 10 breeding pairs, but has been bred in captivity and released successfully.

⚡ CONSERVATION WATCH

Victims of agriculture Thirty-one of the world's 141 species of rails are listed as threatened by the IUCN. Fifteen of these are endangered, three critically so. Nine are already considered extinct. Many live on remote islands, ultra-susceptible to disturbance and predation.

Purple swamphen
Porphyrio porphyrio

Swamphens flick their tails to flash the white underside as they walk about feeding in wetlands and on verges; this is a social signal to others in their group

Inaccessible rail
Atlantisia rogersi

Confined to Inaccessible Island in the South Atlantic

Horned coot
Fulica cornuta

Coots are the most aquatic of all rails

Ranges through Afro-Eurasia to Australasia

White-breasted waterhen
Amaurornis phoenicurus

Common in southeast Asian rice paddies

Corncrake
Crex crex

Little crake
Porzana parva

A secretive inhabitant of Eurasian marshes

Takahe
Porphyrio hochstetteri

Takahes have such vestigial wings that they cannot fly

Gray-necked wood rail
Aramides cajanea

Slender bodies and long legs enable South America's wood rails to run quickly through dense undergrowth

Kagu
Rhynochetos jubatus

The sole member of its family, Rhynochetidae, this bird rarely—if ever—flies

Red-legged seriema
Cariama cristata

Roams woods and grasslands of tropical South America. Runs rather than flies from danger but roosts and nests in trees

The only member of its family, Eurypygidae

Sunbittern
Eurypyga helias

Great bustard
Otis tarda

Colorful neck plumes are flared in display

Colorful tail is raised in display. Males are much larger and more colorful than females

Denham's bustard
Neotis denhami

Bustards are great walkers. 20 out of the 26 species occur in Africa

Houbara bustard
Chlamydotis undulata

Lesser florican
Sypheotides indica

African finfoot
Podica senegalensis

There are only three species of finfoots, one each in Africa, southeast Asia, and tropical America. Feet are not webbed

Deep water
Several species of duck that dive for their food, such as tufted ducks and pochards, sometimes form rafts in deep water, well away from the shore. Divers and grebes also forage in deep water.

Shallows
These are sites where spoonbills, avocets, and a variety of other birds gather food while wading in shallow water.

Mudflats
Many birds like to feed on mudflats. Some waders, such as common sandpipers and Temminck's stints, prefer freshwater to coastal shores for foraging.

WETLANDS

Wetlands are fresh and brackish marshlands where bodies of water are interspersed with reeds and low, swampy vegetation. On the outside, they appear uninviting but to birds they are a haven, providing a wealth of fishes, plant, and invertebrate food, as well as a wide range of cover for resting and nesting. Ducks and geese have developed webbed feet for swimming and flat bills for sieving food from water. Herons and cranes have long legs for wading and long, tapered bills for striking at prey. Waders—curlews, stilts, and snipe—also have long legs for wading but their bills are soft-tipped and sensitive, specialized for detecting microorganisms in mud. Overhead float terns in another niche altogether, their slender bodies and wings specialized for hawking over open water and their short bills adapted to snatch fishes in aerial dives.

Overhead
Passing flocks of birds, such as black terns and geese, flying in their distinctive V-formations

Reedbeds
Water rails and bitterns hide in reedbeds and forage along their margins when undisturbed. Also home to some songbirds, such as reed warblers and grassbirds, they provide nesting and roosting sites for a wide range of other species.

Specialist generalist The stout, shortened bill of the gray crowned crane (*Balearica regulorum*) enables it to snap up and eat almost anything, from tubers dug from mud to plucked seed and shoots, as well as worms, locusts, and small herptiles, all in drying marshes and pasture.

FACT FILE

Barred buttonquail Although this bird generally lives at lower elevations, it also ranges into the Himalayan mountains. It often forages for food, such as seed and insects, in sugarcane, tea, and coffee plantations. It flushes with whirring flight.

- Up to 7 in (18 cm)
- 3–5
- Sexes differ
- Sedentary
- Common

S., S.E. & E. Asia to Philippines & Sulawesi

Hoatzin This prehistoric-looking bird has an extraordinarily large crop. Just a few days after hatching, chicks can climb trees using their feet, bills, and specially adapted wings; the wings have "claws" that later disappear.

- Up to 27 in (69 cm)
- 2–4
- Sexes alike
- Sedentary
- Locally common

N. South America

Limpkin Related to cranes and rails, the limpkin wades in shallow water and uses its long, curved bill to extract snails from their shells. It builds large, flimsy nests of rushes and sticks near the ground. Hunting has reduced its numbers.

- Up to 27 in (69 cm)
- 5–7
- Sexes alike
- Sedentary
- Locally common

C. America to N.E. South America, West Indies

LIMPKIN'S TRACHEA

Cranes and limpkins can make a wide range of calls, from purrs to screams. Their very long tracheas are coiled and fused with their sternums. In that region, the bony rings of the trachea are like thin plates that vibrate, amplifying the sounds produced in the voicebox and allowing the voice to carry for more than 1 mile (1.6 km) in some circumstances. Crane species with better developed tracheas make higher-pitched calls.

folded trachea

sternum

Common buttonquail
Turnix sylvaticus

Barred buttonquail
Turnix suscitator

Despite their quail-like appearance, buttonquails have only three toes. Females are more brightly plumaged than males

Hoatzin
Opisthocomus hoazin

♂

♀

After attracting a mate, a female buttonquail leaves him to incubate and rear the young, and goes off to find another

Barred buttonquail
Turnix suscitator

The relationships of the strange, fowl-sized hoatzin are unclear; some research even associates it with cuckoos

White-breasted mesite
Mesitornis variegatus

♂

Subdesert mesite
Monias benschi

Trumpeters live in South American rain forest. Hump-backed, chicken-like birds, they feed on the ground and can run fast

Gray-winged trumpeter
Psophia crepitans

Limpkin
Aramus guarauna

Swims very well without webbed feet

WADERS AND SHOREBIRDS

CLASS Aves

ORDERS 1

FAMILIES 16

GENERA 86

SPECIES 351

The world's shallow waters and shorelines teem with marine and terrestrial organisms that this order of generally gregarious birds has evolved to hunt. The groups within the order are diverse in bills and feet, allowing them to exploit different resources within aquatic habitats. Typical waders such as sandpipers and plovers patrol shallow waters and shorelines. Gulls scavenge along shorelines, too, but with webbed feet they can swim out to feed on the surface of deeper water. Terns fly even further out and plunge-dive for food. Auks swim underwater after prey, much like penguins. All nest on the ground or in swamps, laying mostly olive-tawny eggs mottled black for camouflage.

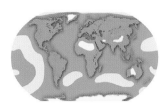

Watery world Some species in this group live next to oceans, along estuaries or seashores; others can live far inland in arid climates in mid deserts.

A WORLD OF DIFFERENCES

Birds within this order exhibit many anatomical differences, as befits their respective niches. Those that wade over mud flats and in shallows, probing for food, have long, often thin legs, necks, and bills. Those that patrol the surf are usually shorter and can scurry out of the way of incoming water. Birds that swim and scoop up food on the water's surface, such as gulls, are stout-billed and web-footed.

Terns that search and dive for marine prey further out on the wing are more capable fliers: they have short legs, pointed bills, and long, narrow wings. These birds are agile in the air and have forked tails for quick maneuvering.

Auks have webbed feet too, but they are set well back on their compact bodies for propulsion underwater. They also use their short wings as flippers.

The diet of these birds ranges from insects and worms to fishes and crustaceans. Some are scavengers.

Walking on water The jacana (above) is a rail-like bird that walks across the surface of still waters by stepping on large lily leaves with its specially elongated toes. For this reason, it is also known as a "lilytrotter."

Best foot forward
Jacanas have splayed, long-nailed toes that distribute their body weight as they walk on floating vegetation.

Holes in the ground Like many waders and shorebirds, puffins (right) often nest in colonies on the shore. Few birds in this order build elaborate nests; like puffins, many lay eggs in squats that they scrape in the ground. Eggs are large so hatchling chicks are already advanced and downy.

Pirate The pomarine jaeger (*Stercorarius pomarinus*) (above) is the largest of the gull-like jaegers. They are big, sturdy, broad-winged birds that scavenge around seabird colonies. They also steal food in flight, chasing other species until they disgorge their stomach contents.

FACT FILE

African jacana This bird uses a high-stepping gait on floating vegetation, probing under plants for insects and snails. It is polyandrous, males making the nest of floating vegetation and incubating the highly glossed eggs.

⚊ Up to 12 in (30 cm)
● 4
✇ Sexes alike
⊘ Sedentary
↟ Common

Sub-Saharan Africa except southwest

Eurasian oystercatcher This shorebird feeds on bivalve mollusks that it opens by cutting the muscle fastening the shells with its chisel-tipped bill. It flocks more than other oystercatchers.

⚊ Up to 18 in (46 cm)
● 2–5
✇ Sexes alike
↻ Migrant
↟ Common

Europe; W., S.W. & E. Asia; N.W., N. & E. Africa

Beach stone curlew Extremely large eyes help this species locate crabs and other shellfish on the reefs and seashores that it patrols alone, or in pairs, at night. Its call is harsh and eerie. It scrapes a simple nest in the sand.

⚊ Up to 22 in (55 cm)
● 1
✇ Sexes alike
⊘ Sedentary
↟ Uncommon

Malay Peninsula to Philippines, Melanesia & N. Australia

BILLS OF FARE

Bills vary with diet and feeding habits. Puffins have big bills with serrated edges used to catch and carry fish underwater. Wading birds have long, slender bills used to probe and pick up small aquatic prey. Gulls have stout bills with vulturine tips for tearing carrion.

Tufted puffin

Common greenshank

Great black-headed gull

Bigger and brighter, females defend breeding territory and mate with several males which brood and rear young

African jacana
Actophilornis africanus

Greater painted-snipe
Rostratula benghalensis

This solitary, polygamous, night-feeder ranges from Africa through southern Asia to Australia

♀

Pheasant-tailed jacana
Hydrophasianus chirurgus

♂

Eurasian oystercatcher
Haematopus ostralegus

Crab plover
Dromas ardeola

Irisbill
Ibidorhyncha struthersii

Black-winged stilt
Himantopus himantopus

Pied avocet
Recurvirostra avosetta

Upcurved bill for sieving plankton from mud. Long legs enable avocets to wade but they can also swim. Widespread across temperate Eurasia and in Africa

Beach stone curlew
Esacus magnirostris

The nine species of stone curlews are cursorial land birds that occur on all habitable continents except North America

Black-tailed godwit
Limosa limosa

Nest in a scrape on the ground; both parents share nesting duties

Collared pratincole
Glareola pratincola

Rusty breeding plumage is lost when bird migrates to winter quarters

Breeds across northern Eurasia and winters from the Mediterranean and Africa to Australia

Eurasian curlew
Numenius arquata

Long, downcurved bills for probing in fresh or saline mud. This species breeds from Europe to central Asia

Spotted redshank
Tringa erythropus

Jerky, nervous feeders, redshanks probe rapidly here and there, in swamp or shore, as they search for microorganisms with their sensitive bills

Southern lapwing
Vanellus chilensis

Common Snipe
Gallinago gallinago

In uniquely black breeding plumage on the Eurasian tundra, winters across southern Eurasia and through central Africa

The only gray lapwing with a crest

American golden plover
Pluvialis dominica

Killdeer
Charadrius vociferus

Feigning a broken wing in distraction display at the nest is a characteristic trait of plovers

In full, black-breasted breeding plumage

FACT FILE

Collared pratincole This bird has short legs, a stumpy bill, and slender wings. Like all pratincoles, it feeds in the air on flying insects over land. It migrates in flocks of thousands.

- Up to 10 in (25 cm)
- 2–4
- Sexes alike
- Migrant
- Locally common

S.W. Eurasia to C. & E. sub-Saharan Africa

Southern lapwing This bird frequents meadows and agricultural fields, where it catches insects and other prey on the ground. Its nests are scrapes in the ground lined with a thin layer of grass.

- Up to 15 in (38 cm)
- 3–4
- Sexes alike
- Sedentary
- Common

N., E. & S. South America

Common snipe The normally secretive common snipe flies in a characteristic zig-zag flight pattern with its bill pointing downward. The tip of the bill has nerve endings that allow the bird to find insects and other organisms by touch as it probes in freshwater fens.

- Up to 10½ in (27 cm)
- 2–5
- Sexes alike
- Migrant
- Common

North & Central America, Eurasia to C. Africa

FLIGHT OF THE SNIPE

Common snipes have a conspicuous display involving "drumming" dives. From a considerable height, the male dives steeply with wings beating and tail fanned. The outer tail feathers are held apart from the rest, to vibrate and produce the drumming sound as the bird falls through the air. The snipe then repeats the display.

Heading down
A common snipe makes a noisy dive. It more typically flies in a distinctive zig-zag pattern.

Green sandpiper This bird's name derives from the greenish sheen to its underparts in summer. It makes piping sounds in flight. It feeds by probing deeply into mud along fresh, inland waterways.

- Up to 9 in (23 cm)
- 3–4
- Sexes alike
- Migrant
- Locally common

W.C. to E.C. Eurasia, C. Africa, S. Asia

Red-necked phalarope The smallest of the three phalarope species, this bird flies swiftly and erratically in flocks. It winters at sea and swims gracefully, carrying its head high and nodding.

- Up to 8 in (20 cm)
- 3–4
- Sexes alike
- Migrant
- Locally common

Arctic, North & Central America, Eurasia

Ruff In spring, the ruff gathers in flocks of hundreds at communal display grounds. The female, or reeve, builds a nest out of fine grasses, either among thick grass or in clumps of sedge.

- Up to 13 in (33 cm)
- 3–4
- Sexes differ
- Migrant
- Locally common

Arctic to W. & S. Eurasia, Africa

CHASING SUMMER

Sandpipers and their allies are transequatorial migrants, exploiting the flushes of summer food on the boreal tundra to breed there, then molting into non-breeding dress and flying to southern shores for more summer feeding from October to April.

Common greenshank
Tringa nebularia

Green sandpiper
Tringa ochropus

Sandpipers probe rapidly for food in favored wetlands, often tidal flats. Their slender bills are pliable and able to sense microorganisms in the ooze

Black marks on the back and breast indicate breeding plumage. Most shanks and sandpipers are monogamous and pairs share nesting duties

Breeds north of Arctic Circle and migrates to southern Europe and sub-Saharan Africa

Full breeding plumage; out of breeding the chestnut turns to white

Little stint
Calidris minuta

Breeds in north Siberian tundra and migrates to Africa, southern Asia, and Australasia

Curlew sandpiper
Calidris ferruginea

Wilson's phalarope
Phalaropus tricolor

Other phalaropes spend winter at sea, but this species migrates from its breeding grounds in the North American midwest to the lakes and mudflats of Andean South America

Red-necked phalarope
Phalaropus lobatus

The male ruff in full breeding regalia. Ruffs congregate in leks at the beginning of breeding to attract and mate with diverse females

♂

Ruff
Philomachus pugnax

♀

Reeves look like ruffs in non-breeding plumage; this is the plumage they wear at winter quarters from Africa to Southeast Asia

Gray-breasted seedsnipe
Thinocorus orbignyianus

Seedsnipes browse on the tips of low, marshy vegetation in the South American highlands

Black-faced sheathbill
Chionis minor

A fatty layer keeps the bird warm and gives it a chubby look

A rudimentary spur on the wing is used as a weapon

Lives by scavenging on sub-antarctic islands and the Antarctic Peninsula

Confined to the Red Sea

White-eyed gull
Larus leucophthalmus

Bonaparte's gull
Larus philadelphia

Jaegers are parasitic; they live in cold seas and chase other seabirds for scraps

Nesting birds have black heads; out of breeding the head molts to white. Lives on the coasts of North America

Long-tailed jaeger
Stercorarius longicaudus

Great black-backed gull
Larus marinus

Widespread around coasts in the Northern Hemisphere

Great black-backed gulls are omnivorous, and usually breed in small colonies

♀

Once thought to be a buttonquail, this Australian bird is now known to be a wader related to the South American seedsnipes. It lives on open plains

Plains wanderer
Pedionomus torquatus

Herring gull
Larus argentatus

In Europe and North America, herring gulls can be distinguished from other large gulls by their combination of a pale gray back with black-tipped wings, pink legs, and pale eyes

FACT FILE

Long-tailed jaeger The long-tailed jaeger has acrobatic courtship flights. It nests within the Arctic Circle and preys on lemmings. Nests are a scrape on the ground. Like other jaegers, this species winters in Southern Hemisphere seas.

- Up to 21 in (53 cm)
- 2
- Sexes alike
- Migrant (inter-polar)
- Common

Arctic, Antarctic, N. & S. Pacific & Atlantic oceans

Herring gull This large, familiar gull can be seen on harbors and beaches, as well as in flocks at garbage dumps and in ploughed fields. It is omnivorous, flies inland to bathe in freshwater, and roosts and nests communally.

- Up to 26 in (66 cm)
- 2–3
- Sexes alike
- Partial migrant
- Common

North & Central America, W., N. & E. Eurasia

JAEGER TAIL FEATHERS

The three species of jaeger are easily recognized by their elongated central tail feathers that taper or are rounded at the tip. The smallest of these birds is the long-tailed jaeger. It grows its central tail feathers—which can project up to 10 inches (25 cm) beyond the other tail feathers—when it is an adult. The function of these feathers is thought to be connected with display, assisting in display flight. Pomarine jaegers even bite theirs off after breeding because they increase drag in normal flight.

Untold tails
Why long-tailed jaegers have projecting central tail feathers is still not really known.

Sandy beaches
When not feeding offshore, terns are fond of loafing in large flocks on beaches. Sanderlings and oystercatchers habitually forage along the shore, and gulls patrol tidelines for carrion.

Cliffs and stacks
These make prime nesting sites for colonies of cormorants, alcids (especially murres and puffins), and some species of gulls.

Offshore
Pelagic birds, such as shearwaters and other tubenosed petrels, usually feed on open seas well offshore.

Surf
The surf zone just offshore may host feeding cormorants and terns and, in the Northern Hemisphere here, rafts of scoters, grebes, murres, loons, and fishing brown pelicans.

SEASHORES

Seafood, in its many forms, brings many groups of birds to the seashore: terns and gannets that plunge-dive from air to sea for fishes; gulls that scavenge; penguins, murres, puffins, and cormorants that chase prey underwater; waders that probe for microorganisms in salty mud and wet sand; and tube-nosed petrels that pick food off the sea surface. The seashore, where land meets sea, brings it all together, providing varied habitats where birds can not only feed, but also rest and nest. These include cliffs, surf-washed rocks, beaches, estuaries, and mangroves. Climate, of course, affects habitat and so influences the bird species present. Alcids and gulls live in colder environments; terns, boobies, and frigatebirds are more common off warmer tropical shores.

From pole to pole Despite overlap, different bird groups are associated with particular habitat: cormorants with cliffs, terns with beaches, shorebirds with estuaries, and so on. Seas fringing the North Pacific coasts, around southern South America, and off New Zealand are particularly rich in seabird life. Auks, gulls, and sea ducks dominate in the north (left), and penguins, cormorants, petrels, and albatrosses in the south.

Nature's banquet table Gulls (above) are highly adaptable inshore seabirds. As natural sources of food have declined or disappeared, they have adapted to scavenging refuse and moved inland in many areas. All seabirds are voracious feeders, as flying and swimming in the open expend a great deal of energy. They belong to five different orders: penguins, tubenoses, pelicans and cormorants, gulls and terns, and shore birds.

DIVING TERNS

Terns resemble gulls but are specially adapted for catching fishes by plunge diving. They have slender, streamlined bodies; heavy heads with strong, thin, tapering bills; long, narrow wings; and forked tails for fast braking and maneuvering. They fly low over oceanic or inland waters, hover briefly, then plunge for food.

Fairy tern
Sterna nereis

Has a more deeply and elegantly forked tail than larger terns

Common tern
Sterna hirundo

Little tern
Sterna albifrons

Migrates in western and northern parts of its range. Nests in scrapes on the ground

Seen here in breeding dress; non-breeding birds have black bills and feet and white foreheads

Sandwich tern
Sterna sandvicensis

Occurs on coasts of west Eurasia, Africa, and the Americas

Confined to sub-antarctic seas in the Indian Ocean

Kerguelen tern
Sterna virgata

All terns have short, webbed feet

Lives along the major rivers of South America

Inca tern
Larosterna inca

Large-billed tern
Phaetusa simplex

Whiskered tern
Chlidonias hybridus

Distinctive white mustache plumes

Both the coloring and the serrated flange on the mid toe are unique to this South American tern

Ranges from Afro-Eurasia to Australasia, on freshwaters. Nests in colonies on floating vegetation

Sooty tern
Sterna fuscata

This pelagic, pan-tropical tern breeds in large colonies, laying a single, red-spotted egg straight on the ground in treeless parts of small islands

Common murre
Uria aalge

Murres live in arctic and sub-arctic seas, sit on the water in large flocks, and dive for a minute or more to chase and catch fishes; feet are webbed

Ancient murrelet
Synthliboramphus antiquus

Breeds colonially like other auks around the North Pacific, but it nests in burrows

Parakeet auklet
Aethia psittacula

Rhinoceros auklet
Cerorhinca monocerata

Crested auklet
Aethia cristatella

Atlantic puffin
Fratercula arctica

Tufted puffin
Fratercula cirrhata

Black skimmer
Rhynchops niger

Lives on coasts of the Americas and large rivers in South America

In skimmers, the lower bill is longer than the upper. They feed by flying just above rather still water with the lower bill immersed, ready to snap up any fishes that come in contact

FACT FILE

Common murre The most widespread of the auk group, common murres nest in large colonies on rocky headlands and offshore islands. Males accompany young after they fledge.

⬧ Up to 17 in (43 cm)
🥚 1
⫽ Sexes alike
〰 Local nomad
🪶 Common

N. Pacific & N. Atlantic oceans

Atlantic puffin In summer, the Atlantic puffin's beak is red, blue, and yellow. In winter, part of the beak is shed; the remaining part is gray-brown with a yellowish tip. Puffins nest in colonies, sometimes using burrows dug by rabbits or shearwaters.

⬧ Up to 14 in (36 cm)
🥚 1
⫽ Sexes alike
🗘 Partial migrant
🪶 Common

Arctic, N. Atlantic Ocean

A LONG WAY DOWN

Murres typically lay just one egg at a time on precarious-looking bare rock ledges on coasts and cliffs. Unlike most eggs, which are oval, murre eggs are pear-shaped. Therefore, if budged, they will roll around in a small circle.

🪶 CONSERVATION WATCH

Auk family The great auk became extinct in the 19th century. Of the other 24 species of the auk family, the IUCN lists 2 as endangered (1 critical) and 3 as vulnerable. All are murrelets that live in the north Pacific Ocean between Japan and the west coast of the United States. Another 31 shorebirds and larids are listed as threatened as well. Introduced rats and foxes at nesting colonies, over fishing, and pollution are taking toll.

PIGEONS AND SANDGROUSE

CLASS	Aves
ORDERS	2
FAMILIES	3
GENERA	46
SPECIES	327

Pigeons and sandgrouse are quite dissimilar and may not even be related. Pigeons and doves are commonplace, tree-dwelling birds that eat fruits and seeds. They have a close association with humans, who have used pigeons for carrying messages. They vary in color from the drab bluish-gray of the familiar street pigeon to the riot of hues that characterize the fruit doves of the Indo-Pacific region. Pigeons feed their young with a milky substance produced in their crops. They also have specialized bills that enable them to suck up water when they drink. By contrast, sandgrouse are dull-colored, fast-flying desert dwellers, with vestigial hind toes that help running.

Abundant Pigeons and doves are found worldwide, except in polar regions. Sand-grouse only inhabit Africa and Eurasia.

FACT FILE

Pallas's sandgrouse This rare nomad breeds on open steppes in Central Asia. Occasionally, large numbers fly for long distances, outside their main range, to grasslands and beaches in order to avoid winter snows that cover their feeding areas. Like other sandgrouse, it has a large crop to hold water as well as food, usually seeds. This species needs to drink daily.

⚊ Up to 16 in (40 cm)
● 2–3
⫽ Sexes differ
⚲ Partial migrant
⚑ Locally common

S. Urals & Transcaspia to Mongolia

Chestnut-bellied sandgrouse As in other sandgrouse, this species disperses to breed in pairs. It lays brown-spotted eggs in a scrape on the ground, the female brooding by day and the male by night. Young can run and leave the nest at hatching, camouflaged in handsomely patterned down. They drink water carried in the male parent's plumage.

⚊ Up to 13 in (33 cm)
● 3
⫽ Sexes alike
⊘ Sedentary
⚑ Common

Semidesert in C. Africa, Arabia & India

Emerald dove This dove is commonly found in rain forests and monsoonal scrub where it forages for fallen fruit on the forest floor, alone or in pairs. It flies low, with evenly beating wings, through forest and nests in low shrubbery. As in other pigeons, nests are flimsy platforms of sticks and eggs are plain cream-white.

⚊ Up to 11 in (28 cm)
● 2
⫽ Sexes differ
⊘ Sedentary
⚑ Common

India & S.E. Asia to E. Australia & Melanesia

Side by side Like other species in this group, green-pigeons roost communally (above). Highly social birds, pigeons, doves, and sandgrouse often flock in large groups numbering thousands. There is actually no real difference between doves and pigeons.

Crowning achievement Three species of spectacular crowned pigeons (right) inhabit the rain forests of New Guinea. The world's largest pigeons, they are distinguished by their filmy crests. Pigeon courtship rituals include bowing and special display flights.

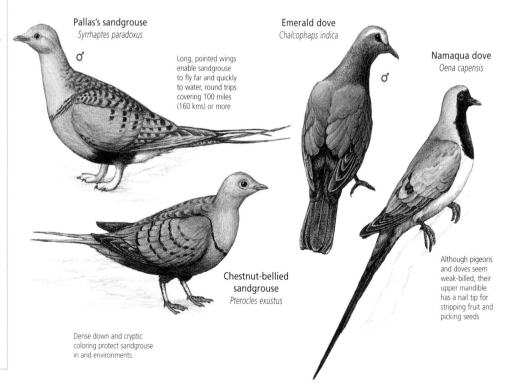

Pallas's sandgrouse
Syrrhaptes paradoxus
♂

Long, pointed wings enable sandgrouse to fly far and quickly to water, round trips covering 100 miles (160 kms) or more

Emerald dove
Chalcophaps indica

Namaqua dove
Oena capensis
♂

Chestnut-bellied sandgrouse
Pterocles exustus

Dense down and cryptic coloring protect sandgrouse in arid environments

Although pigeons and doves seem weak-billed, their upper mandible has a nail tip for stripping fruit and picking seeds

Rock dove
Columba livia

Woodpigeon
Columba palumbus

Widespread in
temperate Eurasia

European turtle dove
Streptopelia turtur

Ranges south to
Ethiopia and Chad
on migration

Emerald- spotted
wood dove
Turtur chalcospilos

A ground-feeder
in the savannas
of east Africa

Crested pigeon
Ocyphaps lophotes

This species
is Australian

Pink pigeon
Nesoenas mayeri

Diamond dove
Geopelia cuneata

Restricted to natural
forest on Mauritius

Stock dove
Columba oenas

Partial migrant
in west Eurasia

Distinct white
mid-back

Lives at high
altitudes in
the Himalayas

Snow pigeon
Columba leuconota

FACT FILE

Rock dove Also known as a feral
pigeon, this bird is familiar to urban
dwellers across the world. Originally
from Eurasia and North Africa, where
it nests on cliffs, it has readily adapted
to living on building ledges in cities.

⚐ Up to 13 in (33 cm)
🥚 2
⚄ Sexes alike
⊘ Sedentary
🜊 Common

S. Europe, Middle East, S.W. & C.E. Asia,
N. Africa; introduced worldwide

Crested pigeon Once found only in
inland Australia, this pigeon has now
spread to the coast in many places.
It is a ground-feeding seed-eater and,
with glossed colors on the wings,
belongs to a group of Australian
pigeons known as the bronzewings.
Slotting at the tips of flight feathers
makes a whistling sound in flight.

⚐ Up to 14 in (36 cm)
🥚 2
⚄ Sexes alike
⊘ Sedentary
🜊 Common

Australia

PIGEON PLUMAGE

Pigeons and doves are plump birds,
clad in dense feathers spread diffusely
over the skin. It is common for tree-
living species to be plumaged in
camouflaging greens while those
feeding on the ground are often
dappled in gray-brown over the back.
Both groups have short feet, better
suited to clambering than walking,
and flush with a clattering of wings.
They can breed opportunistically
whenever food sources are adequate.
Eyes at the side of their heads give
them 360° vision.

*City slickers Rock doves
are one of a hundred or
more bird species found in
Central Park, New York.*

FACT FILE

Madagascan green pigeon This handsome, fruit-eating bird is one of 23 species of green pigeon. It spends most of its time in trees and bushes, climbing in the manner of a parrot. It has complex, soft calls that are not typical of pigeons and doves.

- Up to 13 in (33 cm)
- 2
- Sexes alike
- Sedentary
- Locally common

Madagascar & Comoro Is.

Mourning dove This dove's name derives from its low, mournful cooing. A ground seed-eater, it is a strong, fast flier that may fly considerable distances to find feeding areas or the nearest water source, often at dawn or dusk.

- Up to 14 in (36 cm)
- 2
- Sexes alike
- Partial migrant
- Common

North & Central America, West Indies

Victoria crowned pigeon The only crowned pigeon with a white-tipped crest, this species lives in lowland rain forest. Hunted for food, it remains common only in remote areas of northern New Guinea.

- Up to 29 in (74 cm)
- 1
- Sexes alike
- Sedentary
- Vulnerable

Lowland N. New Guinea

GONE FOREVER

The passenger pigeon (*Ectopistes migratorius*) was one of the world's most plentiful birds, seen across North America in flocks that may have numbered in the billions. But humans hunted them mercilessly, and the last of the species died in 1914.

CONSERVATION WATCH

And still going... Among pigeons, the IUCN lists 12 species as critically endangered, 15 as endangered, and another 33 as vulnerable. Habitat destruction and hunting are root causes. The passenger pigeon, dodo, solitaires, Socorro dove, and choiseul pigeon are all extinct. Several more species in the Pacific are going now.

Madagascan green pigeon
Treron australis

Arboreal fruit-eaters, Indo-African green pigeons have a gizzard modified for grinding seeds as well as fruit

Banded fruit dove
Ptilinopus cinctus

Thin-walled gizzards allow the ingestion of fruit but the passing of seeds

Solitary in the canopy of monsoon forests of the lesser Sundas and northwest Australia

Seychelles blue pigeon
Alectroenas pulcherrima

Bruce's green pigeon
Treron waalia

Turkey-sized crowned pigeons of New Guinea have a uniquely fan-like crest. They eat fruit picked from the forest floor

A common dove throughout temperate North America

Victoria crowned pigeon
Goura victoria

Mourning dove
Zenaida macroura

Lives in wet forests in central America

Gray-headed dove
Leptotila plumbeiceps

Zebra dove
Geopelia striata

Occurs around settlements in southwest Asia

Luzon bleeding-heart
Gallicolumba luzonica

Shy and cryptic species, is vulnerable to snaring

Superb fruit dove
Ptilinopus superbus

♂

Wompoo fruit dove
Ptilinopus magnificus

A nomadic wanderer; males are much brighter than females

Inca dove
Scardafella inca

Solitary in Central America, feeds on seeds on the ground

Common ground dove
Columbina passerina

A ground-feeder, lives in open habitats in tropical America

Nicobar pigeon
Caloenas nicobarica

Tooth-billed pigeon
Didunculus strigirostris

Very short, white tail. The nob on the bill is larger in males

Nests in small colonies over prolonged periods

Pied imperial pigeon
Ducula bicolor

FACT FILE

Luzon bleeding-heart A popular cage-bird, this species is now uncommon in the wild. It is rather solitary and feeds exclusively on rain-forest floors, picking up seeds, fallen berries, and some insects.

⤒ Up to 12 in (30 cm)
● 2
// Sexes alike
⊘ Sedentary
⌁ Uncommon

Luzon, Philippines

Wompoo fruit dove This species can grow to the size of a chicken and is the largest of all fruit doves. It forages on fruit in the sub-canopy of lowland rain forest where it nests. It has a guttural growling call that sounds eerily human.

⤒ Up to 18 in (46 cm)
● 1
// Sexes alike
⊘ Sedentary
⌁ Locally common

E. Australia & lowland New Guinea

Nicobar pigeon This is a colonial pigeon of small islands, commuting extensively between them. Its wanderings are dictated by the seasonal fruiting of food trees. Feeding on the ground on fallen fruits and nuts, it grinds them up with horny plates in its stomach.

⤒ Up to 14 in (36 cm)
● 1
// Sexes alike
~ Nomad
⌁ Locally common

Small islands in Indonesian region

Pied imperial pigeon An arboreal pigeon, this species shifts around south-west Pacific islands seasonally, following the ripening of favored fruits. It will arrive in huge flocks, breed in dense colonies in the forest upper levels, then move on.

⤒ Up to 18 in (46 cm)
● 1
// Sexes alike
~ Seasonal nomad
⌁ Common, declining

Archipelagos in Indonesia to N. Australia

Tooth-billed pigeon This species uses its uniquely thickened and serrated bill to tear open tough-shelled fruit and get to the seed. It also eats wild plantains and aerial yam tubers, carrying out most, if not all, of its foraging in trees.

⤒ Up to 15 in (38 cm)
● no data
// Sexes alike
⊘ Sedentary
⌁ Vulnerable

Samoa in southwest Pacific

PARROTS

CLASS	Aves
ORDERS	1
FAMILIES	3 or more
GENERA	85
SPECIES	364

Parrots and cockatoos form an ancient and highly distinct order of birds, without clear relatives. They are easily recognized by their short, hooked bills, which have incurved mandibles specialized for seed eating; and also by finely scaled feet, which have two toes pointing forward and two pointing backward, specialized for clambering. Most are brilliantly plumaged, colored in shades of green accented by splashes of red, yellow, and blue. Their visual appeal is one reason for their popularity as pets over the centuries. Another is their antics: they can perform acrobatics, hanging on perches with either feet or bills, and can mimic human voices.

Southerly distribution Parrots live primarily in the Southern Hemisphere. They are especially common in lowland tropical rain forests, but some species prefer open, arid regions. The highest concentrations of species occur in Australasia and South America. The most southerly parrot inhabits Tierra del Fuego, Argentina.

A SOCIABLE GROUP

Most parrots eat seeds and nuts (which they crack open with their heavy bills) as well as fruit. They forage among the treetops or on the ground. Lorikeets, on the other hand, are strictly arboreal; they eat soft fruit, and harvest pollen and nectar with brush-tipped tongues.

Although parrots' basic features differ little among species, there is considerable variation in size and shape. Wings can be narrow and pointed, or broad and rounded. Similarly, tails may be long and pointed or short and squarish. Some have ornate feathers. Cockatoos, a separate family from "true parrots," have prominent, erectile head crests. Usually, the sexes are alike and monogamous. Nearly all nest in tree holes and lay plain white eggs.

Parrots are very social birds. They squawk loudly and frequently, and are heard more often than seen in the wild where their green plumage camouflages them. Parrots usually pair for life and separate to breed without holding territory. Almost all nest in scrapes in tree hollows, and all lay plain, dull white eggs.

Group dynamics A colorful gathering of orange-cheeked (*Pionopsitta barrabandi*) and blue-headed (*Pionus menstruus*) parrots at a clay (above), "lick" for salt. Parrots are gregarious and roost and feed in small parties or large flocks.

Fancy feathers Red-and-green macaws (*Ara chloroptera*) (below), though difficult to see in forest foliage, can be recognized by their colorful plumage and long tails. Their tapered wings allow them to fly faster than expected for birds of their size.

Open wide Parrots' bills have a greater range of motion and are more powerful than the bills of other birds. A well-developed hinge on the upper mandible of a parrot's jaw (below) provides leverage that enables the bird to use its bill to climb branches, and a strongly muscled, cutting-edged lower mandible to cut up and crack open large, hard-shelled nuts.

Sounding off Parrots can use their feet like hands, to handle objects. This palm cockatoo (*Progosciger aterrimus*) (above) creates mechanical sounds by drumming a stick against a hollow tree.

Inner view The cutaway shows the adaptations to jaw and bill.

crotch in upper bill for anchoring nut to be husked. The nut is braced there by a muscular tongue specialized for manipulating food

upper hinge

lower hinge

lower bill when jaw is open

cutting tip of lower bill

hook for grabbing food

Aloft Two brilliantly colored red-and-green macaws display a rainbow of hues when they fly. They are among the largest parrots.

Salmon-crested cockatoo
Cacatua moluccensis

Found only in the
South Moluccas
where it is now rare

Females have barred
and spotted plumage
and ivory bills

Red-tailed
black cockatoo
Calyptorhynchus banksii

♂

Cockatiel
*Nymphicus
hollandicus*

♂

Head is gray in
females. Feeds on
seeds on the ground

Palm cockatoo
Probosciger aterrimus

Feeds in the
forest canopy

Endemic to
eucalypt forest in
southeast Australia

Gang-gang cockatoo
Callocephalon fimbriatum

Only males
are red-headed

♂

Pink
cockatoo
*Cacatua
leadbeateri*

♀

Galah
*Eolophus
roseicapilla*

Delicate tone to the
gray on a galah's back
comes from powder
down on the rump.
Females are red-eyed
and males black-eyed

FACT FILE

Palm cockatoo The huge, nut-cracking bill of this species is modified so that it never closes, even at rest, and is larger in males than females. While solitary when feeding, this species roosts in groups.

⤒ Up to 25 in (64 cm)
◗ 1
⫽ Sexes alike
⊘ Sedentary
⚑ Uncommon
🏛 🌲 🜃

Lowland New Guinea, N.E. Australia

Red-tailed black cockatoo This versatile cockatoo feeds both on the ground or in trees by holding nuts with its left foot, while using its right foot for perching. It flies buoyantly, often in large flocks, and enters nest holes tail-first.

⤒ Up to 26 in (66 cm)
◗ 1
⫽ Sexes differ
∼ Local nomad
⚑ Common to rare
🌲 🜃 🜃 🜃

Australia

Cockatiel The smallest and softest-voiced of cockatoos, this species is a popular cage pet. It flocks in the wild, flying gracefully between feeding grounds on pointed wings.

⤒ Up to 13 in (33 cm)
◗ 3–7
⫽ Sexes differ
∼ Nomad
⚑ Common
🜃 🜃

Inland Australia

Galah Resting in trees during the hot midday hours, the galah eats mainly seeds and other plant material on the ground. It gathers in huge flocks and, like other cockatoos, drinks daily.

⤒ Up to 14 in (36 cm)
◗ 2–6
⫽ Sexes alike
⊘ Sedentary
⚑ Common
🜃 🜃 🜃 🜃 🜃

Australia

⚡ CONSERVATION WATCH

It's criminal Illegal trapping for the pet trade threatens parrots and cockatoos as much as habitat loss. Even the eggs of rare species are stolen from the wild, the thieves cutting into nests in hollows and ruining the site for further nesting. The IUCN lists 2 species as already extinct, 15 as critically endangered, 28 as endangered, and 45 as vulnerable. The huge, colorful South American macaws are particularly high in each category.

FACT FILE

Buff-faced pygmy parrot Propped by its stubby tail, this tiny species scrambles around tree trunks, nibbling for lichens and burrowing into termite mounds for termites. Confined to New Guinea, it roosts and nests in termite mounds.

- Up to 3½ in (9 cm)
- 2–3
- Sexes alike
- Local nomad
- Locally common

Lowland N. & E. New Guinea

Rainbow lorikeet Flocks shriek constantly, whether foraging by day or roosting clumped together at night. The tongue of the lorikeet has a tip of brush-like papillae, allowing it to mop up nectar from flowering trees. Its flight is fast and direct on rapidly beating wings.

- Up to 12 in (30 cm)
- 1–3
- Sexes alike
- Local nomad
- Common

E. & S. Australia, Moluccas & New Guinea to New Caledonia

Kea Although its dull color, compact body, and hooked bill may resemble a bird of prey, the kea is primarily a fruit and shoot-eating vegetarian. This bird bounds over the ground in small flocks, nests in crevices under rocks, and roosts in mountain vegetation.

- Up to 19 in (48 cm)
- 2–4
- Sexes alike
- Sedentary
- Uncommon

Montane South I. (New Zealand)

PAMPERED PETS

The familiar budgerigar (*Melopsittacus undulatus*) is one of the world's most popular pet species, on par with the goldfish. It began to be kept in captivity in the middle of the 19th century. Other popular domesticated parrot species include cockatiels and lovebirds. Although pet parrots can mimic human speech, they do not understand a word they are saying.

Tamed In the wild in Australia, budgerigars are all light green and pale yellow. In captivity, they have been bred in a range of colors.

Red-rumped parrot
Psephotus haematonotus

Eclectus parrot
Eclectus roratus

Buff-faced pygmy parrot
Micropsitta pusio

Inhabits woodlands in inland southeastern Australia; feeds on seeds on the ground

This species is widespread in lowland forests in New Guinea and nearby regions

Pesquet's parrot
Psittrichas fulgidus

Eastern rosella
Platycercus eximius

Lives in south-east Australian eucalypt woodlands

Rainbow lorikeet
Trichoglossus haematodus

Kea
Nestor notabilis

New Zealand's keas and kakas are of ancient Gondwanan origin

Black-capped lory
Lorius lory

Widespread in lowland New Guinean rain forests

Blue-crowned hanging parrot
Loriculus galgulus

Alexandrine parakeet
Psittacula eupatria

The tiny ranging parrots of Southeast Asia and Indonesia are among the few groups of parrots with short, blunt tails. They may rest and sleep hanging upside-down in foliage

Swift parrot
Lathamus discolor

Vernal hanging-parrot
Loriculus vernalis

A common feature of the Asian parakeets is a ringed neck

Plum-headed parakeet
Psittacula cyanocephala

A nectar-feeding parrot that looks like a lorikeet but is really related to the Australian rosellas. It breeds only in Tasmania, Australia

Senegal parrot
Poicephalus senegalus

Yellow-collared lovebird
Agapornis personatus

Fischer's lovebird
Agapornis fischeri

Confined to moors around the southern Australian coast

Ground parrot
Pezoporus wallicus

Lovebirds are found only in Africa and Madagascar

FACT FILE

Alexandrine parakeet This parakeet nests in holes that it gnaws in trees, in naturally occurring hollows, or even in chimneys. It lives in small groups that join together to form larger groups for the night. Only the male has a prominent black collar around its neck. The species can be found in forested and cultivated lands.

⏶ Up to 24 in (61 cm)
● 3
✏ Sexes differ
⊘ Sedentary
⌁ Locally common
🌣 ⛰ 🌱

S. & S.E. Asia

Blue-crowned hanging parrot This small parrot is quite common in the forested lowlands of Southeast Asia. It eats buds and flowers as well as fruits, nuts, and seeds in the tree canopy. It gets its name from its habit of sleeping upside-down and nests in tree holes. It wanders around in small groups and is rarely seen alone.

⏶ Up to 5 in (13 cm)
● 3–4
✏ Sexes differ
⊘ Sedentary
⌁ Common
🏛 🌣 🌱

Malay Peninsula, Borneo, Sumatra & nearby islands

BLUE VARIATIONS

Alexandrine parakeets are among those parrot species that also have a mutant blue color variety, due to the suppression of yellow pigmentation. They are popular pets because of their excellent mimicking skills and affectionate behavior. They are named after the legendary Alexander the Great.

Spread out
An Australian eastern rosella in flight shows the wide range of colors and patterns in its plumage.

⚡ CONSERVATION WATCH

Fischer's lovebird This once-common species of parrot, which lives in the wooded steppes and forests of East Africa, is caught in large numbers for the pet trade. Even so, there are still up to a million birds in the wild, at least half of them protected in parks and reserves. "Lovebirds" are named for the close bond between pairs.

FACT FILE

Thick-billed parrot The bill of this species is pale in young birds and darkens as they mature. The parrot eats pine seeds, juniper berries, and acorns. It gathers in nomadic flocks of about half a dozen to several hundred birds.

- Up to 17 in (43 cm)
- 1–4
- Sexes alike
- Nomad
- Endangered

W. Mexico

Hyacinth macaw The largest species in the parrot family, the hyacinth macaw is far less common than it once was due to trafficking and hunting. It depends on a few palm species for food, eating their fruit in crowns or on the ground.

- Up to 3¼ ft (1 m)
- 2–3
- Sexes alike
- Sedentary
- Endangered

N.E. & C. South America

Scarlet macaw This brightly colored bird sometimes supplements its fruit and nut diet with nectar and flowers. It also sometimes ingests clay to help digest the harsh chemicals found in unripe fruit. It nests in large, high tree hollows within dense forest.

- Up to 35 in (89 cm)
- 1–4
- Sexes alike
- Sedentary
- Common

C. & N. South America

BURROWING PARAKEET

Most parrots nest in tree hollows or in cavities in structures such as termite mounds. The burrowing parakeet of Argentina and central Chile, on the other hand, excavates deep burrows in cliffs and banks along rivers or near the ocean. These offer protection from predators.

Thick-billed parrot
Rhynchopsitta pachyrhyncha

Blue-and-yellow macaw
Ara ararauna

Endemic to Amazonian gallery forest

Hyacinth macaw
Anodorhynchus hyacinthinus

Macaws use their massive bills to open hard-shelled nuts and fruits

Scarlet macaw
Ara macao

Maroon-face parakeet
Pyrrhura leucoti.

Military macaw
Ara militaris

Found in pockets of dry, montane forest in north-west South America

Feeds on seeds and fruit, mainly on the ground, in central South America

Nanday parakeet
Nandayus nenday

Burrowing parakeet
Cyanoliseus patagonus

Red-fan parrot
Deroptyus accipitrinus

White-crowned parrot
Pionus senilis

Monk parakeet
Myiopsitta monachus

Canary-winged parakeet
Brotogeris versicolurus

Orange-winged parrot
Amazona amazonica

Cuban parrot
Amazona leucocephala

Kakapo
Strigops habroptilus

Flightless; has cryptic plumage to help it hide in its scrubby habitat, but this has not stopped introduced stoats, rats, and feral cats from exterminating it in its natural range

Like other parrots, the kakapo's feet have two toes forward and two toes back

Blue-fronted parrot
Amazona aestiva

Found in scrubs and savannas of central South America

FACT FILE

Monk parakeet This highly adaptable parrot is found in city parks, on farms, and in gardens as well as in savannas, forests, and palm groves. Unlike other species of parrots, it breeds colonially and builds its own large, complex nests of twigs with several entrances.

- ⚊ Up to 12 in (30 cm)
- ● 1–11
- ∥ Sexes alike
- ⊘ Sedentary
- ⚡ Common

C. & S.E. South America

Blue-fronted parrot This arboreal climbing parrot lives in forests and builds its nests in hollows in trees. It eats fruits and seeds from nuts. Eggs are incubated mainly by the female over the course of about 25 days.

- ⚊ Up to 15 in (38 cm)
- ● 2–4
- ∥ Sexes alike
- ⊘ Sedentary
- ⚡ Common

N.E. & C. South America

Kakapo The world's heaviest parrot, the kakapo is nocturnal and cannot fly because it lacks a sternal keel. It chews leaves or stems to extract their juices. Males court females in leks, booming with their inflated gular air sacs.

- ⚊ Up to 25 in (64 cm)
- ● 1–3
- ∥ Sexes alike
- ⊘ Sedentary
- ⚡ Extinct in natural range

S.W. South Island, New Zealand; introd. to Little Barrier, Maud, Codfish & Pearl Is.

STRIKING RUFF

The red-fan parrot (*Deroptyus accipitrinus*) of Amazonia has a striking ruff of long, colorful erectile feathers on the nape. It raises them when it is excited or angry. It is a noisy, sociable, and conspicuous parrot that usually inhabits jungle interiors, eating fruit in the understory.

Head on
A raised collar

In profile
Ruffled feathers

CUCKOOS AND TURACOS

These two old groups of birds are related by similarities in DNA, but the data are conflicting and the two otherwise differ markedly in development, anatomy, and plumage. Cuckoos are notorious as parasitical birds that trick other species into raising their chicks. However, less than half of their 140 or so species actually engage in such behavior. All cuckoos have feet with two toes pointing forward and two backward, but otherwise differ considerably among themselves in form and behavior. Turacos are more homogeneous: with one exception, they are slender-necked birds with long tails, short, rounded wings, and erectile, laterally flattened crests.

Here, there and everywhere Turacos inhabit savannas and forests. They live only in Africa, south of the Sahara. Cuckoos thrive in a variety of habitats—from open moorland to tropical rain forest—and are virtually cosmopolitan, although they predominate in the tropics and subtropics.

Doing away with the competition
A common cuckoo (left) hatches before the eggs of its host parent, in this case a reed warbler. Within three or four days, the young cuckoo is strong enough to evict the other eggs or hatchlings so that it can monopolize the foster parent's attention and food. Not only different cuckoo species, but different females within a species may each be adapted to parasitize one species of host.

ROBBING THEM BLIND

Some cuckoo species have evolved remarkably devious strategies to get away with brood parasitism, such as laying eggs that closely resemble those of their host.

Most "true cuckoos" are drab, although the bronze-cuckoos of the Old World tropics are shining copper-green. Some are solitary; others breed communally and maintain group territories. Some, such as the roadrunners and ground cuckoos, rarely fly and prefer to run.

Turacos are gregarious, arboreal birds with harsh, barking calls. Helped by an outward-pointing outer toe, they are more agile running among branches than when flap-gliding from tree to tree. Nests are flimsy platforms of sticks.

All savanna-based turaco species have dull plumage but those that favor forests are richly colored, with a unique blue-green pigment. Wing feathers often have a similarly unique red pigment containing copper. All turacos are fruit-eaters.

Flocks in flight Like most parrots, budgerigars (left) band together in flocks to seek food and water, their numbers improving survival prospects.

Hartlaub's turaco
Tauraco hartlaubi

Has the green plumage found in most turacos; lives in equatorial east Africa

All turacos have long, slender tails

Great blue turaco
Corythaeola cristata

The size of a small turkey, this is the largest of all turacos; it lives in tropical Africa and has a distinctive orange belly

Cuckoos of the Afro-Asian *Clamator* group are the only ones with crests

Jacobin cuckoo
Clamator jacobinus

Look at me Unlike most other birds, whose bright plumage colors are caused by refraction of light, turacos such as the Knysna turaco (*Tauraco corythaix*) (below) of South Africa have true pigmentation.

Violet turaco
Musophaga violacea

Violet-blue plumage is characteristic of violet and Ross's turaco species; both live in central west African riverine forests

Great spotted cuckoo
Clamator glandarius

FACT FILE

Common cuckoo This well-known bird inhabits woodlands where it feeds on hairy caterpillars and insects. It has a familiar call from which its name arose. Females in this species are polyandrous and parasitic.

⚲ Up to 13 in (33 cm)
● Up to 12, even 20, singly in host nests
⫻ Sexes differ
↻ Migrant
⚑ Common

Eurasia except S.W.; N.W. & S. Africa

Greater coucal This non-parasitic scavenger has terrestrial habits. It is often mistaken for a game bird due to its size and bushy tail. It has a distinctive dull, booming call, as well as a variety of croaks and chuckles.

⚲ Up to 20 in (51 cm)
● 2–4
⫻ Sexes alike
⊘ Sedentary
⚑ Common

S. & S.E. Asia, Greater Sundas, some islands off Philippines

Greater roadrunner This ground-loving bird is the basis for the famous cartoon character. It inhabits arid regions and deserts with shrubs and cacti. It uses its long tail as a rudder to change direction when it runs quickly. Its diet includes snakes and other reptiles.

⚲ Up to 22 in (55 cm)
● 2–6
⫻ Sexes alike
⊘ Sedentary
⚑ Common

S.W. USA to C. Mexico

FURRY FEAST

Old World cuckoos eat insects and their larvae. They are especially fond of hairy caterpillars, which are shunned by most other birds. Their diet forces common cuckoos to migrate to Africa for the winter.

Common koel
Eudynamys scolopaceus

Like other parasitic cuckoos, males of this Southeast Asian species give monotonous advertising calls, over and over, at night as well as by day during early breeding

Common cuckoo
Cuculus canorus

A female common cuckoo about to place her egg in the nest of another bird—in this case, a reed warbler

Dideric cuckoo
Chrysococcyx caprius

One of the bronze cuckoos, this African parasite has the characteristic glossed green back of the group

Greater coucal
Centropus sinensis

Yellow-billed cuckoo
Coccyzus americanus

A migrant that breeds in North America and winters in South America

Bornean ground-cuckoo
Carpococcyx radiceus

Feeds on insects on the floor of rain forests in Borneo, but roosts and nests in trees, rearing its young

Smooth-billed ani
Crotophaga ani

This non-parasitic bird has a high-ridged bill for parting vegetation as it forages in the woods of South America. It builds communal nests

Rufous-vented ground-cuckoo
Neomorphus geoffroyi

Feeds on the floor of South American forests

Greater roadrunner
Geococcyx californianus

Omnivorous, and an efficient predator on small reptiles; also eats insects, mice, and the eggs of other small birds

OWLS

CLASS	Aves
ORDERS	1
FAMILIES	2
GENERA	29
SPECIES	196

Solitary creatures of the night, owls are instantly recognizable by their forward-facing eyes, face masks, and stout silhouettes. There are two families of owls: barn owls, with heart-shaped faces and elongate bills, and "true owls," with rounded heads and hawk-like bills. Owls usually roost in out-of-the-way spots. Even when out in the open, they tend to perch stoically, camouflaged by their mottled, earth-toned plumage, so they are more often heard than seen. Their stealthy nocturnal habits, coupled with their far-reaching hoots and other eerie-sounding calls, have given rise to many folk superstitions. In lifestyle, however, they are no more than nocturnal birds of prey.

Cosmopolitan birds Both families of owls are widespread; some species such as the barn owl are among the most widely distributed of all birds. Most species inhabit woodlands and forest edges, but some prefer treeless habitats instead.

A bird for all seasons Few owls are migratory. Most boreal species, such as this American great horned owl (*Bubi virginianus*) (above), remain in the north through the winter, sleeping out in the snow and hunting even on dull days for rodents and other prey. Their soft, thick plumage not only silences flight but also insulates superbly.

NIGHT HUNTERS

Owls, which typically become active at twilight, are well adapted to a nocturnal predatory lifestyle. Forward-facing eyes give them binocular vision that helps judge distances and they are able to rotate their heads to see behind them. They can see well in poor light, thanks to their tubular eyes with an abundance of light-sensitive rods. They also rely on an acute sense of hearing; some species even have facial masks to help capture sound waves more effectively.

Owls also have sharp, hooked bills and strong legs with talon-tipped feet. They remain on the alert for prey as they perch on branches or ledges, then swoop down to catch the unwary mammal or insect on the ground. They may also snatch insects or mammals from trees, or catch insects in the air.

When they capture sizable prey with their talons, owls sometimes kill it by reaching down to bite it. Small prey is often lifted to the beak with one foot, in the manner of parrots, and swallowed whole. Larger prey is held with the feet and torn apart with the bill before being eaten.

In most species, females are larger than the males. All hoot or scream as breeding nears. Pairs nest in tree or rock hollows and crevices, laying round, white eggs. Young often leave the nest still partly in down.

STEREO HEARING

Many owls have ears that are asymmetrical in both size and shape. This arrangement enables them to more precisely locate their prey, by noting the subtle difference between the sound signals reaching each ear.

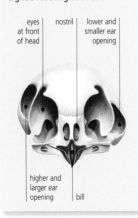

eyes at front of head | nostril | lower and smaller ear opening

higher and larger ear opening | bill

Stealthy flight The eastern screech owl (*Otus asio*) (right) has soft, loose plumage. Its flight feathers have frayed rather than smooth edges, which slows the flow of air over the wings and silences flight.

CONSERVATION WATCH

Favorable future Only 26 of 196 species of owls are threatened: 14 are endangered (4 critically so) and another 12 are vulnerable. Three of the critically endangered are scops owls found only on the Cormoro islands in the Indian Ocean.

HUNTING

Owls are raptors of the night. They hunt in the dark hours for live prey, often warm-blooded animals, quartering their hunting grounds on the wing or swooping down from a vantage perch to ambush. Like hawks, they seize their quarry in their talons and use their strongly hooked bills to carry food or to tear it up to eat. Unlike hawks, they have special adaptations for hunting at night: tubular eyes that have binocular vision to judge distance and pinpoint prey in dim light; enlarged, asymmetric ears to pick up the slightest rustle and coordinate prey position; and soft plumage to deaden the sound of flight. Hearing is so acute in species with sound-conducting facial disks that they can locate the exact position of a shuffling mouse in complete darkness.

Here, a great gray owl swoops on a small rodent somewhere in the boreal forests of the Northern Hemisphere. It hunts in the classical mode of attack used by all owls, striking from a silent aerial sally. Eyes are fixed on the kill; ears are listening, coordinating with the eyes for prey movement; wings are raised, controlling the angle and speed of the swoop; and talons are thrust forward, ready to seize and carry off the victim in one swift pounce. Keen hearing can detect rodents beneath snow, allowing this owl to remain and hunt in boreal forests throughout winter.

KILLER'S INSTINCT

The barn owl belongs to the most specialized group of all owls. Every adaptation that owls have for nocturnal hunting seems to reach its zenith here. Eyes are often smaller, simply because the huge asymmetric ears are so good at finding prey. Their lids close the eye by moving up and down, like human eyes, not forward and backward as in other birds; so owls can appear to wink. No other owl has such large ears or as well-developed facial disks for conducting sound.

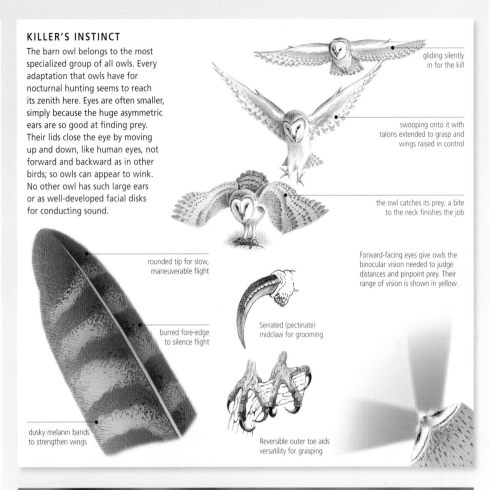

gliding silently in for the kill

swooping onto it with talons extended to grasp and wings raised in control

the owl catches its prey; a bite to the neck finishes the job

Forward-facing eyes give owls the binocular vision needed to judge distances and pinpoint prey. Their range of vision is shown in yellow.

rounded tip for slow, maneuverable flight

burred fore-edge to silence flight

Serrated (pectinate) midclaw for grooming

dusky melanin bands to strengthen wings

Reversible outer toe aids versatility for grasping

Hungry mouths to feed A female great gray owl (right) feeds a rodent to her chicks. Owls can vary their times of breeding and clutch sizes according to availability of food. Hatching is also asynchronous, so that if food becomes hard to come by, the more advanced chicks can survive by eating their younger and weaker siblings. Female owls brood and feed the chicks, while males usually do most of the hunting, bringing food to the female at the nest when she is incubating and brooding.

FACT FILE

Great gray owl This large owl often uses the abandoned nests of other birds. It may not nest in years when food is particularly scarce, whereas in good years, it may lay up to nine eggs.

- Up to 27 in (69 cm)
- 2–9
- Sexes alike
- Sedentary
- Uncommon

N. North America, N. Eurasia

Snowy owl This tundra-lover moves to open, warmer plains in winter. It perches on rocks or in trees and kills its prey—invertebrates, small mammals, or birds—by pouncing in flight. Nests are scrapes in crevices on the ground.

- Up to 27 in (69 cm)
- 3–11
- Sexes differ
- Partial migrant
- Uncommon

N. Eurasia, N. Canada, Arctic

PYGMY OWL DISGUISE

Owls protect themselves from predators primarily by camouflaging themselves against their surroundings and by roosting out of sight. Their nocturnal habits also put them on a different schedule to most bird predators. As further protection, many pygmy owls have spots on the back of their heads that resemble eyes. These are thought to deceive predators into thinking that the owl is already aware of their presence.

Eyes in the back of its head?
Left: real eyes in the face of a pygmy owl; right: false eyes, from feather marks on the back of the head of the same owl.

Ural owl
Strix uralensis

Ranges across the boreal forests of Eurasia; pale gray plumage is distinctive

Great gray owl
Strix nebulosa

Facial disk assists hearing by conducting sound to the ears, like a satellite dish

Black-banded owl
Ciccaba huhula

A canopy insectivore of South American rain forests

Eurasian pygmy-owl
Glaucidium passerinum

Barred owl
Strix varia

Northern hawk owl
Surnia ulula

A tiny owl of north Eurasian forests

Elf owl
Micrathene whitneyi

♂
Snowy owl
Nyctea scandiaca

This predator of forest tundra and taiga preys on mammals and birds, specializing in voles; it nests in hollows and has clutches of six to ten eggs

Breeds in woodpecker holes in Central America

Great horned owl
Bubo virginianus

Verreaux's eagle-owl
Bubo lacteus

The size of a buzzard and one of the largest owls; confined to sub-Saharan Africa, it preys on medium-sized mammals and large birds

Tropical screech-owl
Otus choliba

Found in open South American tropical woods

Spectacled owl
Pulsatrix perscipillata

Lives in dense equatorial forests in Central and South America

Barn owl
Tyto alba

Comb-like central toenail is used for preening. Roosts in hollows, caves, and even buildings

Short-eared owl
Asio flammeus

Has the shortest "ears"—twin crests above the eyes—of its group; found in open country almost worldwide, it hunts small mammals

Long-eared owl
Asio otus

Special combing on the edges of flight feathers silences wing beats

Boreal owl
Aegolius funereus

The palest member of a group of small, mostly New World owls with incomplete facial disks

Burrowing owl
Athene cunicularia

Northern saw-whet owl
Aegolius acadicus

Found in the woods of North America

At its burrow nest on the plains of the Americas

FACT FILE

Barn owl One of the most widespread birds in the world, the barn owl can often be seen hunting rodents along the grassy shoulders and medians of highways. Barn owls have exceptional hearing and can catch prey in total darkness; they also occasionally hunt in daylight. Nests are in crevices.

⚖ Up to 17 in (43 cm)
● 4–7
∥ Sexes alike
⊘ Sedentary to nomad
♟ Common

S. North & South America, sub-Saharan Africa, W. Eurasia to southwest Pacific

Long-eared owl This bird sometimes nests in squirrels' nests. The young are fed by the female, although it is the male owl that does most of the hunting and delivers their diet of small mammals, other birds, and invertebrates. Females are darker and larger than males. Eye color varies with the region, from pale yellow to golden.

⚖ Up to 16 in (40 cm)
● 5–7
∥ Sexes alike
ᒑ Partial migrant
♟ Locally common

C. & S. North America, W. to E. temperate Eurasia

LONG-EARED OWL

To threaten would-be predators approaching her nest, the female long-eared owl spreads her wings, flares her flight feathers, and lowers her head to make herself appear large and ferocious.

NESTS

In most birds, as soon as a breeding pair forms, one or both adults will begin to build a nest. The structure is used to cradle the eggs, house the developing chicks, and help keep them safe from predators. Selecting the nest site and building the nest are tasks that may be performed by either sex, alone or as a pair. Each adult's involvement, the choice of site, technique and building materials, and the energy that is invested in nest-building are characteristics that vary among species. The widely recognized cup-shaped nest is typically built using twigs and other plant matter that is threaded or twisted together to prevent the structure from falling apart. Other nest types include stick platforms, excavated tree hollows, scrapes or burrows in the ground, mud "ovens," and rotting mounds of vegetation. Some birds reuse the nests of others. Some use nests at non-breeding times of the year for sleeping or shelter; such dormitory nests rarely house eggs or young. Bowerbird males build elaborate nests (bowers) on the ground, ornamented with berries, flowers, feathers, and even bones. Such "nests" serve only to attract females, which, after mating, then go off alone to build the actual nest that will house eggs and young. A few birds do not build nests: two penguins, for example, simply incubate their eggs and hold their developing young on top of their feet.

A ready-made home The eastern screech owl (*Otus asio*) (above) makes its nest in available tree hollows. Owls also raise their young in holes in cliffs or in old buildings, and they sometimes reuse the stick nests of crows or hawks. Other birds such as kingfishers also nest in cavities, which they dig in riverbanks or termite mounds. Some birds even use old rabbit holes.

A prickly abode The cactus wren (*Campylorhynchus brunneicapillus*) (right) uses sticks to make a somewhat bulky, domed nest, which it prefers to place among the spines of a cactus. Wrens also build nests for sleeping.

A nest with a view European white storks (*Ciconia ciconia*) (below) often nest on man-made structures, in this case the ruins of a church in Algeria. These birds, which mate for life, pile branches into massive nests that they use for many years.

Easy access A red-throated loon (*Gavia stellata*) (above) joins a chick in a nest built on the edge of a lake in Alaska. Loon nests are often nothing more than shallow scrapes in boggy ground, although some pairs use reeds and water weeds. They are often placed on peninsulas or small islands.

One among many A sociable weaver (*Philetairus socius*) (above) peeks out of its hole in a communal nest. Weavers are renowned for building intricately woven grass nests. They push and pull material into loops and knots in a technique that is similar to basket weaving.

A multi-family dwelling The very large, communal nests (right) of sociable weavers can weigh more than 1 ton (1 tonne) and house hundreds of birds. A small chamber houses each pair. Nests are used for years.

On the rocks A large colony of king cormorants (*Phalacrocorax albiventer*) (left) sit on their nests in the Falkland Islands. This species builds its cone nest on cliff-top slopes using mud and vegetation. Other species use seaweed, guano, or old bones. Those cormorants that nest in trees use twigs.

Home in a cup A vireo (below) sits on her nest in an oak tree. The cup shape is ideal for preventing eggs from rolling out. Fragments of spider-web may serve to bind, and lichen on the outside may help in camouflage.

Spiders' web
for binding

Careful construction Vireos
(right) build cup-shaped nests
using fine grasses, spider's silk,
and strips of bark. They suspend
them from forks in branches in
the mid- to upper levels of trees.

Strips of bark
for camouflage

NIGHTJARS AND ALLIES

CLASS	Aves
ORDERS	1
FAMILIES	5
GENERA	22
SPECIES	118

Similar to owls in nocturnal lifestyle, this order of birds—which comprises oilbirds, frogmouths, potoos, owlet-nightjars, and nightjars—is thought to be distantly related to them. Like owls, nightjars and their allies are active at twilight and at night. They have soft plumage in patterns and shades for camouflage in trees or on the ground. They have rather large heads and large eyes that, as in owls, are tubular and adapted to see well in poor light. But, unlike owls, the eyes are less forward-facing and the bill is wide, adapted for catching insects instead. To detect prey, all have a keen sense of hearing.

Fragmented ranges The oilbird is found only in tropical South American caves. Potoos inhabit open woodlands in Central and South America. Frogmouths and owlet-nightjars live in forests and woods in Australasia. Nightjars occur in a variety of warm-climate habitats across the world.

Trailing behind Nightjars (above) have long tails and wings that help them fly fast yet maneuver. In ancient times, nightjars were accused of stealing milk from goats, hence their nickname of goatsuckers. In reality, it is the insects that gather around livestock that they pursue.

Spot the bird The tawny frogmouth (above) is well camouflaged against its background. These nocturnal birds try to remain inconspicuous during the day. Here one sits motionless on its nest, its shape and color imitating the branch of a tree.

MASTERS OF DISGUISE

These rather unusual-looking night-birds are experts at blending in and often strike curious poses that make them resemble broken-off tree limbs. Their broad, insect-catching bills are surrounded by bristles, for protection and funnelling-in food.

The oilbird is the only member of its family. It is a colonial cave rooster and nester that can navigate in total darkness by relying on echo-location, in a similar way to bats.

Frogmouths are odd-looking birds whose bodies taper from their large, flat, shaggy heads. Their stout bills, hardened with bone, snap shut to trap their prey.

Potoos resemble frogmouths but have thinner bills with fewer bristles. They catch insects while flying and lay their single, purple-brown spotted eggs in bare tree crotches.

Nightjars comprise well over half the species in this group. They fly swiftly but have weak feet, which they rarely use. When threatened, they open and display their brightly colored mouths. Nightjars usually roost on open litter on the ground, laying one to two spotted eggs.

Owlet-nightjars look like a cross between nightjars and owls. Their broad, flat bills are almost hidden by bristles. They hunt by perch-pouncing and lay white eggs in tree-hole nests.

The only regular fruit-eater among nightjar-like birds; feeds mainly on the fruit of palms and other trees

Oilbird
Steatornis caripensis

Common potoo
Nyctibius griseus

Javan frogmouth
Batrachostomus javensis

Tawny frogmouth
Podargus strigoides

Builds downy cup-nests on horizontal branches in rain-forest trees

Camouflages itself at roost by imitating a dead branch; plumage pattern is cryptic

Perch-and-pounce hunters, the Indo-Australian frog-mouths sit motionless on a vantage perch, then, sighting prey, dive down onto it

---

⚡ **CONSERVATION WATCH**

In reasonable shape Only three species of nightjars and their allies are listed as critically endangered by IUCN, two as endangered, and three as vulnerable. Yet others may be under threat as well because so little information is available on these cryptic birds.

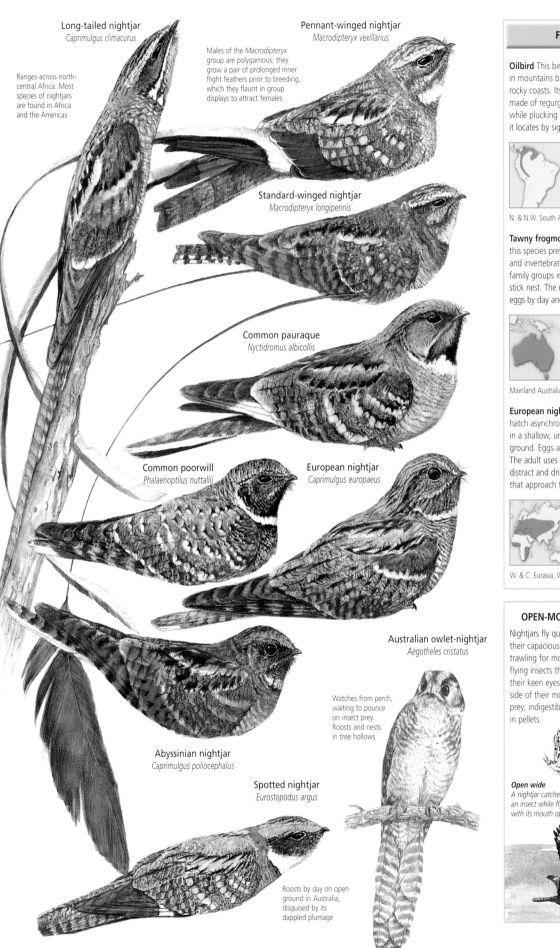

Long-tailed nightjar
Caprimulgus climacurus

Ranges across north-central Africa. Most species of nightjars are found in Africa and the Americas

Pennant-winged nightjar
Macrodipteryx vexillarius

Males of the *Macrodipteryx* group are polygamous; they grow a pair of prolonged inner flight feathers prior to breeding, which they flaunt in group displays to attract females

Standard-winged nightjar
Macrodipteryx longipennis

Common pauraque
Nyctidromus albicollis

Common poorwill
Phalaenoptilus nuttallii

European nightjar
Caprimulgus europaeus

Abyssinian nightjar
Caprimulgus poliocephalus

Spotted nightjar
Eurostopodus argus

Roosts by day on open ground in Australia, disguised by its dappled plumage

Australian owlet-nightjar
Aegotheles cristatus

Watches from perch, waiting to pounce on insect prey. Roosts and nests in tree hollows

FACT FILE

Oilbird This bird lives in caves, mostly in mountains but also sometimes along rocky coasts. Its cup-like nests are made of regurgitated fruit. It hovers while plucking fruits and seeds, which it locates by sight and by smell.

⬌ Up to 20 in (51 cm)
● 1–4
✂ Sexes alike
⊘ Sedentary
✦ Locally common

N. & N.W. South America

Tawny frogmouth A reclusive bird, this species preys on small mammals and invertebrates. It roosts in pairs or family groups in trees, making a small stick nest. The male incubates the white eggs by day and the female by night.

⬌ Up to 21 in (53 cm)
● 1–3
✂ Sexes alike
⊘ Sedentary
✦ Common

Mainland Australia & Tasmania

European nightjar This bird's eggs hatch asynchronously in a nest made in a shallow, unlined scrape on the ground. Eggs are color-camouflaged. The adult uses a special display to distract and drive away any predators that approach the nest.

⬌ Up to 11 in (28 cm)
● 1–2
✂ Sexes differ
↻ Migrant
✦ Common

W. & C. Eurasia, W. & S.E. Africa

OPEN-MOUTHED FEEDING

Nightjars fly quickly through the night, their capacious mouths fully open, trawling for moths, beetles, and other flying insects that they pursue with their keen eyesight. Bristles on either side of their mouths help trap their prey; indigestible parts are regurgitated in pellets.

Open wide
A nightjar catches an insect while flying with its mouth open.

HUMMINGBIRDS AND SWIFTS

CLASS	Aves
ORDERS	1
FAMILIES	3
GENERA	124
SPECIES	429

Any common ancestry between these dissimilar birds would have to be very old indeed. Nevertheless, hummingbirds and swifts do have significant anatomical similarities, such as the relative length of their wing bones. This is related to two distinguishing features for both groups: their very rapid wing beats and flight behavior. Hummingbirds are also known for their tiny size, bright iridescent colors, and hovering flight. The average weight of many of these birds is less than one-third of an ounce (8.3 g); the bee hummingbird is the smallest known species of bird, at a mere one-tenth of an ounce (2.5 g). Swifts are relatively bigger birds that are the fastest fliers of the avian world.

Prevalent throughout Swifts are widely distributed, but are most numerous in the tropics. Hummingbirds are confined to the New World; most live in its tropical belt.

FREQUENT FLIERS

Swifts and treeswifts spend most of their time in the air, using their narrow, swept-back wings to maneuver after insects, especially swarming mayflies and termites. Several species make migrations over land and ocean to reach Southern Hemisphere wintering quarters.

Predominantly dark colored, swifts have short legs with strong claws for gripping their roosts as they sleep upright in holes and crevices. Some cave swiftlets nest and roost in total darkness, deep in caves. They are among the few birds capable of navigating by echolocation, using clicking calls.

Hummingbirds have long, very narrow bills that they poke into flowers for nectar, hovering in front of the blossoms to collect the sweet fluid with their twin-tubed tongues. They also supplement their diet with insects for protein.

Swifts and hummingbirds can become torpid to conserve energy, lowering their metabolism and body temperatures while resting. Both lay plain white eggs.

Compact caretaker A green hermit hummingbird (*Phaethornis guy*) (above) feeds her chicks. In hummingbirds, females build the nest and rear the chicks. Hermit nests are a long cup of plant material held together with spiderweb and anchored to the underside of a hanging leaf.

Spit it out The salivary glands of many swifts (left) enlarge during the breeding season. They use secretions from these glands to glue together sticks to form their nests, which they attach in colonies to vertical walls of hollow trees or rock faces. The nests of some species of cave-dwelling swifts are made entirely of saliva and are highly sought after in some Asian cuisines.

Eating on the fly The whirring sound made by the wings of hummingbirds (right) gives them their name. They can hover while they feed thanks to the anatomy of their wings, which they can turn completely over on the backstroke as well as on the forestroke, counteracting the tendency to drift off in any one direction.

Whiskered treeswift
Hemiprocne comata

Square tail and broad white rump bar distinguish this species; it feeds at great heights over the skies of Africa and Southwest Asia

Little swift
Apus affinis

Alpine swift
Tachymarptis melba

Treeswifts build half-saucer nests of feathers and bark agglutinated with saliva on the open branches of tall forest trees

Breeds at high altitudes across southern Eurasia and migrates to Africa and India; can sleep on the wing

Crested treeswift
Hemiprocne coronata

Treeswifts range from Southeast Asia to the New Guinea region

Treeswifts fly out from exposed set perches to hunt insects; they all have either white mustache stripes or short crests on the face

Common swift
Apus apus

The most familiar and widespread swift in Eurasia; migrates to winter exclusively in sub-equatorial Africa

Asian palm swift
Cypsiurus balasiensis

Breeds in eastern North America in spring, cementing its half-cup nest of sticks with saliva to walls of chimneys—hence the name

Chimney swift
Chaetura pelagica

African palm swift
Cypsiurus parvus

With long, forked tail and tapered wings, palm-swifts are the most streamlined of all swifts; they roost and nest mostly in palms

---

FACT FILE

Crested treeswift This species feeds by sallying out on the wing from high, bare perches on rain-forest edges. It drinks in midair. Both parents share nesting duties, incubating eggs that are glued to the frail nest floor by saliva.

- Up to 10 in (25 cm)
- 1
- Sexes alike
- Mainly sedentary
- Locally common

India to Indochina

Chimney swift Wheeling overhead in loose groups, this swift gives high-pitched twittering calls as it flies. Its sweeping glides on back-swept wings and stumpy tail distinguish it from swallows to which it is unrelated.

- Up to 5 in (13 cm)
- 2–7
- Sexes alike
- Migrant
- Common

E. North America, N.W. South America

African palm swift This bird's nest is a small, flat pad of down that it glues to a leaf. The female then uses saliva to glue one or two eggs to the pad. The parents incubate the eggs in a vertical position. Chicks hook themselves to the pad until they can fly.

- Up to 6 in (15 cm)
- 1–2
- Sexes alike
- Sedentary
- Locally common

Sub-Saharan Africa, Madagascar

AERIAL EXISTENCE

Swifts live in the air, some species even sleeping there in communal "rafts" on migration and at winter quarters. They may also copulate in midair. The female signals her interest by holding her wings in an inverted V-shape and gliding downward. The male pursues her, then gently lands on her back. They then mate as they glide downward.

Mating
A male and female swift mate as they glide together.

Violet-capped woodnymph
Thalurania glaucopis

Red-billed streamertail
Trochilus polytmus ♂

Whitetip
Urosticte benjamini ♂

Confined to Jamaica. Females lack tail streamers

Flower feeding Ingested nectar (right) passes into a crop, which takes about four minutes to fill. It is then emptied directly into the intestine where it is digested.

Green-crowned brilliant
Heliodoxa jacula ♂

Spends over 70 percent of each day perching—partly to offset energy costs of flight

♂

Ecuadorian hillstar
Oreotrochilus chimborazo

Lives close to the snowline in the high Andes; roosts and nests in caves and crevices for protection from cold

♂

Swallow-tailed hummingbird
Eupetomena macroura ♂

White-tipped sicklebill
Eutoxeres aquila

White-whiskered hermit
Phaethornis yaruqui

♂

White-necked jacobin
Florisuga mellivora

Migrates up and down woodlands and gardens in coastal South America

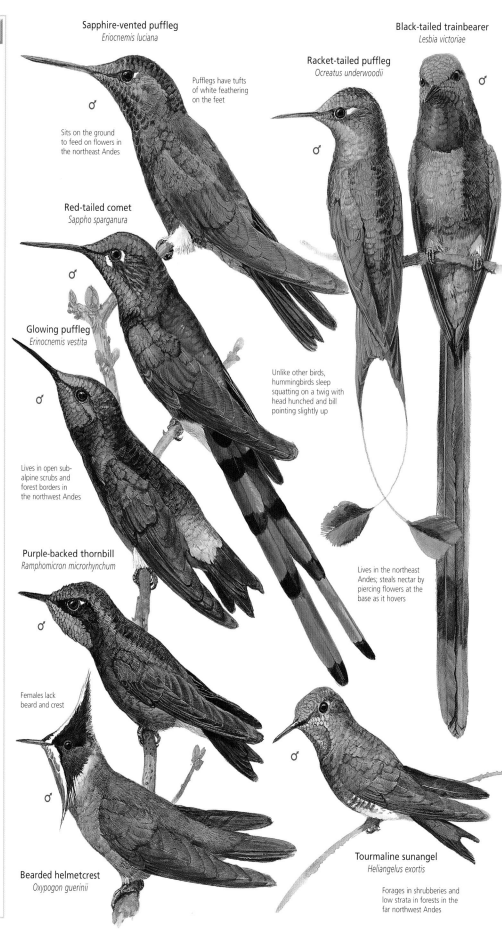

FACT FILE

Racket-tailed puffleg The foot tufts in some males of this species are bright orange, not white. It occurs in temperate and subtropical mountain forests in the Andes, feeding by hovering both inside forest and in regrowth. Females build a tiny cup-nest of fiber and lichen perched on horizontal twigs low in trees.

🔺 Up to 6 in (15 cm)
🥚 2
⚥ Sexes differ
↻ Local migrant
🔹 Common

N.W. Andes, South America

Red-tailed comet Males have uniquely tapered red tails and establish feeding territory in nectar-rich patches of dry, sparse woodland at mid-altitudes in the Andes. This species feeds at low to mid heights in trees and shrubberies. Nests are bulky cups made from moss, lichen, and animal hair, and are hidden under rocks in ravines.

🔺 Up to 8 in (20 cm)
🥚 2
⚥ Sexes differ
⊘ Sedentary
🔹 Common

C. Andes, South America

Purple-backed thornbill The short bill of this species can only rifle nectar from short-tube flowers, but holes made by flower-piercers in longer corollas may be used opportunistically as well. Most feeding is done along the upper strata of the forest edge. Female purple-backed thornbills build small, cup-shaped nests in trees.

🔺 Up to 3½ in (9 cm)
🥚 2
⚥ Sexes differ
⊘ Mostly sedentary
🔹 Uncommon

N. & C. Andes, South America

Bearded helmetcrest This species lives in wet forests and shrubberies right up to the snowline in the Andes. The males occur more often on open hillsides while the females usually live in gorges. Females appear to be non-territorial and often secrete their nests close together under shelter along the rocky banks of streams. To gather nectar this species usually clings to flower heads like a woodpecker.

🔺 Up to 5 in (13 cm)
🥚 2
⚥ Sexes differ
⊘ Sedentary
🔹 Locally common

High N.W. Andes, South America

Sapphire-vented puffleg
Eriocnemis luciana
♂

Pufflegs have tufts of white feathering on the feet

Sits on the ground to feed on flowers in the northeast Andes

Red-tailed comet
Sappho sparganura
♂

Glowing puffleg
Eriocnemis vestita
♂

Lives in open sub-alpine scrubs and forest borders in the northwest Andes

Purple-backed thornbill
Ramphomicron microrhynchum
♂

Females lack beard and crest

Bearded helmetcrest
Oxypogon guerinii
♂

Black-tailed trainbearer
Lesbia victoriae

Racket-tailed puffleg
Ocreatus underwoodii
♂

♂

Unlike other birds, hummingbirds sleep squatting on a twig with head hunched and bill pointing slightly up

Lives in the northeast Andes; steals nectar by piercing flowers at the base as it hovers

Tourmaline sunangel
Heliangelus exortis
♂

Forages in shrubberies and low strata in forests in the far northwest Andes

Confined to the mountains of
Costa Rica and Panama; males
dive about in aerial displays to
defend breeding territory

Scintillant hummingbird
Selasphorus scintilla
♂

Rufous hummingbird
Selasphorus rufus
♂

Vervain hummingbird
Mellisuga minima
♂

Wedge-billed hummingbird
Schistes geoffroyi
♂

Occurs in north
Andean cloud forests

This bumblebee-size,
second-to-smallest bird
in the world, lives in
Jamaica and Hispaniola
in the West Indies

**Ruby-throated
hummingbird**
Archilochus colubris
♂

Hooded visorbearer
Augastes lumachella
♂

Black-eared fairy
Heliothryx auritus

Occurs in lowland
rain forest in northern
South America

Marvelous spatuletail
Loddigesia mirabilis
♂

Most hummingbirds need
to visit 1,000–2,000 flowers
per day to satisfy their
energy needs

FACT FILE

Rufous hummingbird One of a
handful of North American species,
this brilliant midget migrates from
its summer breeding home in the
northwest, to winter from California
to the Gulf of Mexico. Males don
duller, non-breeding plumage then.
Its tiny, neatly bound cup-nests are
perched on twigs in trees and bushes.

⚊ Up to 3½ in (9 cm)
● 2
⫻ Sexes differ
↻ Migrant
♣ **Locally common**

W. Canada to California, C. Mexico &
Gulf of Mexico

Ruby-throated hummingbird A
familiar breeder in gardens in the
eastern United States, this species has
wings that whirr at up to 200 beats
per second in display flight. It lays
down fat for its annual migrations
between its summer range and Central
America, and is able to accumulate
just enough reserves for its non-stop
flight across the Gulf of Mexico.

⚊ Up to 3½ in (9 cm)
● 2
⫻ Sexes differ
↻ Migrant
♣ Common

E. North America to C. America

Hooded visorbearer This species
is found only in dry cactus scrubs in
the central Brazilian hills. Like other
hummingbirds, males hover in front of
females to show off their glittering faces
in courtship. Bound into vertically forked
twigs, nests are tiny cups of interwoven
plant wool and seeds, decorated with
moss and smoothed by spiderweb.

⚊ Up to 4 in (10 cm)
● 2
⫻ Sexes differ
⊘ Sedentary
♣ Uncommon

C.E. Brazil, South America

Marvelous spatuletail Only four
feathers make up the tail of this
remarkable bird which, in the male,
comprises two that are awl-shaped
and two that are extraordinarily long
curved wires with spatulate tips. It is
confined to forest edge and scrub in
a tiny corner of the Peruvian Andes.
Little is known of its breeding.

⚊ Up to 7 in (18 cm)
● 2
⫻ Sexes differ
⊘ Sedentary
♣ Endangered

N. Peru, South America

FACT FILE

Crimson topaz This visually stunning bird is the second-largest hummingbird. It lives in the Amazon region where it keeps to the forest canopy, making it difficult to observe. The male's long tail streamers cross halfway down.

- ⤒ Up to 9 in (23 cm)
- ● 2
- ⫻ Sexes differ
- ⊘ Sedentary
- ⫯ Locally common

N. South America

Giant hummingbird The largest of hummingbirds, this giant is dull and brownish. It flies more like a swift, with slow beats interspersed with glides, and perches at flowers for nectar. Females place their nests in cacti for protection.

- ⤒ Up to 9 in (23 cm)
- ● 1–2
- ⫻ Sexes differ
- ⊘ Sedentary
- ⫯ Locally common

Andean W. South America

Sword-billed hummingbird At over four inches (10 cm), the bill is uniquely longer than this bird's body. It is specialized for probing flowers with long, pendant corollas which the bird approaches by hovering from below.

- ⤒ Up to 9 in (23 cm)
- ● Unknown
- ⫻ Sexes differ
- ⊘ Sedentary
- ⫯ Locally common

Andean N.W. South America

Black-throated mango This small bird prefers to feed on nectar from red flowers in the forest canopy, and even hawks above it. During courtship flights its wings beat twice as fast as normal.

- ⤒ Up to 5 in (13 cm)
- ● 2
- ⫻ Sexes differ
- ⸖ Partial migrant
- ⫯ Common

N.W., N.E. & E.C. South America

AGGRESSIVE BREEDERS

Hummingbirds are polygamous. Males other than hermits are aggressively territorial, protecting and competing for feeding grounds for themselves and to attract females. Mating is brief. Females then leave to carry out all nesting duties and become just as defensive about breeding territory.

Crimson topaz
Topaza pella

Great sapphirewing
Pterophanes cyanopterus

Lives on the fringes of cloud forest in the northern Andes

Giant hummingbird
Patagona gigas

Collared inca
Coeligena torquata

Characteristic blue head, white breast, and white sides to the tail. Lives in the cloud forests of the northern Andes

Sword-billed hummingbird
Ensifera ensifera

Green-backed firecrown
Sephanoides sephanoides

Locally common and partly migratory in southern South America

Wedge-tailed hillstar
Oreotrochilus adela

Buff-winged starfrontlet
Coeligena lutetiae

A buff wing patch identifies this north Andean species

One of five species of hillstars that, as their name indicates, live high in the South American Andes

Black-throated mango
Anthracothorax nigricollis

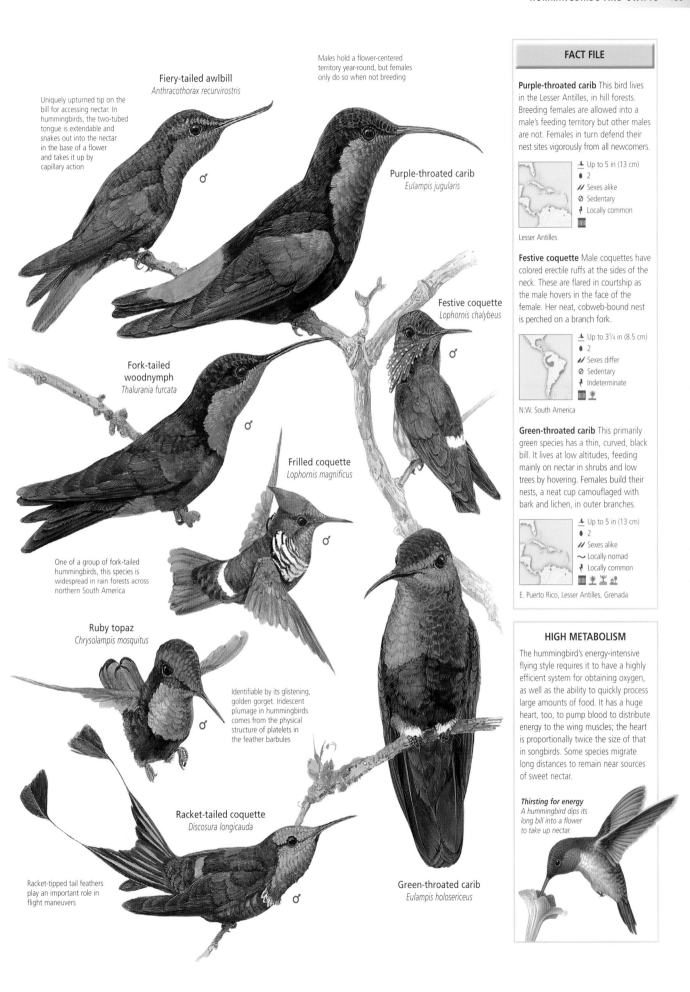

Uniquely upturned tip on the bill for accessing nectar. In hummingbirds, the two-tubed tongue is extendable and snakes out into the nectar in the base of a flower and takes it up by capillary action

Fiery-tailed awlbill
Anthracothorax recurvirostris

Males hold a flower-centered territory year-round, but females only do so when not breeding

Purple-throated carib
Eulampis jugularis

Festive coquette
Lophornis chalybeus

Fork-tailed woodnymph
Thalurania furcata

Frilled coquette
Lophornis magnificus

One of a group of fork-tailed hummingbirds, this species is widespread in rain forests across northern South America

Ruby topaz
Chrysolampis mosquitus

Identifiable by its glistening, golden gorget. Iridescent plumage in hummingbirds comes from the physical structure of platelets in the feather barbules

Racket-tailed coquette
Discosura longicauda

Racket-tipped tail feathers play an important role in flight maneuvers

Green-throated carib
Eulampis holosericeus

FACT FILE

Purple-throated carib This bird lives in the Lesser Antilles, in hill forests. Breeding females are allowed into a male's feeding territory but other males are not. Females in turn defend their nest sites vigorously from all newcomers.

⤒ Up to 5 in (13 cm)
◖ 2
✳ Sexes alike
⊘ Sedentary
⚑ Locally common
▥

Lesser Antilles

Festive coquette Male coquettes have colored erectile ruffs at the sides of the neck. These are flared in courtship as the male hovers in the face of the female. Her neat, cobweb-bound nest is perched on a branch fork.

⤒ Up to 3¼ in (8.5 cm)
◖ 2
✳ Sexes differ
⊘ Sedentary
⚑ Indeterminate
▥ ✳

N.W. South America

Green-throated carib This primarily green species has a thin, curved, black bill. It lives at low altitudes, feeding mainly on nectar in shrubs and low trees by hovering. Females build their nests, a neat cup camouflaged with bark and lichen, in outer branches.

⤒ Up to 5 in (13 cm)
◖ 2
✳ Sexes alike
∿ Locally nomad
⚑ Locally common
▥ ✳ ⚘ ⛰

E. Puerto Rico, Lesser Antilles, Grenada

HIGH METABOLISM

The hummingbird's energy-intensive flying style requires it to have a highly efficient system for obtaining oxygen, as well as the ability to quickly process large amounts of food. It has a huge heart, too, to pump blood to distribute energy to the wing muscles; the heart is proportionally twice the size of that in songbirds. Some species migrate long distances to remain near sources of sweet nectar.

Thirsting for energy
A hummingbird dips its long bill into a flower to take up nectar.

HUMMINGBIRD FLIGHT

HUMMINGBIRD FLIGHT

Flying forward Hummingbirds flap their wings up and down to move forward.

Hovering Hummingbirds move their wings in a rapid figure-eight motion to hover in stationary position.

Flying upward By altering the wing angle of the movements, many directional changes are possible. Here, a more up-and-down angle allows a controlled vertical rise.

Flying backward Hummingbirds flap their wings above and behind their heads to move backward.

Free movement The wings of this scintillant hummingbird (right) are shown turned backward for a split second as it hovers to suck nectar. A unique joint system at the shoulder allows such free movement.

Most birds can only fly forward, but hummingbirds can also fly backward, sideways, and straight up or down. They can even switch direction without turning their bodies. They can accomplish this thanks to their specialized physiology and anatomy, with wings that can be turned through 180 degrees. To maintain hovering, they regularly beat their wings up to 80 times per second. Their flight feathers take up almost the entire wing, and their breastbones, to which major wing muscles are anchored, are deep and strong.

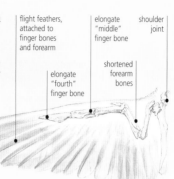

flight feathers, attached to finger bones and forearm

elongate "middle" finger bone

shoulder joint

elongate "fourth" finger bone

shortened forearm bones

Hummingbird wing structure
This arrangement transfers enormous power to the flight feathers.

Positioning agent The scintillant hummingbird (*Selasphorus scintilla*) (below) can position itself at just the right angle to reach the nectar in the flower. Its wings hover at blurring speed to keep it in position while its body remains quite still.

MOUSEBIRDS

CLASS Aves
ORDERS 1
FAMILIES 1
GENERA 2
SPECIES 6

The mousebird gets its name from its odd habit of creeping and crawling among bushes and clinging upside down, with its long tail held high. Herbivores, their diets include wild or cultivated fruit and even seedlings. They are therefore sometimes considered pests. They build cup-nests in bushes, lay sepia-marked eggs, and can cannibalize their young if they stray from the nest. Mousebirds dislike rain and cold, huddling together and sometimes becoming torpid. Their feathers are replaced randomly and have long aftershafts.

Only in Africa Mousebirds live in a wide range of African habitats south of the Sahara, from almost-dry bushland to the edge of forests.

Spread out Blue-naped mousebirds (*Urocalius macrourus*) (left) demonstrate one of the unusual characteristics of this bird family: a perching style in which the feet are kept almost level with the shoulders.

This way or that Mousebirds have unique feet with two reversible outer toes that can point either forward or backward. Because of this, they can imitate the toe arrangements of all other birds. It helps when scrambling and clinging to vegetation.

All points of the compass The toes of mousebirds can splay in all directions.

White-headed mousebird
Colius leucocephalus

Endemic to the horn of Africa; little is known of its habits but, like other mousebirds, it roosts in family groups and has only ten tail feathers

Speckled mousebird
Colius striatus

Ranges over tropical and eastern Africa; monogamous, but members of each communal group may help to rear young

TROGONS

CLASS Aves
ORDERS 1
FAMILIES 1
GENERA 6
SPECIES 39

The best known of these brilliantly colored birds is the resplendent quetzal, the national bird of Guatemala, which was considered divine by the Aztecs. Female trogons are duller than males, and lay plain-white to buff eggs in tree cavities. Both sexes brood. Trogons are secretive and territorial, perching while they scan for food. They eat insects and small herptiles; some species also eat fruit. Males stage displays that include chases through trees.

Pan-tropical beauties Trogons are found in the tropics of the Americas, Africa, and Asia. Arboreal birds, they live in rain forests and monsoon scrubs.

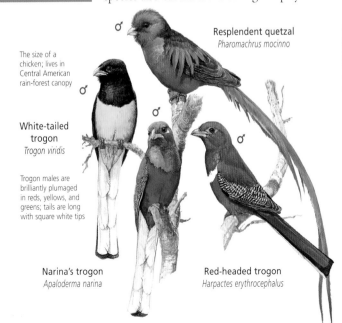

The size of a chicken; lives in Central American rain-forest canopy

Resplendent quetzal
Pharomachrus mocinno

White-tailed trogon
Trogon viridis

Trogon males are brilliantly plumaged in reds, yellows, and greens; tails are long with square white tips

Narina's trogon
Apaloderma narina

Red-headed trogon
Harpactes erythrocephalus

Sticking out A male resplendent quetzal (above) peers from its nest in a tree hollow. Trogons nest in such hollows or excavate nest holes in dead trees. Although male trogons may group to display to several females, they are monogamous and share nesting duties.

KINGFISHERS AND ALLIES

CLASS	Aves
ORDERS	1
FAMILIES	11
GENERA	51
SPECIES	209

Kingfishers and their allies include the Central American motmots and todies, and the Afro-Asian bee-eaters, rollers, hoopoes, and hornbills. Despite their diversity of form, all have short feet specialized for perching with three part-fused forward toes. Many species have brilliantly colored plumage, and all nest in holes that they dig in soil or in rotten trees with their bills. Eggs are plain white and spherical. Kingfishers stand out with their robust, straight bills which have sharply pointed or slightly hooked tips. The former is best suited for striking at and grasping fishes and other prey in water, and the latter for holding and crushing prey caught on land.

Waters and woods Kingfishers and their relatives occur in a variety of aquatic and wooded environments around the world. Most species live in Africa and Southeast Asia. Ground and cuckoo rollers are found only in Madagascar. "Non-fishing" kingfishers favor tropical rain forest and woodland.

DIFFERENT HABITS

Most kingfishers are generalized predators that eat a variety of terrestrial and aquatic invertebrates and vertebrates. To hunt, they sit quietly on a perch from which they survey their surroundings. Spotting prey, they swoop down and seize it in their bills. After bringing it back to a perch, they immobilize it by striking it repeatedly against a branch.

Todies are small, stocky birds with flattened bills that sally from perches to capture insects in midair and from under leaves. They are found only in the West Indies.

Motmots are solitary birds similar to bee-eaters in rich rufous-and-green plumage. They sally quickly out after insects and fruit high within the forest. Bee-eaters themselves are much more gregarious. They are masters at catching stinging insects, snatching them in midair then returning to a perch to wipe off the sting before swallowing.

Rollers are stout birds with thickened bills and patches of iridescent blue in their plumage. They hunt by pouncing from bare "sentinel" perches or by extended hawking on the wing.

The ground-feeding hoopoe is a solitary bird and the sole member of its family. Its arboreal relatives, the wood hoopoes are more gregarious and have short, curved claws to help them climb and probe crannies on tree trunks and branches for insects.

Hornbills are large birds with massive, colored bills and bill casques. Communal and noisy fliers, they call in unison as their broad wings thresh the air. They are mainly arboreal fruit eaters, able to manipulate food in the bill with great dexterity. For protection, brooding females wall themselves into nest holes in trees with mud and droppings.

Mother's helpers Carmine bee-eaters (*Merops nubicus*) (above) congregate at a nesting colony in Botswana. Many species of kingfishers and their allies are cooperative breeders, helping to raise other adults' chicks. This can increase fledging success dramatically.

Giant kingfisher
Megaceryle maxima

Pied kingfisher
Ceryle rudis

Widespread in sub-Saharan Africa and southern Asia; lives along rivers, lakes, and waterways; dives for fishes from perches

Dagger-like bills are typical of kingfishers; this species, widespread in sub-Saharan Africa, is the largest of all kingfishers and as big as a chicken

Belted kingfisher
Megaceryle alcyon

Short, wedge-shaped tail, characteristic of many kingfishers

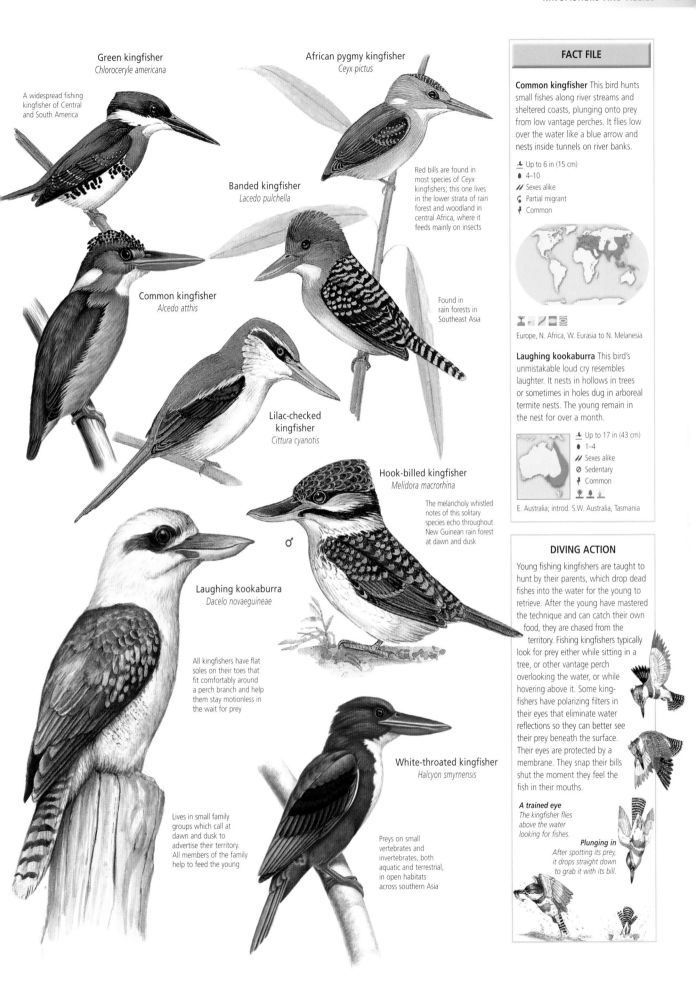

Green kingfisher
Chloroceryle americana

A widespread fishing kingfisher of Central and South America

African pygmy kingfisher
Ceyx pictus

Red bills are found in most species of *Ceyx* kingfishers; this one lives in the lower strata of rain forest and woodland in central Africa, where it feeds mainly on insects

Banded kingfisher
Lacedo pulchella

Found in rain forests in Southeast Asia

Common kingfisher
Alcedo atthis

Lilac-checked kingfisher
Cittura cyanotis

Hook-billed kingfisher
Melidora macrorhina

The melancholy whistled notes of this solitary species echo throughout New Guinean rain forest at dawn and dusk

♂

Laughing kookaburra
Dacelo novaeguineae

All kingfishers have flat soles on their toes that fit comfortably around a perch branch and help them stay motionless in the wait for prey

Lives in small family groups which call at dawn and dusk to advertise their territory. All members of the family help to feed the young

White-throated kingfisher
Halcyon smyrnensis

Preys on small vertebrates and invertebrates, both aquatic and terrestrial, in open habitats across southern Asia

FACT FILE

Common kingfisher This bird hunts small fishes along river streams and sheltered coasts, plunging onto prey from low vantage perches. It flies low over the water like a blue arrow and nests inside tunnels on river banks.

- Up to 6 in (15 cm)
- 4–10
- Sexes alike
- Partial migrant
- Common

Europe, N. Africa, W. Eurasia to N. Melanesia

Laughing kookaburra This bird's unmistakable loud cry resembles laughter. It nests in hollows in trees or sometimes in holes dug in arboreal termite nests. The young remain in the nest for over a month.

- Up to 17 in (43 cm)
- 1–4
- Sexes alike
- Sedentary
- Common

E. Australia; introd. S.W. Australia, Tasmania

DIVING ACTION

Young fishing kingfishers are taught to hunt by their parents, which drop dead fishes into the water for the young to retrieve. After the young have mastered the technique and can catch their own food, they are chased from the territory. Fishing kingfishers typically look for prey either while sitting in a tree, or other vantage perch overlooking the water, or while hovering above it. Some kingfishers have polarizing filters in their eyes that eliminate water reflections so they can better see their prey beneath the surface. Their eyes are protected by a membrane. They snap their bills shut the moment they feel the fish in their mouths.

A trained eye
The kingfisher flies above the water looking for fishes.

Plunging in
After spotting its prey, it drops straight down to grab it with its bill.

Caught in the act A common kingfisher (*Alcedo atthis*) (left) catches a fish. Despite their name, most kingfishers live on land and eat a variety of foods, including insects.

Cuban tody
Todus multicolor

All todies have short, straight tails and the same plumage pattern. Both sexes dig the nest and brood

Blue-crowned motmot
Momotus momota

Widespread in tropical America, centered in Amazonian forests and woodlands

Red-bearded bee-eater
Nyctyornis amictus

♂

Lives in tall, Southeast Asian rain forests; sits on bare vantage perches and nests in burrows. One of few solitary bee-eaters

All motmots have racket-tipped tails, which they twitch sporadically side-to-side at perch. Both sexes dig a burrow nest and brood

European bee-eater
Merops apiaster

Carmine bee-eater
Merops nubicus

Blue-bellied roller
Coracias cyanogaster

European roller
Coracias garrulus

Hawks for aerial insect prey from high bare perches in gracefully elaborate maneuvers

Grows prolonged central tail feathers when breeding, which is tied to the rainy season. Nests are burrows in earth banks

Dollarbird
Eurystomus orientalis

FACT FILE

Cuban tody This adaptable species is found in wooded thickets throughout Cuba. It typically catches insects from the underside of a leaf in the course of an arc-like flight. Its nest is a burrow.

⚊ Up to 4½ in (11.5 cm)
● 3–4
✂ Sexes alike
⊘ Sedentary
⚊ Locally common

Cuba, Isla de la Juventud

European bee-eater Relying on flying insects for food, this species migrates to southern Africa for winter. It nests in colonies inside tunnels that pairs dig with their beaks and legs.

⚊ Up to 11 in (28 cm)
● 4–10
✂ Sexes alike
↻ Migrant
⚊ Common

S.W. Eurasia, N.W., C.W. & S. Africa

Carmine bee-eater The two regional populations of this species undergo three-stage migrations each year. They live in large colonies of up to 1,000 pairs. They ride on the backs of large mammals, waiting to catch insects.

⚊ Up to 11 in (28 cm)
● 2–5
✂ Sexes alike
↻ Migrant
⚊ Common

Sub-Saharan & S.C. Africa

Dollarbird This bird gets its name from circular white patches on its wings that resemble American silver dollar coins. It eats mainly insects caught on the wing and nests in shallow tree hollows.

⚊ Up to 13 in (33 cm)
● 3–5
✂ Sexes alike
↻ Partial migrant
⚊ Common

S. & S.E. Asia to E. Australia & N. Melanesia

⚡ CONSERVATION WATCH

Hotspots of danger The world's 5 ground rollers live in Madagascar; 3 of them are listed as vulnerable by IUCN. Of the 26 endangered and vulnerable species of kingfishers and allies, 9 live in the Philippine region, including the critically endangered sulu (*Anthracoceros montani*) and rufous-headed (*Aceros waldeni*) hornbills. Four of the 12 threatened kingfishers also occur there. Habitat destruction and, for hornbills, hunting are the causes.

CAVITY NESTS

The hoopoe (below) nests in cavities. Some sites are reused. The young are initially cared for by the female and later by both parents. In most species of the related hornbills, which also nest in natural cavities, the female closes the entrance hole and remains with the chicks for months. The male feeds the entire family through the hole.

Long-tailed ground roller
Uratelornis chimaera

Rufous-headed ground roller
Atelornis crossleyi

Forages alone for insects on the floors of Madagascan rain forest. Pairs nest in a burrow dug in soft earth

Common hoopoe
Upupa epops

Flocks only on migration

Cuckoo-roller
Leptosomus discolor

Cuckoo-rollers give loud, mournful whistles as they glide over Madagascan forests; the calls are among the most characteristic on the island

♂

Hunts insects in flocks on tree trunks in African woodlands

Red-billed hornbill
Tockus erythrorhynchus

Green wood hoopoe
Phoeniculus purpureus

Feeds mostly on the ground in African savannas, dipping in dung and debris for small insects

Northern ground hornbill
Bucorvus abyssinicus

Feeds on the ground, walking about in pairs or small family groups and picking up a range of vertebrate and invertebrate prey by stabbing. Booms characteristically at dawn

♂

Great hornbill
Buceros bicornis

♂

Monogamous and territorial birds that nest in large hollows in tall rain-forest trees; the male feeds his mate and chicks through a small hole in the entrance for the period of incubation and rearing, up to about 100 days

JACAMARS AND PUFFBIRDS

CLASS Aves	
ORDERS 1	
FAMILIES 2	
GENERA 15	
SPECIES 51	

Jacamars and puffbirds are arboreal birds with pointed bills and short, weak feet suitable only for perching. Because these species have a foot with two toes pointing forward and two backward, they have usually been associated with woodpeckers and their allies. Yet, they have other traits that link them to the kingfishers and rollers, particularly in their head bones. Like many kingfisher allies, they dig burrows in the ground for nesting, have long incubation periods, and their nest sanitation is poor; eggs are plain white. Because recent DNA studies are noncommittal as to where these species belong, the jacamars and puffbirds have been placed here—in their own group—for the time being.

Tropical residents Jacamars and puffbirds are forest-dwellers of Central and northern South America. The great majority live in the rain forests of Amazonia.

Raised to attention Jacamars are showy, noisy birds. With their slender, curved bills and usually glossy green and orange plumage they resemble bee-eaters. When perched, jacamars such as the rufous-tailed jacamar (*Galbula ruficauda*) (far left), often move the head rapidly from side to side and hold it at a jaunty angle with bill part raised.

Puffed up Puffbirds are silent birds in dull brown or gray plumage and have stout bills. They often squat motionless on a branch, heads hunched and plumage fluffed. Like the white-eared puffbird (*Nystalus chacuru*) (left), they resemble an unobtrusive ball of feathers, hence their common name. One group of puffbirds, the nunbirds, are blacker. They have red bills and a more erect stance.

A SALLYING LIFE

Jacamars and puffbirds are sedentary birds and feed mostly alone, sallying on the wing for insect prey from vantage perches within the interior of forest or on its wooded edges. Both groups perch motionless for long periods and parents in these species share all nesting duties—but the similarities end.

Jacamars are noisy, showy, slender-bodied birds that hawk for flying insects in swift, darting movements. They wait for particular prey, such as large-bodied butterflies, but also eat wasps and bees—without removing the sting. It has been suggested that they are immune to the venom.

Jacamars nest in simple, horizontal burrows dug deep into soft bark or termite mounds. All 18 species are monogamous, but in some species other members of the local territorial group help in rearing the young. They sleep in dormitory burrows.

Unlike jacamars, puffbirds are silent, dumpy, and dull-plumaged. All except the swallow-wing puffbird hunt simply by swooping down from perches on rounded, rapidly beating wings. They pick up stationary prey, whether insects or small herptiles, from foliage, tree trunks, or the ground. Intention to swoop is signaled by a twitching of the tail. They can see sharply in dim light with their large eyes and forage in lower strata of forest edges and bamboo, especially near streams.

The burrow nests of puffbirds are dug on flat ground and slope downward. Some species make attempts at camouflage, covering newly excavated earth with leaves and sticks. Although all 33 species are monogamous, some do have helpers at the nest from their own family group. Sociable birds, the groups roost side-by-side on tree branches.

Black nunbird
Monasa atra

Paradise jacamar
Galbula dea

Great jacamar
Jacamerops aureus

Takes insects from leaf surfaces as well as in the air. Has expanded its diet to spiders and small reptiles

Spotted puffbird
Bucco tamatia

White-necked puffbird
Notharchus macrorhynchos

Swallow-wing puffbird
Chelidoptera tenebrosa

Found on the borders of humid forests in Amazonia; hunts from perches in the lower tree strata

Only puffbird to hawk for insects in the air, darting out from perches high up on the forest edge

Widespread in Central and northern South America. Nests in holes excavated in termite mounds

WOODPECKERS AND ALLIES

CLASS Aves	
ORDERS 1	
FAMILIES 3	
GENERA 53	
SPECIES 347	

These three families of birds—barbets and toucans, honeyguides, and woodpeckers—look different but share certain anatomical features, such as zygodactyl feet, with two toes in front and two at the back. They also lack down feathers and lay white eggs. Most species are colorful; some are even gaudy. They are primarily tropical birds that live in trees and nest in their cavities, in termite mounds, or in the ground. Woodpeckers and barbets typically excavate their own nest holes in trees; their abandoned holes are then often used by other species. Woodpeckers sometimes live within sight of large cities and are frequent visitors to bird-feeding stations.

Wide ranges Barbets live in New and Old World tropics, toucans in tropical America, and honeyguides in Afro-Asia; woodpeckers are more widespread.

Hanging on An acorn woodpecker (*Melanerpes formicivorus*) (far left) clings to a pine tree studded with acorns. These birds store their acorns in holes in special storage trees, which they fiercely defend. They then rely on these food stores during the lean winter months. They live in oak and mixed oak woodland in western America and may be monogamous or polygamous, depending on the area.

Sticking out A toco toucan (*Rhamphastotos toco*) (left) eats a goiaba fruit. These odd-looking birds have frilled tongues and often serrated bills, which they use adroitly to pick fruits from trees. They also sometimes prey on untended eggs or nestlings. They are the only toucans that live outside rain forest, frequenting riverside growth and savannas.

SPECIALIZED FEATURES

Woodpeckers are usually heard before they are seen. Their strong, often chisel-tipped bills to drum on tree trunks to signal their territory. Bony, muscle-cushioned skulls help protect them from the impact. They use their strong, long-clawed toes to grip the bark and their straightened tail feathers to prop themselves against the trees. Woodpeckers hop rather than walk.

Feeding varies. Some species forage on the ground for ants or flycatch in open areas, but most work over the trunks of trees, probing crevices or tunneling into wood with their bills for insects. Their remarkable tongues can be extruded for over 2 inches (5 cm) and are barbed, sticky, or brush-tipped to spear larvae, bind ants, or lap up sap.

Despite their large, gaudy-colored bills, which can be up to a third or more of their body length, toucans are often surprisingly inconspicuous as they perch on branches amid foliage. They feed mainly on fruit, as do the brightly colored and patterned barbets which have relatively stout, bristled, and sometimes notched bills. Barbets roost in tree holes or burrows.

Dull-plumaged honeyguides eat wax from beehives, as well as insects. Their name comes from the fact that one of their species leads humans to beehives.

Most species in these families are solitary, sedentary, and monogamous. Only toucans gather regularly in small feeding parties. Some sociable African barbets nest in pair groups of 200 or more birds, all residing in one dead tree. Honeyguides are brood parasites of hole-nesting birds. They lay one egg in the nest of each host bird.

Black-spotted barbet
Capito niger

Widespread in Amazonia

Blue-throated barbet
Megalaima asiatica

Hairy-breasted barbet
Tricholaema hirsuta

Most Southeast Asian barbets are green, matching forest foliage

A solitary barbet; forages for fruit and insects in upper strata of central African forests

Red-and-yellow barbet
Trachyphonus erythrocephalus

Lives in open, wooded, and riverine habitats in central east Africa

Double-toothed barbet
Lybius bidentatus

The double notch on the heavy bill helps it nip off fruit and snap up insects

Red-fronted tinkerbird
Pogoniulus pusillus

The African tinkerbirds are the smallest barbets, they eat mistletoe fruits

Greater honeyguide
Indicator indicator

Congregates in groups at sources of beeswax, is otherwise rather solitary

Yellow-rumped honeyguide
Indicator xanthonotus

This Himalayan honeyguide is one of only two species of the group to occur outside Africa

Lesser honeyguide
Indicator minor

Flashing the tail in flight is used as a signal to lead immatures (and others) to beehives

Black-necked aracari
Pteroglossus aracari

Curl-crested aracari
Pteroglossus beauharnaesii

A canopy-feeder in southwest Amazonia

An acrobatic fruit feeder of east Brazil

Emerald toucanet
Aulacorhynchus prasinus

Distinctively striped bill; this species lives in montane rain forest in the northern Andes

Toco toucan
Ramphastos toco

Bills are used for grasping fruit, preying on small animals, robbing birds' nests, and intimidation

Gray-breasted mountain-toucan
Andigena hypoglauca

Zygodactyl toes with two forward and two backward, an arrangement better fitted for clasping perches than for running

Moderately attenuated tail that is often cocked temporarily at perches or during vocalizations

Toucans roost in tree holes. Each group has dormitory hollows, several birds cramming into one, their tails pushed back up over their heads to make space

Channel-billed toucan
Ramphastos vitellinus

Broad crimson breast band and dark bill. Occurs in lowland rain forests of tropical South America and eats palm nuts, fruits, and insects. Drinks from bromeliads or by holding its bill open in rain

---

FACT FILE

Greater honeyguide This bird is known for leading humans to the hives of wild honeybees. The humans harvest the comb and leave the remains for the bird, which is particularly fond of the wax.

⤒ Up to 8 in (20 cm)
● Sets of up to 5
⫽ Sexes alike
⊘ Sedentary
⤙ Common

Sub-Saharan Africa excl. Congo basin & S.W.

Lesser honeyguide Like other honeyguides, the lesser honeyguide is a brood parasite. Newly hatched young use hooks on their bills to kill the host's chicks and push them out of the nest or break the host's eggs before hatching.

⤒ Up to 6½ in (16.5 cm)
● Series of 2–4
⫽ Sexes alike
⊘ Sedentary
⤙ Locally common

Sub-Saharan Africa excl. Congo basin & S.W.

Emerald toucanet Males and females signal their territory with monotonous growling notes; the male's voice is deeper. As in other toucans, there is no aerial display. This species sometimes appropriates the nesting holes of other birds, or excavates its own.

⤒ Up to 14½ in (37 cm)
● 1–5
⫽ Sexes alike
⊘ Sedentary
⤙ Locally common

Mexico, S. Central & N.W. South America

Toco toucan The toco toucan lives in family groups or flocks. It nests in holes in trees and often pecks noisily at tree branches. In this species, two birds will sometimes clash their bills together.

⤒ Up to 24 in (61 cm)
● 2–4
⫽ Sexes alike
⊘ Sedentary
⤙ Locally common

N.E. South America

🐦 CONSERVATION WATCH

Woodpecker wake The IUCN lists 12 species of woodpeckers and their allies as threatened: 6 as vulnerable, 3 endangered, and 3 critical. The critically endangered species are all woodpeckers. One of them, the ivory-billed woodpecker, has just been found on the mainland. It had not been seen there since the 1970s and was thought extinct.

FACT FILE

Northern flicker This woodpecker lives in diverse wooded habitats. It hops on the ground to dig mostly for ants that it sweeps up with its tongue; arboreal probing and fruit-eating are rarer except in winter.

- Up to 14 in (36 cm)
- 4–9
- Sexes alike
- Partial migrant
- Common

North America, Central America, Cuba

Yellow-bellied sapsucker The male and female of this species have different colored throat patches. At nesting grounds, the bird makes distinctive drumming sounds with alternating rapid and slow thumps.

- Up to 8 in (20 cm)
- 4–7
- Sexes differ
- Migrant
- Common

C.N. to S.E. North America, Central America

Ground woodpecker This species feeds almost entirely on the ground. It is specialized to eat ants by digging its bill into ants' nests, head down, and sticking out its tongue. It also nests on the ground, in 3 ft (1 m) long burrows, dug mostly by the male.

- Up to 12 in (30 cm)
- 2–5
- Sexes alike
- Sedentary
- Locally common

Cape Province to Transvaal & Natal (Africa)

SUCKING SAP

The yellow-bellied sapsucker is one of several North American woodpeckers that peck rows of holes in the trunks of both deciduous trees and conifers. They feed on the sap that accumulates in the holes, as well as on the insects that are attracted to the sap. These sap wells, dug in late summer and fall, are also exploited by other birds and mammals.

Hunting sap
A sapsucker at work drilling sap wells on a birch tree.

Northern wryneck
Jynx torquilla

One of only three Eurasian migratory woodpeckers. Curved bill is used to open anthills on ground

Guianan piculet
Picumnus minutissimus

Curved bill is used to open anthills

Northern flicker
Melanerpes formicivorus

Barred backs and black chest patches are characteristic of flickers. Their nine species occur through North and South America

Yellow-bellied sapsucker
Sphyrapicus varius

♂

Gray woodpecker
Dendropicos goertae

♂

Widespread in central African woods, feeds by pecking on tree branches for ants and other insects

Red-headed woodpecker
Melanerpes erythrocephalus

Feeds on both insects and seeds in forests, and stores nuts and seeds for winter. Endemic to eastern North America

♂

Golden-tailed woodpecker
Campethera abingoni

Ground woodpecker
Geocolaptes olivaceus

♂

Brown-capped woodpecker
Dendrocopos moluccensis

Lives in woodlands in India and the Sundra island arc

Rufous woodpecker
Celeus brachyurus

An active and solitary tree-and-ground forager; rarely remains long in any spot

Blond-crested woodpecker
Celeus flavescens

♂

Yellow head, red cheek splash, and gold mottled back identify this species; it lives in the forests and savannas of central east South America; forages on arboreal ants

Black woodpecker
Dryocopus martius

♂

Pileated woodpecker
Dryocopus pileatus

♀

♀

An Indian species; lives in dry to moist woodlands; forages at all levels in trees on ants and other insects

♂

Black-rumped woodpecker
Dinopium benghalense

♂

Gray-headed woodpecker
Picus canus

Digs funnel-shaped holes into ants' nests

A stiffened, tapered tail helps to prop woodpeckers as they clasp upright trunks and branches in their feeding. This arboreal forager lives in Southeast Asia

Green woodpecker
Picus viridis

Greater yellow-naped woodpecker
Picus flavinucha

Widespread in Eurasia; has similar habits to the green woodpecker

FACT FILE

Rufous woodpecker This bird appears frequently in gardens. It has the unusual habit of building its nest by digging a burrow in the middle of a tree-ant nest, so gaining a ready food supply at its doorstep. It also feeds on termites.

⬆ Up to 10 in (25 cm)
● 2–3
⫻ Sexes alike
⊘ Sedentary
♟ Common

S. & S.E. Asia to Borneo & Sumatra

Pileated woodpecker This large, adaptable woodpecker can even be seen within sight of skyscrapers. It eats primarily ants, which it extracts from rotting trees and fallen logs using its frilled, sticky tongue. It also eats fruit.

⬆ Up to 18 in (46 cm)
● 2–6
⫻ Sexes differ
⊘ Sedentary
♟ Rare

C.W. & E. North America

Green woodpecker This bird has a distinctive flight pattern, alternating three or four wingbeats with undulations with wings closed. It feeds on meadow ants, fruits, and other insects.

⬆ Up to 13 in (33 cm)
● 4–8
⫻ Sexes differ
⊘ Sedentary
♟ Common

Europe to trans-Caucasia, N.W. Africa

Grounded
The green woodpecker feeds mainly on the ground but nests in tree holes.

TONGUE AND GROOVE

The hairy woodpecker is typical of the family in that it bores a hole in a tree trunk and uses its long bill to extract insects from the interior. Woodpeckers have extremely long tongues that can be extended well beyond the end of the bill. The muscled base of the tongue loops over and behind the skull.

PASSERINES

CLASS	Aves
ORDER	Passeriformes
FAMILIES	96
GENERA	1,218
SPECIES	5,754

Passeriformes are by far the largest order of birds—with nearly 100 families and 5,800 species—and attest to great evolutionary success. Arising some 80–70 million years ago on the southern supercontinent Gondwana, they have proven to be remarkably adaptable and have reached every continent except Antarctica. Passerines are distinguished by their size, specialized feet, and complex, muscled voice box. Being small has energetic and environmental advantages; their feet can perform many functions in many situations; and their voice boxes can sing, allowing them to communicate and mark territory easily. They have exploited more niches in more habitats than any other order of birds.

SKILLED VOCALIZERS

Passerines are typically small to medium-sized birds that vary much in plumage color, from often drab to stunningly brilliant. Bills are adapted to diet. Most eat invertebrates on the ground, in trees, or captured by hawking on the wing. Others specialize on seeds (finches), fruit (orioles), and nectar (sunbirds). While most species of passerines are monogamous, what polygamy there is goes hand-in-hand with ornate display plumage (birds-of-paradise).

The toes of passerines are free and, unlike those in other birds, all join the "leg" at the same level, three of them directed forward and the fourth and innermost backward. All are worked by a unique arrangement of free tendons that enables the toes to grasp and hold on to a perch involuntarily, whether a branch, a small rock, or even a blade of grass. For this reason, passerines are traditionally called "perching birds."

Wings vary to fit environmental needs. In shrub and ground dwellers,

Small but powerful singer The yellow warbler (*Dendroica petechia*) sings from a branch. Its bright song has been phrased as "sweet sweet sweet, I'm so sweet." Warblers are members of the suborder Oscines, whose members have the most elaborately muscled voice boxes and are therefore the best singers.

they are usually short and rounded for maneuverability; in birds of open spaces they tend to be tapered, to cover distance and evade predators. All are suited to rapid take-offs. The outermost flight feathers, however, are reduced and few passerines can sustain high flight speed.

Song and the capacity to sing set passerines apart from all other birds. Unlike mammals, which produce sound in their larynx, birds use a voice box known as a syrinx. This unique structure at the base of the windpipe, or trachea, consists of two chambers and relies on up to four inner pairs of muscles to control the tension of its three elastic, vibrating membranes. The bird's trachea,

On the hunt A blue tit (*Parus caeruleus*) (above) hovers beside an oak tree as it scans the branches for insects. Hardy and enterprising, many tits vary their diet with the seasons, eating seeds during winter when other prey is harder to find. In spring, they turn to insect protein for breeding.

A good match The iiwi (*Vestiaria coccinea*) (right) is a Hawaiian honeycreeper whose slender, curved bill matches the sickle shape of the flower blossoms on which it feeds. At least 11 species in its small subfamily, which has played an important role in Hawaiian culture, are now extinct.

Mealtime A noisy pitta (*Pitta versicolor*) (left), an Australian native, sits on a perch after a successful attempt to catch some worms. Pittas are terrestrial forest foragers and nesters, and are among the most colorful of birds. Land snails are favored prey for this species. Some other insect-eating passerines hunt their prey in flight.

Hungry mouths to feed A marsh wren (*Cistothorus palustris*) (right) feeds its chicks at a nest on Long Island, in New York, United States. All passerine young are altricial, meaning they are born naked, helpless, and blind. The nestlings gape to indicate that they want to be fed. Parents have such a strong feeding instinct that they occasionally even feed other species.

interclavicular air sac, and mouth modify the sound that is produced. The two chambers allow the bird effectively to sing a duet by itself.

Such passerines are known as "songbirds" or oscines. According to molecular evidence, they arose in the Australian sector of Gondwana and spread throughout the world. Another group, particularly common in South America, has simpler, more poorly muscled voice boxes that produce only simple, stereotyped songs. They are called suboscines and include the pittas and broadbills of the Old World tropics, and the tyrant flycatchers and antbirds of the New.

Wading in An American dipper (*Cinclus mexicanus*) (left) stands in a waterhole. The five species of dippers, which do not have webbed feet but use their wings to propel them when hunting for insects underwater, are the only truly aquatic birds in the passerine order. They prefer to hunt in the clear, running water of shallow streams.

Small passengers A group of yellow-billed oxpeckers (*Buphagus africanus*) (below) sits on the back of a buffalo in Africa. Also known as tickbirds, they can be seen riding on different species of large mammals, pecking for ticks on their hides. Some related starlings eat parasites on livestock, but also swoop down to eat insects disturbed by the grazers.

Displaying A male three-wattled bellbird (*Procnias tricarunculatus*) (below) gets close to a female in a cloud forest in Costa Rica. Bellbirds are among the world's loudest birds. During the breeding season, the male stands on a display perch high in the tree canopy and emits a clang akin to a sledgehammer hitting an anvil. It can be heard up to half a mile (1 km) away.

PASSERINE ORIGINS

Modern molecular and paleogeographic evidence has turned around the old notion that passerines arose in Eurasia about 30–20 million years ago and from there spread throughout the world. Older fossil passerines have now been found in Australia that date back to beyond 40 million years ago. Australia then was much farther south, out of touch with Eurasia, having just separated from the remnants of the southern supercontinent, Gondwana. More molecular and anatomical evidence then weighed in. First, it revealed that Australia's songbirds are unrelated to their look-alike warblers, robins, and flycatchers in Eurasia—they converged on them in appearance simply because they adapted, independently, to the same ecological niches. Then it was determined that the Australasian and South American passerine lineages are much older and more diversified than any in the Northern Hemisphere. Today, it is thought that passerines arose on Gondwana more than 80 million years ago, and that they split into South American suboscines, Afro-Old World suboscines, and Australasian songbirds as those continents broke away from Gondwana. Only after that, did Eurasia get its ancestral songbirds, from Australia, in reverse.

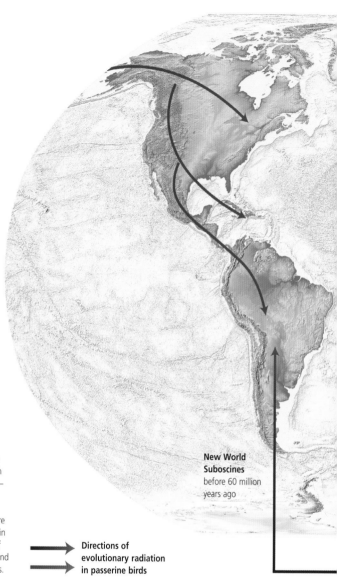

New World Suboscines before 60 million years ago

Southern Hemisphere Both suboscines and songbirds are characteristic passerine families in the southern lands. The sub-oscines include the New Zealand wrens, the Madagascan asities, and the great tropical American radiation of tyrannids, antbirds, and ovenbirds. The songbirds include diverse Australasian families of few species. Apart from the tropical American radiation, the passerine bird faunas of these lands have a character that is ancient.

Northern Hemisphere In the boreal north, characteristic passerine families are all of songbirds. Their number is not much greater than those of the southern lands—43 versus 40—yet the number of their species is more than treble—3,450 versus 1,090. The northern families, too, are more closely related to one another than those in Australasia. Their character, then, is one of recent and vigorous evolution, radiation, and dispersal, producing a multitude of species.

→ **Directions of evolutionary radiation in passerine birds**

Suboscine flycatcher, *Pyrocephalus rubinus*

Suboscine antshrike, *Thamnophilus doliatus*

Madagascan paradise-flycatcher, *Terpsiphone mutata*

Boreal finch, *Carduelis chloris*

Boreal chickadee, *Parus atricapillus*

Old World Suboscines
before 60 million years ago

Australasian Oscines
before 50 million years ago

New Zealand Wrens
85–80 million years ago

Australian songbird, *Dasyornis broadbenti*

Australian songbird, *Cinclosoma castanotus*

New Zealand wren, *Xenicus gilviventris*

FACT FILE

Old World suboscines Members of this group have poorly muscled voice boxes and comprise 52 species in four families: the New Zealand wrens, the Madagascan asities, and the broadbills and pittas found throughout tropical Afro-Asian forests.

Family Acanthisittidae These wrens are tiny, stump-tailed birds that live in Antarctic beech forests or the alpine screes in mountains above, gleaning for insects. Both parents share breeding duties, building rough, hooded nests in crevices and brooding white eggs.

Genera 2
Species 4 (2 extinct)

New Zealand

Family Eurylaimidae Broadbills are stout, arboreal birds with broad heads, broad, flattened bills, and short legs. Most species eat insects, as well as small herptiles and fruit. They build hanging, domed nests and lay plain or speckled cream eggs.

Genera 9
Species 14

Tropical Africa, S.E. Asia,
Gr. Sundas, S. Philippines

Family Pittidae Pittas are insect-eating birds with short tails. Brilliantly colored, they hop among leaf litter on forest floors. Their domed nests, built near or on the ground, resemble piles of debris. All give loud, double whistle calls.

Genera 1
Species 30

C. Africa, S.E. Asia to N. & E. Australia, Melanesia

⚡ CONSERVATION WATCH

Waifs in woe Many Old World suboscines are confined to islands where they are susceptible to disease, introduced predators, and habitat disturbance. Two species of New Zealand wrens have already been exterminated since European settlement; and one of these is known only from the 17 birds killed by a lighthouse keeper's cat. Two broadbills, nine pittas, and one asity are also listed as threatened.

Green broadbill
Calyptomena viridis,
family Eurylaimidae

♂

Southeast Asian broadbills are brightly plumaged in greens, reds, and blacks

Cream head-spots shine in Southeast Asian forests, possibly for social signaling

Long-tailed broadbill
Psarisomus dalhousiae,
family Eurylaimidae

♂

Red-bellied pitta
Pitta erythrogaster,
family Pittidae

Ranges from the Philippines to Australia. As in most pittas, the sexes look alike

Rifleman
Acanthisitta chloris,
family Acanthisittidae

Banded pitta
Pitta guajana,
family Pittidae

Feeds quietly on the floor of Indo-Malaysian rain forest and seldom calls. Females are finely barred all over the belly

♂

Forages in hopping spirals up tree trunks and branches, flicking its wings

Velvet asity
Philepitta castanea,
family Philepittidae

♂

Male asities have bright eye wattles of blue and green skin. They gather to display in leks and are endemic to Madagascar

Alpine rock wren
Xenicus gilviventris,
family Acanthisittidae

Eared pitta
Pitta phayrei,
family Pittidae

Lives above the treeline in the southern alps. Like the rifleman, it lays its eggs at 2-day intervals

Endemic to Southeast Asia; distinct in having "ears" and short "legs" with a long hind claw

Barred becard
Pachyramphus versicolor,
family Cotingidae

A forest fruit-eater
along the mountains
between Costa Rica
and north Bolivia

Masked tityra
Tityra semifasciata,
family Cotingidae

♂

Widespread from
Mexico to Amazonia.
Tityras are monogamous
and nest in tree holes

Wire-tailed manakin
Pipra filicauda,
family Pipridae

♂

Lives in stream-
side forests in
upper Amazonia

Bearded manakin
Manacus manacus,
family Pipridae

♂

Male erects hairy
feathers under its
chin in display

Lance-tailed
manakin
Chiroxiphia lanceolata,
family Pipridae

♂

In display, a pair
of males cartwheel
about each female on
low branches, giving
rhythmical, whining
calls. The dominant
male will win the right
to mate with her

Blue-crowned
manakin
Pipra coronata,
family Pipridae

♂

♂

Ranges from upper Amazonia
to Costa Rica. Male manakins
have contrastingly colored
crowns or heads

White-crowned manakin
Pipra pipra,
family Pipridae

Occurs in forests through
Amazonia to Costa Rica.
Males spread white crown
feathers out when displaying

Golden-headed manakin
Pipra erythrocephala,
family Pipridae

♂

FACT FILE

New World suboscines There are
10 families and almost 1,170 species of
New World suboscines, in two major
groups. One comprises the manakins,
cotingas, and tyrant flycatchers which
have a voice box extending from the
base of the trachea on to the bronchii,
as in most birds. The other comprises
the antbirds, gnateaters, tapaculos,
ant-thrushes, ovenbirds, and wood
creepers. Their voice box is confined
just to the base of the trachea. Both
groups are centered in tropical America.

Family Pipridae Stump-tailed manakins
pluck fruit as they fly through the forest.
Females are green but males brilliantly
colored, a sign of polygamy. To attract
females, they gather on the ground or
in trees, and bound and flutter about
making mechanical sounds with their
modified wings. Females sling thin,
hammock-like nests in lower forest
strata, and rear broods alone. Clutches
are of two, brown-spotted eggs.

Genera 13
Species 48

S. Mexico to subtropical
South America

Bearded manakin Males clear display
courts on the ground, leaving a vertical
sapling used as the main display perch.
There, they execute astonishing jumps
while the wings make loud, whirring
and snapping sounds. Females visit
males at their courts and dance with
them before mating on the main perch.

Up to 4½ in (11.5 cm)

2

Sexes differ

Sedentary

Common

S. Mexico to Brazil

Ritual brushing
During courtship,
the male wire-tailed
manakin rapidly brushes
the female's throat
with the wire-like tips
of his tail feathers.

⚡ CONSERVATION WATCH

Rare gem discovered Of the four
threatened manakins, the striking
white Araripe manakin, with black
wings and red crest, is listed as
critical. Discovered in 1996 in Brazil,
it has a known range of only two-
thirds of a mile square (1 km²) and
numbers less than 250 individuals.

FACT FILE

Family Cotingidae Cotingas are small to mid-sized birds of the tree tops. Most males are ornamented with bizarre crests, beards, and wattles, and are exquisitely plumaged. These species are polygamous, the males displaying in leks. Once mated, the usually much duller females undertake nesting duties unaided and lay clutches of one to four, brown-blotched eggs. Males of some species, such as the plantcutters and purpletufts, wear dull, female plumage and are monogamous, sharing in nesting duties. Diet is diverse, some species eating fruit—for which they have large mouths to swallow items whole—and others insects—which they catch by sallying in the forest canopy.

Genera 33
Species 96

Mexico to South America

Bearded bellbird As in other bellbirds, males display vocally on high, exposed perches, uttering far-carrying calls that sound like a hammer hitting an anvil. Attracted females, plumaged in dull green streaked with yellow, meet them within the forest below to mate.

⬆ Up to 11 in (28 cm)
🥚 1
✇ Sexes differ
⊘ Sedentary
⚑ Locally common

N. Colombia, Venezuela, N. & N.E. Brazil

Crimson fruitcrow Contradicting its name, this species eats mainly insects. The display flight of males is spectacular, the birds flying steeply up above the forest canopy, then sailing down slowly with wings and tails spread and plumage fluffed into a large, crimson ball.

⬆ Up to 14 in (36 cm)
🥚 probably 1
✇ Sexes differ slightly
⊘ Sedentary
⚑ Rare

N. lower Amazonia

⚡ CONSERVATION WATCH

Tiny population There are believed to be fewer than 50 individuals remaining of the kinglet calyptura (*Calyptura cristata*), a very small, yellowish cotinga that lives north of Rio de Janeiro, Brazil. This altitudinal migrant has been all but exterminated by deforestation. Another 17 species of cotingids are listed as threatened, 6 of which are considered endangered.

Bearded bellbird
Procnias averano,
family Cotingidae

Bellbirds are fruit-eaters; in this species, the male beard is made up of numerous bare, black wattles

Turquoise cotinga
Cotinga ridgwayi,
family Cotingidae

Amazonian umbrellabird
Cephalopterus ornatus,
family Cotingidae

Males of this upper Amazonian fruit-eater display in small groups, calling with crest spread and long, feathered breast wattle inflated

Crimson fruitcrow
Haematoderus militaris,
family Cotingidae

Sharpbill
Oxyruncus cristatus,
family Cotingidae

Capuchinbird
Perissocephalus tricolor,
family Cotingidae

Rufous-tailed plantcutter
Phytotoma rara,
family Cotingidae

Polygamous males erect a cowl of feathers around the neck, raise the tail, and fluff out tufts of orange under-tail feathers while calling in display

Males call alone for mates from high bare branches, their wattles enlarged

Three-wattled bellbird
Procnias tricarunculata,
family Cotingidae

Guianan cock-of-the-rock
Rupicola rupicola,
family Cotingidae

In display, males drop to the ground, prostrating themselves in a spectacular show

This fruit-eater lives in the forest canopy in Nicaragua and Panama

Scale-crested pygmy tyrant
Lophotriccus pileatus,
family Tyrannidae

Confined to mountain forests from the northern Andes to Costa Rica; inconspicuous; sallies for insects in mid-forest strata

Golden-crowned spadebill
Platyrinchus coronatus,
family Tyrannidae

Yellow-bellied elaenia
Elaenia flavogaster,
family Tyrannidae

Black-capped
pygmy tyrant
Myiornis atricapillus,
family Tyrannidae

Inactive, solitary insect-eater of forest canopy from Costa Rica to Ecuador

Rufous-browed
tyrannulet
Phylloscartes superciliaris,
family Tyrannidae

Ruddy-tailed flycatcher
Terenotriccus erythrurus,
family Tyrannidae

Bronze-olive
pygmy tyrant
Pseudotriccus pelzelni,
family Tyrannidae

An insectivore of lower undergrowth in mountain forests of the northern Andes

Torrent tyrannulet
Serpophaga cinerea,
family Tyrannidae

Widespread in lower strata of lowland rain forest from Amazonia to southern Mexico; sallies for insects from set perches

Its nest is a substantial cup of fiber placed in a low, horizontal tree fork over a stream

FACT FILE

Family Tyrannidae This, the largest of passerine families, comprises warbler- to flycatcher-like insectivores that live mostly in trees and shrubberies. Well over half the species are South American. Despite resembling Old World flycatchers and tits, they have a suboscine voice box and make only simple rasping, hissing, and whistled calls. They feed mostly by sallying on the wing or gleaning among twigs and foliage. Monogamy is the rule and the sexes usually look alike. Although males help in chick-rearing, only females incubate their clutches of two to five brown or black-blotched eggs. Nests vary in form and position.

Genera 98
Species 400

South America, West Indies, North America

Golden-crowned spadebill This little tyrant lives inside rain-forest interiors, perching in tall shrubs and low trees, peering about, and then suddenly darting up to scoop insects and spiders from the undersides of leaves or twigs. It forages in pairs.

🐦 Up to 3½ in (9 cm)
● 2
⫻ Sexes alike
⊘ Sedentary
🐦 Locally common

Amazonia, Central American isthmus

Torrent tyrannulet Alone or in pairs, this species forages along fast-flowing mountain streams amid forest. It perches on rocks and roots, flutters out to catch insects on the wing, or runs and stops along banks to pick them up, flicking its tail up as it goes.

🐦 Up to 4½ in (11.5 cm)
● 2
⫻ Sexes alike
⊘ Sedentary
🐦 Locally common

N.W. Andes to Costa Rica

CONSERVATION WATCH

Failing fragments The mishima tyrannulet (*Zimmerius villarejoi*) lives within a protected area in Peru but is still listed as vulnerable because of its tiny, fragmented range. Kaempfer's tody-tyrant (*Hemitriccus kaempferi*) and the Minas Gerais tyrannulet (*Phylloscartes roquettei*) are two fragmented Brazilian species that do not occur inside reserves and are considered critically endangered. All 24 species of tyrant flycatchers are listed as threatened.

DIET SPECIALIZATION

Different species within the Tyrannidae family exploit very particular niches within their environments, allowing dozens of species to coexist in some areas. In some cases this is due to different food preferences, such as for fruit as opposed to insects. But in the majority of cases it can be attributed to slightly different combinations of prey size, habitat, vegetation type, foraging position, and capture technique.

On different continents, passerines of quite different origin have taken on parallel forms and lifestyles in parallel ecological niches.

Ground feeders The American white-browed ground tyrant (below right) is similar to the Eurasian northern wheatear in its long legs, upright stance, and similar plumage pattern.

Foliage gleaners The South American tufted tit-tyrant (below left) bears a strong resemblance to its Old World counterpart, the crested tit, with which it also shares a similar feeding strategy.

Scissor-tailed flycatcher
Tyrannus forficatus, family Tyrannidae

Great kiskadee
Pitangus sulphuratus, family Tyrannidae

Royal flycatcher
Onychorhynchus coronatus, family Tyrannidae

Females build loose, hanging nests with a side entrance

Breeds in boreal forests of North America and migrates to winter in Central and South America

Flattened, slightly hooked bill for catching insects in flight in Tropical America

Eastern kingbird
Tyrannus tyrannus, family Tyrannidae

One of the largest tyrants; an aggressive insect-eating North American migrant

Olive-sided flycatcher
Contopus cooperi, family Tyrannidae

Sulfur-bellied flycatcher
Myiodynastes luteiventris, family Tyrannidae

Erectile crest is raised in excitement

Tufted flycatcher
Mitrephanes phaeocercus, family Tyrannidae

Black phoebe
Sayornis nigricans, family Tyrannidae

Lives in open habitat, including parks and gardens, where it catches insects on the wing. Ranges along the western American mountains, from Oregon to Argentina

Long tail for maneuverability in flight

Sallies out after flying insects in Central America mid-forest strata, returns to perch and shivers tail upon landing

Barred antshrike
Thamnophilus doliatus,
family Thamnophilidae

Follows army ants
and mixed bird
flocks only casually

♂

Fasciated antshrike
Cymbilaimus lineatus,
family Thamnophilidae

Widespread in
Amazonia and the
American isthmus;
forages sluggishly
through undergrowth
of tropical rain forest

♂

Great antshrike
Taraba major,
family Thamnophilidae

♂

Spot-crowned antvireo
Dysithamnus puncticeps,
family Thamnophilidae

Occurs from far
northwest South
America to
Costa Rica

♂

♂

Rufous-winged antwren
Herpsilochmus rufimarginatus,
family Thamnophilidae

♂

Dot-winged antwren
Microrhopias quixensis,
family Thamnophilidae

Like many antwrens,
this species perch-gleans
actively and builds
suspended nests

♂

Pygmy antwren
Myrmotherula brachyura,
family Thamnophilidae

Found in upper
forest strata
in Amazonia

♀

Forages alone on the floor of
lowland rain forest in Amazonia
and the American isthmus

Wing-banded antbird
Myrmornis torquata,
family Thamnophilidae

FACT FILE

The Clamatores The next six families
are of New World suboscines that have
a voice box confined to the base of the
trachea. Although brightly marked,
they are cryptically toned in browns
and most live in forest undergrowth
and shrubberies. They occur in Central
and South America.

Family Thamnophilidae The antbirds
are so called because they follow
columns of army ants. This is one of
their two main feeding strategies,
finding invertebrate food flushed out
by the swarming marauders. The other
is to join mixed flocks of foraging birds,
again to exploit prey disturbed by the
noise and movement. Each pair holds
to a permanent territory—antbirds are
monogamous, mate for life, and the
sexes share all nesting duties. They build
cup-shaped nests of vegetable matter
in undergrowth and the female lays two
or three white to buff eggs that are
marked in red-browns and dusky tones.

Genera 46
Species 206

Neotropical America

White-faced antbird
*This antbird waits
above a marauding
swarm of army
ants, ready to
pounce on any other
insects it disturbs.*

Barred antshrike This species spends
most of its time alone in undergrowth
in disturbed forests. It peers about,
drops on to insect prey on the ground,
and gleans up through clumps of low
vines. Nests—thin cups of tendrils—are
slung on a horizontal fork in thickets.
Females are reddish-brown.

⤒ Up to 6½ in (16.5 cm)
● 2
✸ Sexes differ
⊘ Sedentary
⚑ Locally common

S.E. Mexico to N. Argentina

Spotted antbird
Hylohylax naevioides,
family Thamnophilidae

Ranges from the American isthmus to Ecuador; forages in forest substrata, often follows army ants

Ferruginous-backed antbird
Myrmeciza ferruginea,
family Thamnophilidae

In lower Amazonia, this species forages on the ground and often follows army ants

Black-throated huet-huet
Pteroptochos tarnii,
family Rhinocryptidae

This south Chilean forest dweller nests in a hole at the end of a 6-foot (2 m) long tunnel. It sings simple, penetrating songs

White-plumed antbird
Pithys albifrons,
family Thamnophilidae

Black-bellied gnateater
Conopophaga melanogaster,
family Conopohagidae

Females differ from males in their gray faces and breasts

A professional follower of army ant swarms in Central America

Ocellated antbird
Phaenostictus mcleannani,
family Thamnophilidae

Silvery-fronted tapaculo
Scytalopus argentifrons,
family Rhinocryptidae

This Costa Rican species creeps about on the ground, fossicking in all manner of nooks and crannies

Rufous-vented tapaculo
Scytalopus femoralis,
family Rhinocryptidae

Lives underneath primary and secondary rain forest in central Peruvian Andes

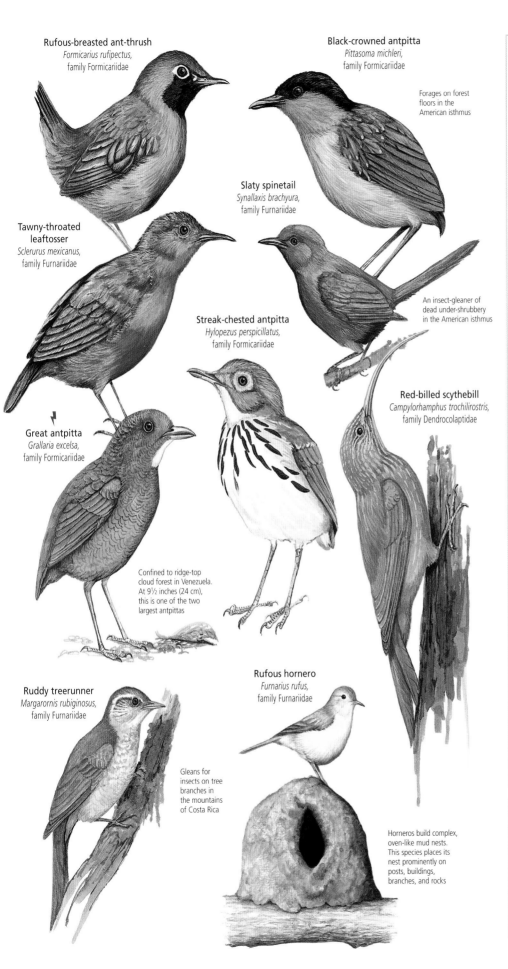

Rufous-breasted ant-thrush
Formicarius rufipectus,
family Formicariidae

Black-crowned antpitta
Pittasoma michleri,
family Formicariidae

Forages on forest floors in the American isthmus

Slaty spinetail
Synallaxis brachyura,
family Furnariidae

Tawny-throated leaftosser
Sclerurus mexicanus,
family Furnariidae

Streak-chested antpitta
Hylopezus perspicillatus,
family Formicariidae

An insect-gleaner of dead under-shrubbery in the American isthmus

Red-billed scythebill
Campylorhamphus trochilirostris,
family Dendrocolaptidae

Great antpitta
Grallaria excelsa,
family Formicariidae

Confined to ridge-top cloud forest in Venezuela. At 9½ inches (24 cm), this is one of the two largest antpittas

Ruddy treerunner
Margarornis rubiginosus,
family Furnariidae

Gleans for insects on tree branches in the mountains of Costa Rica

Rufous hornero
Furnarius rufus,
family Furnariidae

Horneros build complex, oven-like mud nests. This species places its nest prominently on posts, buildings, branches, and rocks

---

FACT FILE

Family Formicariidae Contrary to their name, the ground-antbirds do not associate with army ants. All are solitary, secretive, and long-legged for foraging for invertebrates. They fall into two groups: the ant-thrushes, which walk with tail pumped up and nest in tree cavities; and the antpittas, which hop, bob, and wing-flick, and nest in shrubbery. Clutches are of two varicolored eggs, from plain white in ant-thrushes to plain blue or buff marked with browns in antpittas.

Genera 7
Species 62

C. Mexico to subtropical South America

Family Furnariidae Ovenbirds are famous for building oven-like nests of mud; yet as a family they are unrivaled for the variety of nests that they make, from holes in trees and burrows in the ground, to cups and domes of plant matter in vegetation as well. All are rather small, brown birds and most eat insects. Monogamous, both sexes share all nesting duties and many roost in their nests when not breeding. Females lay plain white eggs.

Genera 55
Species 236

S. Mexico to South America

Family Dendrocolaptidae The woodcreepers are tree-climbing relatives of the ovenbirds. Small and brown with streaks or bars, they have thin, straight to curved bills—good for probing trunks and branches for invertebrates and herptiles. Their spine-tipped tails are used as a prop. These birds may be monogamous or polygamous. When they are polygamous, females nest alone in tree holes. Eggs are plain white, in clutches of two to three.

Genera 13
Species 50

Mexico to N. temperate South America (C. Argentina)

CONSERVATION WATCH

Declining forest dweller Twelve ground-antbirds, one woodcreeper, and 26 ovenbirds are threatened. The Alagoas foliage-gleaner and royal cinclodes are critically endangered. Fewer than 250 royal cinclodes survive in Andean forests that continue to be cleared.

Singing A marsh wren (*Cistothorus palustris*) sings while perching on a common cattail in Alberta, Canada. This tiny bird is a perennial singer, except during the molting season. The size of song repertoires varies by population.

Well-researched singers Zebra finches (*Taeniopygia guttata*), widespread in the dry regions of Australia, are among the best-studied songbirds. To make their songs heard far afield, birds may sing from the highest perches available. This is also one reason that many species prefer to sing in the morning, when the clear air helps carry the sound farther. Birds can produce sounds with higher frequencies than the human voice.

Volume matters Male zebra finches (far left) sing far more loudly when other birds are present, in order to prompt females (left) to respond to their advances and to ward off other males.

SONG

Bird songs have inspired musicians, poets, and other artists through the ages. The syrinx, the resonating chamber in which bird sounds are produced, is a complex structure that is best developed in the group of passerines known as oscines or songbirds. Different species can be distinguished by their songs, although some birds, such as the village indigobird, are very skilled at mimicking other birds. Songs are generally partly or entirely learned, and different dialects often exist among neighboring populations. In most species, it is the males that sing, to attract females or to warn other males to stay away from an established territory. Studies have shown that males can distinguish the songs of their neighbors from the songs of other males. Sometimes birds sing in duets.

Repertoires matter Most male songbirds can sing two or more different songs. Female zebra finches have been shown to consistently prefer males with more complex songs.

Stimulating sounds Songs help coordinate the reproductive cycles of mates. They can prompt females to ovulate, build nests, and lay eggs.

Begging to be fed Four hungry northern mockingbird chicks (*Mimus polyglottos*) beg for food. Parents respond not only to gaping mouths but also to feeding calls. Calls are shorter and less complex than songs and can signal threats, hunger, sexual interest, and various other elements of social behavior.

Great bowerbird
Chlamydera nuchalis,
family Ptilonorhynchidae

Male adorns its bower with white bones and pale green berries

Golden bowerbird
Prionodura newtoniana,
family Ptilonorhynchidae

♂

Satin bowerbird
Ptilonorhynchus violaceus,
family Ptilonorhynchidae

♂

Builds twin towers of sticks over 5 feet (1.5 m) high, that it decorates with lichen, moss, and flowers

♂

Always decorates its bower with blue or violet-colored objects

Noisy scrub-bird
Atrichornis clamosus,
family Atrichornithidae

First discovered in south-west Australia in 1842, this species was lost to science for over 100 years before its rediscovery

♂

Treecreepers have a uniquely muscled voice box and give ringing, whistled calls. This species lives in east Australian wet eucalypt forests

♂

A lyrebird singing in display posture

♂

Superb lyrebird
Menura novaehollandiae,
family Menuridae

Red-browed treecreeper
Climacteris erythrops,
family Climacteridae

FACT FILE

The oscines or songbirds All remaining families that follow belong to the vast suborder of songbirds, with complexly structured and muscled voice boxes. Recent molecular studies place them in four main groups: the Ancient Australasians, the Meliphagoids, the Corvidans, and the Passeridans.

The Ancient Australasians

Family Menuridae Male lyrebirds, the largest of songbirds, display on mounds in an exploded lek, singing and dancing with extraordinary power and shimmering their lyre-shaped tails over their heads. Females alone build rough, domed nests and rear a single chick from an olive, blackish-marked egg.

Genera 1
Species 2

S.E. Australia

Family Climacteridae The Australian treecreepers have fused forward toes that work like calipers as they hop up trunks and branches, probing into crannies for their main food: ants. They are monogamous, live in pairs or small groups, and roost and nest in holes in trees. Clutches are of two to four cream eggs marked in black or red-brown.

Genera 2
Species 7

Mainland Australia,
E. & W. New Guinea

Family Ptilonorhynchidae Bowerbirds are renowned for building bowers—ornamented platforms, towers, or avenues of sticks on the ground where males sing and dance to attract females. Mostly arboreal fruit-eaters, bowerbirds are polygamous and females carry out nesting duties alone.

Genera 8
Species 18

N., C. & E. Australia,
New Guinea

Bower on display *Male bowerbirds build elaborate bowers, which they decorate with small, colored objects.*

FACT FILE

The Meliphagoids This group of five families and 270 species is centered in Australasia. It is dominated by honeyeaters, which comprise over 60 percent of the species. According to molecular data, two aberrant families in the group, the Australasian babblers and logrunners, are closely related to the Corvidans as well.

Family Maluridae Fairy-wrens are cock-tailed, undergrowth foragers that have only six to ten tail feathers. Females are the matriarchs in fairy-wren social groups, guarded territorially by males which help rear the young. The female nest-builds and broods alone.

Genera 5
Species 28

Australia, Tasmania, New Guinea, Aru Is.

Standing out
The brilliantly colored male fairy-wrens stand out, none more so than the splendid fairy-wren, a species that lives in Australia's western and interior scrublands.

HONEYEATING

Nectar is a rich source of energy that is exploited by different groups of birds in different ways. Versatile honeyeaters have moderately long bills and channeled tongues that are deeply frayed at the tip. This allows them access to both massed flower heads and tubular flowers, in which their tongues literally mop up the nectar.

⚡ CONSERVATION WATCH

Misjudged rarities The only two fairy-wrens listed as threatened are the Mallee emu-wren and white-throated grasswren. But the so far unsung thick-billed grasswren is in a far more hazardous state. Eighty percent of its range has disappeared since European settlement.

Canopy feeder in New Guinea, Australia, and Indonesia. Has a loud clanking song that male and female may give in duet

Helmeted friarbird
Philemon buceroides,
family Meliphagidae

Variegated fairy-wren
Malurus lamberti,
family Maluridae

Western spinebill
Acanthorhynchus superciliosus,
family Meliphagidae

♂

Iridescent blue head characterizes many malurid wrens

Slender bill and tubular tongue for taking nectar from long-tubed epacrid and protead flowers

♂

White-cheeked honeyeater
Phylidonyris nigra,
family Meliphagidae

Bar-breasted honeyeater
Ramsayornis fasciatus,
family Meliphagidae

Wattlebirds are named for the colored lobes of skin that hang from their cheeks

Regent honeyeater
Xanthomyza phrygia,
family Meliphagidae

Yellow wattlebird
Anthochaera paradoxa,
family Meliphagidae

Bell miner
Manorina melanophrys,
family Meliphagidae

This is the largest honeyeater, up to 20 inches (51 cm) long, and is confined to Tasmania, Australia

Calls day-in, day-out, with continuous, bell-like "tinks"—the note that gives it its name. Lives in southeast Australian forests

Brown honeyeater
Lichmera indistincta,
family Meliphagidae

A widespread
Australian species;
calls like a
reed-warbler

Crimson chat
Epthianura tricolor,
family Meliphagidae

♂

Follows erratic rains
in desert Australia.
Like other honeyeaters,
must drink regularly

Red-headed honeyeater
Myzomela erythrocephala,
family Meliphagidae

♂

Males are brightly
pied, females are
dull gray

♂

Pied honeyeater
Certhionyx variegatus,
family Meliphagidae

Lewin's honeyeater
Meliphaga lewinii,
family Meliphagidae

**Black-chinned
honeyeater**
Melithreptus gularis,
family Meliphagidae

Tui
Prosthemadura novaeseelandiae,
family Meliphagidae

One of two honeyeater
species found in
New Zealand

A large, communal
honeyeater that nests
in the disused nests
of other birds

Blue-faced honeyeater
Entomyzon cyanotis,
family Meliphagidae

Unusual fusing of
the skin over the
nostrils, the function
of which is unclear

FACT FILE

Family Meliphagidae Honeyeaters
are the largest bird family in Australasia.
Living in trees and shrubbery, they are
small to mid-sized gray and green birds
and the sexes are usually alike. Curved
bills and brush-tipped tongues allow
them to pursue different foods—nectar,
fruit, and insects—as opportunities offer.
Species more dependent on nectar
tend to be nomadic in their search
for flowering. Many honeyeaters
congregate at food sources where
they create aggressive peck-orders.
Though monogamous, they often
mate only for breeding. Females
carry out most nesting duties,
building cup-nests slung in
foliage. Their clutches of one
to five eggs are usually pale
pink with red and dusky spots.

Sweet meal An
eastern spinebill forages
on eucalypt blossom.

Genera 44
Species 174

Australia & Melanesia to L. Sundas,
Sulawesi & Oceania

Pied honeyeater This irruptive nomad
of Australia's arid zone has developed
a pointed wing with reduced flight
feathers for covering vast distances
quickly to flushes of flowers. Males
have a spectacular display flight, flying
vertically up, then diving down with
wings closed and tail fanned. They assist
the female with building the nest, which
can be completed in a matter of days,
with young fledged in under a month.

↥ Up to 7 in (18 cm)
● 2–4
✚ Sexes differ
～ Nomad
↧ Locally common

Inland Australia

CONSERVATION WATCH

Island dweller The mao (*Gymnomyza
samoensis*) of Samoa is a large,
endangered honeyeater. Slash-and-
burn farming techniques and the
introduction of non-native trees
have threatened its forest habitat.
Half a dozen other Pacific island
honeyeaters are already extinct.

FACT FILE

Family Pardalotidae Pardalotes are tiny birds that creep about in eucalypt trees to glean larvae, insects, and exudates with their scoop-shaped bills. Breeding males beam out territorial calls from a vantage perch and help to incubate three to five white eggs in burrows.

Genera 1
Species 4

Australia, Tasmania

Cavity dweller Pardalotes, such as the spotted pardalote, typically nest in tree cavities or in tunnels in the ground; they have also been known to nest in buildings.

Family Acanthizidae Scrubwrens and gerygones are small, hopping insect-gleaners. All have dull plumage and all build domed nests in foliage or crevices, in trees or the ground. Males help with nesting duties except incubation of eggs.

Genera 14
Species 60

Australia to S.E. Asia, New Zealand, & Melanesia

Family Pomatostomidae Australasian babblers resemble some Asian babblers in appearance and the way they hop, fossicking for insects; but they are much more social. They build domed tree nests where they roost and breed together.

Genera 2
Species 5

Australia, lowland New Guinea

Anyone home? An Australian gray-crowned babbler visits one of its nests, a bulky dome of twigs.

Family Orthonychidae Chattering noisily, logrunners work over the rain-forest floor in search of invertebrates, foraging in groups. Their pelvis and legs have a unique structure that allows them to scrape litter away sideways.

Genera 1
Species 3

E. Australia, montane New Guinea

Spotted pardalote
Pardalotus punctatus,
family Pardalotidae

Males give a whistled pinging to advertise territory, sitting on a high perch and turning about to send the call in all directions

Chestnut-breasted whiteface
Aphelocephala pectoralis,
family Acanthizidae

A rare South Australian species. Like other whitefaces, has a thickly muscled stomach to digest seeds

White-browed scrubwren
Sericornis frontalis,
family Acanthizidae

Different species occupy different niches in all strata of vegetation, right to the ground

Most gerygones, scrub-wrens, and thornbills live in Australia and New Guinea

Fairy gerygone
Gerygone palpebrosa,
family Acanthizidae

Lives in inland east Australia

Yellow-rumped thornbill
Acanthiza chrysorrhoa,
family Acanthizidae

Builds huge, domed dormitory nests in open trees

Chestnut-crowned babbler
Pomatostomus ruficeps,
family Pomatostomidae

Spine-tipped tail is used as a prop in litter to balance while scraping outward, first with one foot, then the other, to expose food on the forest floor

Logrunner
Orthonyx temminckii,
family Orthonychidae

Female logrunners undertake all nesting duties, building a domed nest of sticks and moss on the forest floor and laying a single white egg per clutch

NEW GUINEAN DISCOVERIES

If the world's songbirds arose on the Australian part of Gondwana over 60 million years ago, where are their ancestral stocks today? Gondwana's songbirds evolved in cool rain forests of laurel, Antarctic beech, and myrtle. But when Australia broke from Gondwana, 10-5 million years ago, it drifted north into desert latitudes and dried out. Ancestral songbirds either perished or changed rapidly to adapt. About the same time, crustal pressures forced up a huge mountain range along Australia's north rim. It was the backbone of New Guinea. There, the Gondwanan rain forests and their songbird waifs took refuge. Not surprisingly, DNA research has uncovered new families of songbirds in New Guinea; and they are probably not the last.

Satinbirds Male satinbirds (family Cnemophilidae) are so brilliantly plumaged in blacks, yellows, and oranges that they were thought to be birds-of-paradise. Yet they are monogamous, build domed nests, and have no extrovert displays. Females are dull olive without barring. Their three species live in the foliage of mountain forests, eating fruit.

Longbills DNA shows that the slaty-chinned longbill (*Toxorhamphus poliopterus*), a tiny bird that darts through the forest, is one of the berrypeckers. Yellowish breasted and short-tailed, the four species of longbills have long, curved bills with distinctively toothed edges and deeply channeled, brush-tipped tongues for taking nectar as well as insects.

GONDWANA'S ARK

The 15,000-foot (4,500-m) high mountain spine of New Guinea holds most of that great island's songbirds. All of the birds-of-paradise and bowerbirds are centered there. So too are its endemic songbird families: berrypeckers, satinbirds, and several others still to be worked out. They live above 3,000 feet (915 m), in tall, cool, Gondwanan rain forests of Antarctic beech, laurels, myrtles, and araucariads found elsewhere today only in New Zealand, Chile, and tiny pockets in east Australia.

Ancient ancestors New Guinean songbirds are found in rain forests throughout the region. Scientists believe there are still songbird families within these forests yet to be discovered.

Berrypeckers Small foliage-gleaners and fruit-eaters of forest shrubberies, berrypeckers (family Melanocharitidae) have short bills with distinctively serrated edges and no bristles around the gape as so many songbirds have. Monogamous, they build neat, felt-like cup-nests on branches and decorate them with lichen. Males are mostly glossed black over the back, with often gray or cream breast and white tail bar; females are dull olive and larger. There are 12 species. The fan-tailed berrypecker (*Melanocharis versteri*) (above) is a young male changing from juvenile to adult plumage; its size reduces with the change.

Unique species Two unusual members of the berrypecker family are the tit berrypecker (*Oreocharis arfaki*) (male and female below), and crested berrypecker (*Paramythia montium*). They have unique hair-like plumes in the flanks. Unlike other solitary berrypeckers, these species gather in small, noisy flocks to forage for insects through the mid and upper forest. They build untidy cup-nests of fiber in foliage.

Scarlet minivet
Pericrocotus flammeus, family Campephagidae ♂

Flocks at food sources; males are usually much more brightly colored than females

Bar-bellied cuckoo-shrike
Coracina striata, family Campephagidae

Black-faced cuckoo-shrike
Coracina novaehollandiae, family Campephagidae

Ranges from the Malay Peninsula through western Indonesia to the Philippines

Its call is a grinding, metallic churr

Ranges nomadically through the woodlands of Australia

Varied triller
Lalage leucomela, family Campephagidae ♂

Saddleback
Philesturnus carunculatus, family Callaeatidae

Varied sitella
Neositta chrysoptera, family Neosittidae

Joins mixed feeding bird flocks as a tactic for finding food, picking up insect prey disturbed by other birds

Scrub greenlet
Hylophilus flavipes, family Vireonidae

Black-capped vireo
Vireo atricapilla, family Vireonidae

Rufous-browed peppershrike
Cyclarhis gujanensis, family Vireonidae

Australasian figbird
Sphecotheres viellioti,
family Oriolidae

Differs from other
orioles in several ways.
It is gregarious, noisy,
builds shallow nests,
and has bare skin
around the eye

Malay rail-babbler
Eupetes macrocerus,
family Eupetidae

Forages on the
forest floor in
Southeast Asia's
rain forests

Eastern whipbird
Psophodes olivaceus,
family Eupetidae

Crested shrike-tit
Falcunculus frontatus,
family Falcunculidae

Lives in eucalypt
woodlands and
forests of northern,
eastern, and
southern Australia

Eurasian golden oriole
Oriolus oriolus,
family Oriolidae

Golden whistler
Pachycephala pectoralis,
family Pachycephalidae

Crested bellbird
Oreoica gutturalis,
family Pachycephalidae

Males have black
bills and females
leaden-gray

Gray shrike-thrush
Colluricincla harmonica,
family Pachycephalidae

Geographic variation in color
patterns in the golden whistler
are considerable in both sexes,
but in most populations, the
female is plain gray-brown

FACT FILE

Family Eupetidae Whipbirds and jewel-babblers are insect-eaters. Rail-babblers, often richly toned in blues and reds, are slender-headed birds with long legs. They walk secretively over the rain-forest floor, building nests of dead leaves and roots there. Whipbirds are dull, thick-headed, crested birds with short, strong feet for jumping in shrubbery where they nest.

Genera 4
Species 10

S., E. & C. Australia, New Guinea, Sumatra, Malaysia

Family Falcunculidae Shrike-tits work over branches in the forest midstage, stripping and prising off loose bark and moss with their stout, hooked bills to expose invertebrate food beneath. The sexes differ in throat markings or the presence of wattles. They commonly forage in small parties, the members of which may help the senior pair to feed young in their cup-nest, high in trees.

Genera 2
Species 4

Australia & montane New Guinea

Family Oriolidae Solitary, orioles forage through forests and woods for insects and fruit. Most are red-billed and richly colored in yellows. Their territorial call is a sweet but monotonous, rolling gurgle. Females, helped by their mates, build a bulky bag-nest suspended in trees. They incubate two to five brown-spotted eggs.

Genera 2
Species 29

Australia & New Guinea to temperate Eurasia, sub-Saharan Africa

Family Pachycephalidae Whistlers and shrike-thrushes comprise two families, but they are similar in form and forage alone for invertebrates, moving by perch-and-pounce in forest mid-strata. Their territorial songs are rich, fluted whistles. Monogamous, both sexes may share nesting duties, building loose, cup-shaped nests of roots, fiber, and dead leaves.

Genera 9
Species 55

Australia, New Guinea, Melanesia, Micronesia

FACT FILE

Family Platysteiridae Shrike-flycatchers and batises are small, stump-tailed insect-catchers. They hop about in trees to sally or hover-glean for insects, often taking prey flushed by their whirring wings or mixed feeding flocks of birds. Pair bonds are strong; males help females to rear young and to build neat cup-nests.

Genera 6
Species 28

Sub-Saharan Africa

Family Malaconotidae Bush-shrikes and helmetshrikes have stout, hooked bills for grasping and pulling food apart: mainly large invertebrates. These they pounce on from perches, tethering the kill with their feet. They vary from solitary to social, and both sexes build their cup-nest in tree crotches.

Genera 10
Species 52

Africa & S. Arabia

Family Vangidae Vangas are the tree shrikes of Madagascar, but their bills have diversified from thickened and hooked to slender and curved, for catching insects on the wing, probing into crevices, hop-gleaning up trunks, and grabbing small herptiles. Rough cup-nests are placed in an upright fork or woven on to horizontal branches.

Genera 15
Species 22

Madagascar

Family Artamidae Butcherbirds and woodswallows occupy diverse niches. Carnivorous butcherbirds have stout, hooked bills for grasping and ripping; currawongs crow-like bills for scavenging; and woodswallows short, wide bills to catch insects on the wing. Most are pied and all have slit nostrils.

Genera 6
Species 24

Australia & Melanesia
to S.E. Asia & India

⚡ CONSERVATION WATCH

African angst All threatened species in these families are Madagascan or African: six bush-shrikes and five vangas. In Madagascar, habitat destruction is particularly serious.

White-browed woodswallow
Artamus superciliosus,
family Artamidae

♂

An inland
Australian
nomad

All birds in the
Artamidae family
have uniquely sunken
nostrils; most species
forage and roost
in groups

Dark newtonia
Newtonia amphichroa,
family Vangidae

Chinspot batis
Batis molitor,
family Platysteiridae

♂

Males have a
black breast band.
Lives in woods of
southeast Africa

Pairs hold
territory and
duet in courtship

Brubru
Nilaus afer,
family Malaconotidae

**Brown-throated
wattle-eye**
Platysteira cyanea,
family Platysteiridae

Tylas vanga
Tylas eduardi,
family Vangidae

Black-crowned tchagra
Tchagra senegala,
family Malaconotidae

Wanders African
savannas in flocks,
breeds in communal
groups. Helmetshrikes
are social while African
bush-shrikes are solitary

White helmetshrike
Prionops plumatus,
family Malaconotidae

♂

This species carols
in duet with others
of its flock

Australian magpie
Gymnorhina tibicen,
family Artamidae

Strong feet adapted
for ground feeding

Fantails flirt their tails and wings to help flush insects. This is a Southeast Asian species

Yellow-bellied fantail
Rhipidura hypoxantha,
family Rhipiduridae

Rufous fantail
Rhipidura rufifrons,
family Rhipiduridae

Widespread in rain forests of east Australia and Melanesia

Yellow-breasted boatbill
Machaerirhynchus flaviventer,
family Machaerirhynchidae

♂

Greater racket-tailed drongo
Dicrurus paradiseus,
family Dicruridae

Sexes in the Rhipiduridae family look alike and share nesting duties

Willie wagtail
Rhipidura leucophrys,
family Rhipiduridae

Long-tailed shrike
Lanius schach,
family Laniidae

Ranges from central India to the Philippines, Lesser Sundas, and New Guinea; it is sedentary

Shrikes perch on low vantage perches in the open and dive on to prey

Birds in the Laniidae family have strong, hooked bills for ripping their food open, and can impale it on barbs to dismember or store

Masked shrike
Lanius nubicus,
family Laniidae

Red-backed shrike
Lanius collurio,
family Laniidae

Drongos are distinctively glossy black and fork-tailed, often with long outer streamers

FACT FILE

Family Machaerirhynchidae Boatbills are small, rain-forest salliers that sit on bare twigs, tails quivering, then dart out to snap up insects. Their broad, flat bills are specialized for this, and they forage alone, cocking the tail when excited. Nests are meager, shallow saucers of tendrils slung in branchlet forks. Males are brighter than females.

Genera 1
Species 2

N.E. Australia, New Guinea

Family Dicruridae Drongos are large, black, sallying insect-eaters. Their stout bills are fitted for dealing with hard-shelled insects and surrounded by protective bristles. Both sexes share nesting duties and sling their shallow, cup-shaped nests in branchlets.

Genera 2
Species 22

Sub-Saharan Africa, S.& E. Asia to E. Australia & N. Melanesia

Family Rhipiduridae Fantails are small, fan-tailed flycatchers that pirouette and sally around undergrowth hyperactively and alone. Their bills are short and wide, and surrounded by long bristles. Pairs build small, neat cup-nests of fiber bound with cobweb which they perch on a twig and furnish with a slender tail.

Genera 1
Species 43

Australasia & Melanesia, Oceania, S.E. Asia & India

Family Laniidae Shrikes are solitary predators of insects and small vertebrates. Sexes are usually alike, monogamous, and territorial. They place their cup-shaped nests of interwoven tendrils, twigs, and leaves in trees or shrubbery.

Genera 4
Species 30

North America, Africa, Eurasia to montane New Guinea

Perching *The long-tailed shrike is a solitary, aggressive bird of the open country. It perches conspicuously on poles or trees as it looks for food.*

DISPLAYS AND LEK BEHAVIOR

Because birds respond strongly to visual signs, much of their communication revolves around displays. These may serve a number of functions, including courtship, greeting, threat, submission, or distraction of predators. Courtship displays themselves vary widely, and may involve ritualized flying, constructing elaborate structures, demonstrating skills, or performing such singular actions as the male manakin's brushing of the female's throat with his tail feathers. In some cases, only the male displays, and the female is merely a spectator; in other cases, the male and female perform together. Many courtship displays involve showing off plumage, especially that found on the most visible parts of the body, such as the head, neck, breast, upper wings, or tail. In some cases, many males gather together in staging areas called leks, where they compete to attract females. Most birds are monogamous, forming pairs for one or more breeding seasons.

Trying to impress A male great bowerbird (*Chlamydera nuchalis*) (above) displays in front of a female who inspects his handiwork in the bower he has constructed. The species of bowerbirds in which the males are relatively drab build more elaborate bowers than those in which the males are more colorful. Bowers may take different shapes and may be decorated with various small objects. After mating, female bowerbirds go away to build separate, cup-like nests in trees.

All together Male raggiana birds-of-paradise (below) perch in groups and vie with each other for the attention of females by simultaneously quivering their long, lacy, colorful flank plumes (which they spread for maximum effect) and by cawing hysterically.

Groupings Male raggiana birds-of-paradise typically gather in groups of three to eight. Other species such as the greater bird-of-paradise (Paradisaea apoda) may gather in groups of as many as 20. Most species, however, display singly.

Choosing a suitor Dull female raggiana birds-of-paradise visit the lek to observe the males' displays. Studies have shown that most females mate with the same male, presumably the one that is most dominant, judged by prowess in display.

Spectacular gatherings Birds-of-paradise, which live in the forests of New Guinea, eastern Indonesia, and Australia, are justly famous for their ornate plumage and their impressive displays. Males of different species have different courtship rituals; the best known are those of the *Paradisaea* genus—such as the raggiana bird-of-paradise (*Paradisaea raggiana*) (above)—in which the males congregate in leks in the forest, spreading their colorful plumes while posturing and dancing on high, bare branches. Females observe the show, mate, then leave to nest on their own.

Elegance in the forest A male superb lyrebird (*Menura novaehollandiae*) (left), which lives in the forests of southeastern Australia, is renowned for having one of the most stunning of avian displays. To attract a mate, it makes use of its unique tail, the two outer feathers of which are shaped like a Greek lyre, hence its name. The bird stands on a mound and spreads its tail into a spectacular fan. It then throws its tail forward over its head and vibrates the plumes as it dances and sings.

Going solo The male western parotia (*Parotia sefilata*) (right) of New Guinea may perform in dispersed leks or by itself. It stands in a small, cleared performing ground on the forest floor and dances to attract females. Most songbirds perform by themselves, even the superb bird-of-paradise and riflebirds, which surround themselves with raised wings.

Saving the best display for last When a visiting female raggiana bird-of-paradise (below, right) shows enough interest in a courting male to land on his perch, he begins his most impressive show. He leans forward until his body is nearly inverted, then extends his colorful wings and clasps them together, giving the female a better view of his brilliant plumage. This is a very strenuous exercise for the male. After mating, the female will fly off and the male will resume his displays in the quest for another mate. The males are not involved in the raising of offspring.

Inspiring humans The display dances of male raggiana birds-of-paradise have inspired the native people of eastern New Guinea to adorn themselves with the bird's plumes and perform ceremonial dances of their own. The raggiana bird-of-paradise is the national bird of Papua New Guinea. Trade in them is controlled, and non-nationals cannot possesss a bird-of-paradise or its plumes.

Different strokes Male birds-of-paradise have different routines, depending on their species. King birds-of-paradise (Cicinnurus regius) invert themselves even more than the raggiana, by hanging under branches.

Showing interest A female raggiana bird-of-paradise observes her suitor's private display, gauging his desirability as a mate. She also casually pecks at his beak. By primarily choosing to mate with the same male—the one who outshines his rivals—the females optimize the quality of male genes they pass on to their offspring.

FACT FILE

Family Paradisaeidae Polygamy and exquisite plumage reach their zenith in male birds-of-paradise, one driving the other for the attraction of females. Males flaunt their plumes in song-and-dance displays, in trees or on the ground, in groups or alone, and in greatest diversity in mountain rain forests. Females are dull and barred. After mating, they build rough cup-nests of twigs and rear the usually single young alone. Only one small group, the manucodes, is monogamous and females are glossy black like males. All species are arboreal and feed on a variety of fruits and some invertebrates. They bound and run around foliage like rodents to pick off their food. Display calls, ranging from raucous rasps to hysterical cawing, hardly match the beauty of plumage; one species, the brown sicklebill, rattles explosively like a machine gun.

Genera 16
Species 40

New Guinea & satellite islands, E. Australia, N. Moluccas

Family Picathartidae Bald crows are long-legged, long-tailed birds that forage on the rain-forest floor in rocky terrain. They live alone, in pairs, or in small social groups. Graceful and rather silent, they spring over the ground in hops, short runs, and short flights, picking up larger invertebrates from the ground, foliage, and sometimes from the edge of army ant swarms. Though monogamous, they are not territorial or aggressive. Different pairs often build their large cup-nests of mud near one another, attaching them to shelves in caves and open rock faces. Both male and female share all nesting duties, and feed their young mostly on worms.

Genera 1
Species 2

Equatorial W. Africa (Guinea to Gabon)

⚡ CONSERVATION WATCH

Blue beauty The uniquely plumed blue bird-of-paradise (*Paradisaea rudolphi*), which lives in montane forests in New Guinea, is one of three vulnerable members of the Paradisaeidae family. Threats to its survival include loss of habitat and hunting for its feathers. Both bald crows from the diminishing rain forests of west equitorial Africa are also listed as vulnerable.

White-necked picathartes
Picathartes gymnocephalus,
family Picathartidae

Occurs from Guinea to Ghana where it is sedentary, never moving far from breeding sites, and is vulnerable to on-going forest clearing

King bird-of-paradise
Cicinnurus regius,
family Paradisaeidae

A secretive gem of lowland rain forests throughout New Guinea

Arfak astrapia
Astrapia nigra,
family Paradisaeidae

Velvet sheen gorget. Lives in mountains in western New Guinea

Magnificent riflebird
Ptiloris magnificus,
family Paradisaeidae

White plumes are raised in display. Endemic to the north Moluccas

Twelve-wired bird-of-paradise
Seleucidis melanoleucus,
family Paradisaeidae

Wallace's standardwing
Semioptera wallacii,
family Paradisaeidae

Western parotia
Parotia sefilata,
family Paradisaeidae

Wire-like head plumes are twirled in display

A specialist feeder on pandanus fruit in the swamp rain forests of lowland New Guinea

Asian paradise-flycatcher
Terpsiphone paradisi,
family Monarchidae

Like other Afro-Asian paradise-flycatchers, this species is crested, black-headed and, in males, has a long, attenuated tail

♂

Spectacled monarch
Monarcha trivirgatus,
family Monarchidae

Darts about shrubbery on the wing within Australian rain forests, flirting its white-tipped tail to help flush insects

Black-naped monarch
Hypothymis azurea,
family Monarchidae

Rufous-winged philentoma
Philentoma pyrhopterum,
family Prionopidae

White-eared monarch
Monarcha leucotis,
family Monarchidae

♂

♂

Monarchs have weak feet that are suited for little else than perching. These blue species live in Southeast Asia

Pied monarch
Arses kaupi,
family Monarchidae

♂

Satin flycatcher
Myiagra cyanoleuca,
family Monarchidae

Migratory in east Australia

♂

Ranges from central south Asia through Southeast Asia to western islands of the Sunda arc

Magpie-lark
Grallina cyanoleuca,
family Monarchidae

Large and long-legged; one of only two species of ground-foraging monarchs. Widespread in woodlands of Australia

Apostlebird
Rich gray and thrush-sized, apostlebirds (Struthidea cinerea) roost and nest in trees but forage entirely on the ground. They pick up mainly seeds for which their short finch-shaped bill is adapted.

MUD NESTERS

Time and again, birds have turned to mud to form and bind their nests. When mixed with plant fiber, it dries into a firm layer that sticks to rock and wood. Albatrosses and flamingos build simple mud nests on the ground. But it is the passerines that have mastered the art, in the multichambered "ovens" built by the horneros, and the inverted flasks of some swallows. Two Australian species build bowl-shaped mud nests which they perch on horizontal branches, well above the ground. They are the apostlebird and the white-winged chough, which are placed in their own endemic Australian family, Corcoracidae.

True adobe builders This nest of the apostlebird (above), with whitish eggs sparingly spotted in black and lavender, is characteristic of the family. The nest structure is true adobe, mud being used to bind dry plant stems and fiber into a wall and then left to dry; the nest lining is made of fiber.

Common habits and habitats Apostlebirds (left) and choughs may look different, but they have much in common. Both are ground-foragers with long, bushy tails and rounded wings; they walk about with tails teetering up and down, and fly slowly in flap-and-glide style. They also have a peculiar ring of cartilage in the eye which enables them to bulge the eye in excitement or threat. Both are found through much of eastern Australia.

White-winged chough A white-winged chough (*Corcorax melanorhamphos*) sits in its mud nest (right). Unlike apostlebirds, choughs have a slender bill that they use to shuffle through leaf litter in search of invertebrate food. Like apostlebirds, they are intensely social, living in flocks of a dozen or more—hence the name for apostlebirds—and all help one another in nest-building, brooding, and rearing the chicks.

Family of feeders A lone white-winged chough (left), is seen here feeding young, but a large band of helpers is needed to ensure successful rearing. Without them, nesting fails and the group eventually perishes. If a helper bringing food to the nest in difficult times is seen to swallow the morsel itself, the rest of the group attack and punish it.

COOPERATIVE BREEDING

About 3 percent of all bird species breed cooperatively, meaning that additional birds—either juveniles or adults—help the parents raise their young. Recent studies have shown that this phenomenon is more prevalent among passerines than was previously thought. There are two forms of cooperative breeding. One involves non-breeding birds only helping parents protect and rear their nestlings. The other, called communal breeding, involves some shared parentage (whether shared maternity, paternity, or both) of the offspring that a group of adults are raising together.

Family flocks Gray-crowned babblers (*Pomatostomus temporalis*) (above) are highly sociable birds that live in small flocks of a dozen or so—typically the senior breeding pairs and offspring of previous years—all year round. The junior birds help the parents with nest building and feeding duties, feeding not only the young but also the brooding female on and off the nest. They also help to build dormitory nests where all cram in to sleep at night.

Staying behind *Like many other Australian birds, juvenile superb fairy-wrens (left and right) from an earlier brood frequently remain with their parents to help raise their younger siblings. This increases the chances of similar genes surviving.*

Tidying up *An immature (or eclipse) male superb fairy-wren (right) removes a fecal sac from the nest. Helpers carry out various chores, including tidying the nest, procuring food, and protecting the nestlings from predators.*

A lighter load *The mother (left) brings food to her nestlings. Her workload is considerably eased by the presence of her helpers. Studies have shown that chicks raised in communal settings are fed more insects per hour than those raised in a nuclear family setting.*

A group effort The superb fairy-wren (*Malurus cyaneus*) (right) is one of the many communally breeding species of passerines. It is common in southeastern Australia, including in suburban gardens. Why cooperative breeding evolved in some species of birds and not in others is still something of a mystery, especially in light of the patchy distribution of the phenomenon among genetically related types of birds. Ornithologists believe it is probably related to a combination of factors, including environmental constraints (with respect to the availability of unoccupied breeding territories or sexually mature mates) and life-history traits, such as mortality rates and dispersal tendencies. Helpers may include birds whose own attempts at nesting have failed that season.

Standing guard *The father (left) of the brood perches near the nest. Among superb fairy-wrens, fertilization is more likely to occur with a partner outside the group than within the pair itself. Studies have shown that per capita reproductive success does not increase with group size.*

FOOD STORAGE HABITS

Many corvids hide surplus food in caches, to which they return later. Their ability to recall the exact location of their caches has intrigued scientists, who believe that corvids rely on landmarks and possess a well-developed spatial memory. Here, a North American Clark's nutcracker buries nuts for later.

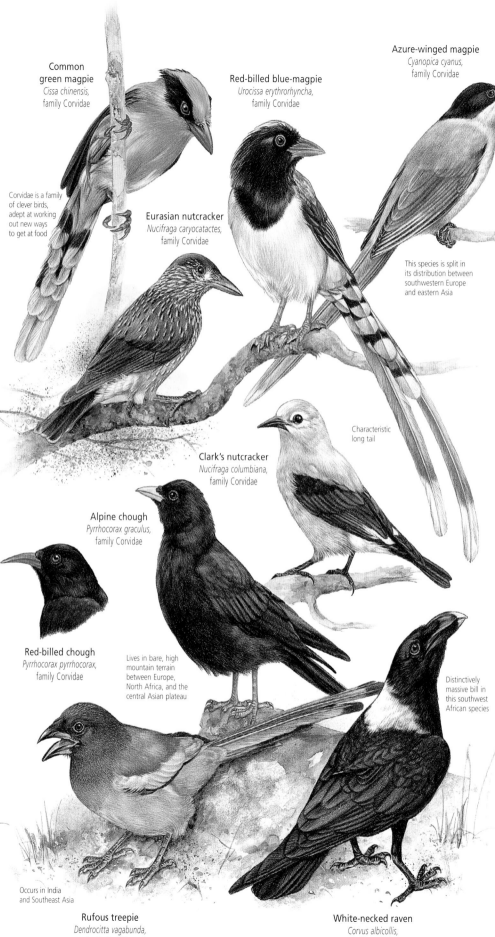

Common green magpie
Cissa chinensis,
family Corvidae

Red-billed blue-magpie
Urocissa erythrorhyncha,
family Corvidae

Azure-winged magpie
Cyanopica cyanus,
family Corvidae

Corvidae is a family of clever birds, adept at working out new ways to get at food

Eurasian nutcracker
Nucifraga caryocatactes,
family Corvidae

This species is split in its distribution between southwestern Europe and eastern Asia

Clark's nutcracker
Nucifraga columbiana,
family Corvidae

Characteristic long tail

Alpine chough
Pyrrhocorax graculus,
family Corvidae

Red-billed chough
Pyrrhocorax pyrrhocorax,
family Corvidae

Lives in bare, high mountain terrain between Europe, North Africa, and the central Asian plateau

Distinctively massive bill in this southwest African species

Occurs in India and Southeast Asia

Rufous treepie
Dendrocitta vagabunda,
family Corvidae

White-necked raven
Corvus albicollis,
family Corvidae

Bohemian waxwing
Bombycilla garrulus,
family Bombycillidae

Widespread in
boreal forests of the
Northern Hemisphere

Red tips on inner
flight feathers
are wax—hence
the name

Long-tailed silky-flycatcher
Ptilogonys caudatus,
family Bombycillidae

Sedentary insectivore
of mid and upper
forest strata;
endemic to Costa
Rica and Panama

Endemic to western India;
prefers groves of royal
palms, where it eats fruit

Palmchat
Dulus dominicus,
family Dulidae

Northern scrub robin
Drymodes superciliaris,
family Petroicidae

This Australian scrub
robin is superficially
thrush-like

White-browed robin
Poecilodryas superciliosa,
family Petroicidae

White-faced robin
Tregellasia leucops,
family Petroicidae

Sits sideways on the trunks
of trees and saplings in
New Guinea, watching
and waiting to pounce

A perch-pouncer
in drier woodlands
throughout inland
Australia

Red-capped robin
Petroica goodenovii,
family Petroicidae

Gray hypocolius
Hypocolius ampelinus,
family Bombycillidae

A fruit-eater; breeds
in southwest Asia
and winters south
to Arabia and
northeast Africa

FACT FILE

The Passeridans The remaining 44 families of 3,460 species are passeridan songbirds—a vast group that exploded through Eurasia, Africa, and the Americas out of ancestral corvidan lineages. These ancestral stocks, perhaps allied to the Australasian robins, dispersed into the Northern Hemisphere about 30–20 million years ago. Most passeridans have a double pit in the upper arm bone.

Family Petroicidae These small, Australasian robins are the region's perch-and-pounce insectivores, working methodically through the lower strata of trees and diving on to prey, often on the ground. The sexes are usually alike and monogamous, the exception being a group that is the reddest breasted of all robins. All build neat, cup-shaped nests in trees and under shrubbery.

Genera 13
Species 45

Australia, New Guinea,
New Zealand, S.W. Pacific

Family Bombycillidae Waxwings are mid-sized, finely plumaged, gregarious, arboreal birds with crests and a corvidan-like structure of the upper arm bone. But according to DNA data, they are passeridans. Some eat more berries while others, such as the silky flycatchers, eat more insects—caught often on the wing. All build bulky nests of interlocked twigs in trees, and the duties of brooding the clutch of three to six bluish eggs vary.

Genera 5
Species 8

North America to N.W. South America, Eurasia

Family Dulidae The palmchat, a mid-sized arboreal fruit-eater that favors palm berries, is the only member of its family. It is a gregarious bird, commonly weaving a huge, communal nest of twigs and vine stems into the crown of tall royal palms. Dozens of pairs nest in it together, each with its own chamber where both sexes incubate their clutches of two to four purple-gray, blotched eggs, and rear their young.

Genera 1
Species 1

Hispaniola (West Indies)

FACT FILE

Tits Small, plump, and restless, tits are tree-living insectivores that have strong legs for hopping about foliage and short bills for gleaning for insects and seeds. They are gregarious, lay large clutches of eggs incubated by the female, and occur through the Northern Hemisphere and sub-Saharan Africa. Sexes are alike.

Family Paridae Tits and chickadees are often black-capped, whitish-cheeked, and crested. They nest in tree holes and sometimes on the ground, have speckled, red-brown eggs, and rear their young on insects, particularly caterpillars. Out of breeding they eat seeds as well.

Genera 3
Species 54

North America, Africa & Eurasia to Japan & L. Sundas

Family Remizidae The olive and brown penduline tits have finely tipped bills and are always social, with helpers additional to parents at nests. They build hanging, felted nests, with complex entrances, which may be used for both roosting and nesting. Eggs are plain white.

Genera 5
Species 10

S. North America, Eurasia, sub-Saharan Africa

Family Aegithalidae Long-tailed tits are distinguished by their autumn tones, attenuate tails, and intricate, domed nests bound into branches and lined with hundreds of feathers. They are gregarious in and out of breeding. They roost in tightly packed groups on a twig.

Genera 4
Species 11

W. North America, Eurasia to Java

Black-throated tit
Aegithalos concinnus,
family Aegithalidae

This long-tailed tit lives in mountain forests from the Himalayas to Southeast Asia

Penduline tit
Remiz pendulinus,
family Remizidae

Fire-capped tit
Cephalopyrus flammiceps,
family Remizidae

Both are Eurasian penduline tits

Great tit
Parus major,
family Paridae

Grayish plumaged titmice are widespread in North America

Tufted titmouse
Parus bicolor,
family Paridae

Nests in trees and holes, including artificial nesting boxes across Eurasia

Inhabits woods, parks, and gardens

Sultan tit
Melanochlora sultanea,
family Paridae ♂

Blue tit
Parus caeruleus,
family Paridae

Azure tit
Parus cyanus,
family Paridae

Frequents mountain forests between the Himalayas and Southeast Asia

Found in temperate forests of Europe to Iran and northwest Africa. Females are slightly duller than males

Yellow-cheeked tit
Parus spilonotus,
family Paridae

White-eyed river martin
Pseudochelidon sirintarae,
family Hirundinidae

White-banded swallow
Atticora fasciata,
family Hirundinidae

Occurs in open areas across
northern South America;
nests in crevices in rocks,
stumps, and buildings

White-winged swallow
Tachycineta albiventer,
family Hirundinidae

Frequents the forested
rivers of Amazonia where
it nests in burrows. The
white-banded swallow
does not migrate

♂

Black lark
Melanocorypha yeltoniensis,
family Alaudidae

Horned lark
Eremophila alpestris,
family Alaudidae

♂

This large lark
digs for food in the
deserts of northern
Africa and south-
western Asia

Greater hoopoe-lark
Alaemon alaudipes,
family Alaudidae

Greater short-toed lark
Calandrella brachydactyla,
family Alaudidae

Breeds in
temperate Eurasia
and migrates south

♂

Chestnut-backed
sparrow-lark
Eremopterix leucotis,
family Alaudidae

FACT FILE

Family Hirundinidae Swallows and
martins are the songbird equivalent of
swifts, streamlined and swift of wing for
hawking for flying insects, and weak of
foot just for perching at rest. Many have
streamer tails. They feed in the sky over
all habitats, singly or in groups. They
usually nest in colonies, either in holes or
burrows, or attach mud nests of pellets
to walls, some of them bottle-shaped.
Females build the nest from mud
brought by males; eggs are white.

Genera 20
Species 84

Widespread except polar regions

Family Alaudidae Larks such as the
skylark have inspired poets with their
song-flights in display during spring.
Unlike other songbirds, their voice box
lacks a band of cartilage, and their hind
claw is elongated into a spur. Larks live
and nest in open grassland and are
fawn-plumaged for camouflage. They
walk and run to glean invertebrates
and seeds. Females build cup-
shaped nests of grass and incubate
their gray-freckled eggs alone.

Genera 19
Species 92

Widespread except C. & S. South America,
S.W. Australia

Courtship
*Display flights of
the male horned
lark (*Eremophila
alpestris*) involve
complicated
circling maneuvers.*

CONSERVATION WATCH

Under threat The Bahama swallow
(*Tachycineta cyaneoviridis*) is a
vulnerable native of the Caribbean.
It often builds nests near human
settlements where it is prey to
introduced predators. Four other
swallows and six larks are listed as
threatened, two of them critically.

FACT FILE

Family Pycnonotidae Bulbuls are common, smallish, gray or green songbirds of the Old World tropics. Many are crested and most are active, noisy, and arboreal, in either tree foliage or shrubberies. Their "average" songbird form confers great versatility in behavior. Rounded wings and long, squarish-tipped tails give them good maneuverability and strong flight. Feet are weak and suited only for perching and scrambling. Bills, however, are short and slender, slightly hooked, and surrounded by bristles; they are used to pick fruit, glean, and pounce on insects. Bulbuls have adapted to both open woodlands and forests. Most species forage in foliage but those in open habitats have become specialized ground feeders. Most also eat fruit, but some glean insects from leaves while others take nectar and buds.

Bulbuls are monogamous and, although gregarious in roaming bands when not breeding, pairs defend nest territory. The sexes look alike and both share all nesting duties, including incubation. They build rough, cup-shaped nests that are usually perched, but sometimes suspended, in lower tree strata and shrubbery. Clutches are of two to three, rarely to five, whitish or pinkish eggs freckled heavily brown and dusky.

Genera 22–26
Species 118–130

Sub-Saharan Africa, Madagascar, S. Asia to Philippines & Moluccas

Red-whiskered bulbul A familiar bird of forest edges, secondary growth, and gardens, this species scrambles actively among foliage for fruit and insects, giving bright chirrups. It breeds in territorial pairs and flocks loosely in winter. A popular cage bird, this bulbul has been introduced to east Australia, Hawaii, and parts of the United States.

⬆ Up to 8 in (20 cm)
● 2–4
∥ Sexes alike
⊘ Sedentary
⚑ Common

Himalayas, E. India, S.E. Asia

⚡ CONSERVATION WATCH

Bulbuls take a battering Thirteen species of bulbuls are listed as threatened globally. One, the Liberian greenbul (*Phyllastrephus leucolepis*), in the devastated woods of southeast Liberia is critical; and two more, Progogine's greenbul in east Zaire and the streak-breasted bulbul in the central Philippines, are both endangered.

Common bulbul
Pycnonotus barbatus,
family Pycnonotidae

Lives in Africa, in shrubbery of all kinds and lacks color around the eye

White-spectacled bulbul
Pycnonotus xanthopygos,
family Pycnonotidae

Madagascar bulbul
Hypsipetes madagascariensis,
family Pycnonotidae

Black-crested bulbul
Pycnonotus melanicterus,
family Pycnonotidae

White-throated bulbul
Criniger flaveolus,
family Pycnonotidae

Ranges from the Himalayas to Burma, north Thailand, and southwest China at lower altitudes. Frequents forest and scrub

Red-whiskered bulbul
Pycnonotus jocosus,
family Pycnonotidae

Lives in gardens and scrub from Pakistan and India to Burma and southwest China. Introduced in Fiji

Red-vented bulbul
Pycnonotus cafer,
family Pycnonotidae

White-cheeked bulbul
Pycnonotus leucogenys,
family Pycnonotidae

Zitting cisticola
Cisticola juncidis,
family Cisticolidae

Gives clicking calls in display flights. Ranges from south Europe to north Australia

A common garden bird in south and east Australia and New Zealand; causes frequent damage to cultivated fruit crops

Silvereye
Zosterops lateralis,
family Zosteropidae

White eye-rings are found in most white-eyes

Oriental white-eye
Zosterops palpebrosus,
family Zosteropidae

Tailorbirds range from India to the Philippines and Indonesian archipelagos

Cinnamon-breasted warbler
Euryptila subcinnamomea,
family Cisticolidae

Rufous-tailed tailorbird
Orthotomus sericeus,
family Cisticolidae

♂

Hill prinia
Prinia atrogularis,
family Cisticolidae

Golden-headed cisticola
Cisticola exilis,
family Cisticolidae

♂

This male is in full breeding dress; in most Australian populations males have a streaked non-breeding plumage

Bar-throated apalis
Apalis thoracica,
family Cisticolidae

Apalises are the only cisticolids which are commonly grayish. All live in Africa

FACT FILE

Old World warblers and babblers
The next four families are small, somber songbirds that live mostly within the cover of vegetation where they forage for insects and sing sweetly when breeding. Some, such as the babblers and white-eyes, are gregarious but others are solitary. Fledglings, unlike Old World thrushes and flycatchers, are plain-plumaged without spotting.

Family Cisticolidae Cisticolas, prinias, and tailorbirds are tiny, tawny to russet or gray-backed insect-eaters that live in undergrowth, whether in forest, open woodland, or grass field. They glean unobtrusively in ones and twos, and rarely break cover except for conspicuous display flights or singing when breeding. Deep purse or bottle-shaped nests of fiber are secreted in deep growth, and tailorbirds and some cisticolas sew large, protective leaves around their nests. Eggs are whitish to pale blue, spotted in red-browns.

Genera 25
Species 127

Africa, Madagascar, S. Europe to S. & E. Asia & Australasia

Family Zosteropidae White-eyes are so-called because most species have an eye-ring of dense white feathers. Plain, yellowish-green birds, they roam in groups through shrubberies in forests, parks, and gardens, gleaning for insects or piercing fruit with their finely pointed bills. They lap up pulp and juice as they go with their fringed tongues. Both sexes share nesting duties, building cup-shaped nests of fiber slung from the rim in shrubberies. They brood plain, pale blue eggs.

Genera 14
Species 95

Sub-Saharan Africa, S. & E. Asia to Australasia

CONSERVATION WATCH

More island problems Although fewer in species, 19 white-eyes are listed as threatened, compared to only seven cisticolids. Another seven are critically endangered or already extinct, and are confined to small islands from Mauritius to Micronesia and Norfolk Island.

Family Sylviidae The core Old World warblers are small, sweet-voiced birds of woods and grass fields. Bills are straight, narrow, and mostly short. Many breed in high latitudes and migrate to the tropics for winter; their navigation has a strong genetic component. There are four subfamilies: the west Pacific grassbirds, the Afro-Eurasian bush and reed warblers, the Afro-Asian leaf warblers, and the typical Eurasian warblers. All eat insects and forage unobtrusively by hop-gleaning in foliage and rank herbage, often alone. Both sexes usually share nesting duties, building cup-shaped nests of fiber in deep foliage or grass tussocks and reeds. They brood clutches of three to six, white to buff, usually spotted eggs.

Genera 48
Species 265

Africa, Eurasia to Australasia & Oceania, W. Alaska

Garden warbler A "typical" warbler, this sleek-bodied insectivore hop-gleans in the foliage of trees and shrubberies, and flocks to feed on fruit as well in winter. Both sexes share nesting duties, building stout, cup-shaped nests in shrubberies and trees, and brooding creamy, brown and gray spotted eggs.

⏳ Up to 5½ in (14 cm)
● 3–6
∥ Sexes alike
↻ Migrant
⸙ Common

W. temperate Eurasia & sub-Saharan Africa

Pallas's leaf warbler Like many leaf warblers, this species is a dumpy citrine-washed bird with crown or brow stripes. Though feet are weak, it is lively in manner, hop-gleaning among outer foliage from shrubberies to the tops of trees. When breeding, males sing rather unobtrusive songs from set perches. Most leaf warblers build a domed nest hidden in tree crevices. Some species use crevices on the ground while others hang their nests in foliage. Eggs are usually plain white, and brooded by the female alone.

⏳ Up to 4 in (10 cm)
● 3–6
∥ Sexes alike
↻ Migrant
⸙ Locally common

E. temperate Eurasia to Southeast Asia

Rufous-faced warbler
Abroscopus albogularis,
family Sylviidae

Mostly sedentary in upper forest foliage and bamboo stands, from the east Himalayas and south China through all Southeast Asia

Garden warbler
Sylvia borin,
family Sylviidae

Its song is a vigorous, mellow warbling. Like many warblers, this species is grayish-plumaged and swift-flighted

Southern hyliota
Hyliota australis,
family Sylviidae

A bird of the treetops in miombo woodlands, south central Africa. Females and juveniles are brown-backed

Barred warbler
Sylvia nisoria,
family Sylviidae

Red-capped crombec
Sylvietta ruficapilla,
family Sylviidae

Pallas's leaf warbler
Phylloscopus proregulus
family Sylviidae

Wood warbler
Phylloscopus sibilatrix,
family Sylviidae

Breeds in temperate woodlands and forests of western Eurasia and migrates to winter in tropical rain forests of central Africa

Chestnut-crowned warbler
Seicercus castaniceps,
family Sylviidae

Widespread in rain forests of Southeast Asia, from the Himalayas to Sumatra

Icterine warbler
Hippolais icterina,
family Sylviidae

This west Eurasian breeding warbler winters in the woodlands of central southern Africa

Great reed warbler
Acrocephalus arundinaceus,
family Sylviidae

Breeds across temperate Eurasia and migrates to sub-Saharan Africa in winter

River warbler
Locustella fluviatilis,
family Sylviidae

Breeds in thickets along rivers in temperate west Eurasia. Migrates to winter in central east Africa

Slaty-bellied tesia
Tesia olivea,
family Sylviidae

Lives in forest undergrowth in the hills and mountains of Southeast Asia, west to the Himalayas

Little grassbird
Megalurus gramineus,
family Sylviidae

Cape grassbird
Sphenoeacus afer,
family Sylviidae

Confined to undergrowth along streams in South Africa

African yellow warbler
Chloropeta natalensis,
family Sylviidae

Lives within pockets of rank grassland and shrubbery around edges of woodlands and forest in sub-Saharan Africa

Skulks in tangled undergrowth in forest edges of east South Africa, running over the ground like a mouse

Barrat's scrub warbler
Bradypterus barratti,
family Sylviidae

FACT FILE

Great reed warbler This species and its allies live in reed beds, marshes, or within forest undergrowth. Nearly all are plumaged in plain brown. Strong-legged and most often solitary, they hop and flutter about actively, if unobtrusively, under cover. They glean for invertebrates both in undergrowth and on the ground. Male breeding song, given from under cover, is strong, varied, often metallic, and sometimes monotonous. Both sexes share nesting duties, building deep, cup-shaped nests of fiber laced around reed stems or undergrowth. They incubate clutches of two to six bluish white eggs, marked brown-gray and blackish purple, or wholly reddish in species of *Cettia*. This species breeds across Eurasia, migrating to winter in sub-Saharan Africa.

⌀ Up to 7½ in (19 cm)
● 4–6
∥ Sexes alike
↻ Migrant
⤢ Locally common

Temperate Eurasia & Africa

Little grassbird Like most members of its group, this species is brown, striped with black on the back, and has a ragged, thin tail. It usually skulks about in grass beds where it varies its invertebrate diet with seeds. When flushed, it flutters feebly to the nearest patch of cover. Songs from breeding males, of several thin, whistled notes, are neither loud nor protracted. Other members of the group, notably the Australian songlarks, make spectacular song flights in breeding display, uttering ringing, metallic notes that carry for half a mile. Grassbirds build deep cup-nests hidden in grass tussocks, and, like other members of their group, lay pinkish white eggs that are densely speckled red. Only females appear to incubate.

⌀ Up to 5½ in (14 cm)
● 3–5
∥ Sexes alike
∼ Regional nomad
⤢ Locally common

Australia (incl. Tasmania) & New Guinea

⚑ CONSERVATION WATCH

Warblers are worrying Thirty-one species of Old Word warblers are listed as threatened, eight of which are considered endangered. One of them, the Hawaiian millerbird, is critical. Five of the remaining endangered species are also reed warblers or swamp dwellers, three of them found on small islands. The draining and pollution of their swamps is serious.

Gray-headed parrotbill
Paradoxornis gularis,
family Timaliidae

A seed-eater of Southeast Asian hill forests

Cutia
Cutia nipalensis,
family Timaliidae

♂

Works over trunks of trees like a nuthatch. Sedentary in mountain forests from Himalayas to Southeast Asia

Whiskered yuhina
Yuhina flavicollis,
family Timaliidae

Large wren-babbler
Napothera macrodactyla,
family Timaliidae

Fluffy-backed tit-babbler
Macronous ptilosus,
family Timaliidae

Keeps to undergrowth close to the ground on the Malay Peninsula, Sumatra, and Borneo

Arabian babbler
Turdoides squamiceps,
family Timaliidae

A richly colored babbler with varied song and red-brown spotted eggs. Ranges from south China to Burma

White-crested laughingthrush
Garrulax leucolophus,
family Timaliidae

A Southeast Asian laughing-thrush, which is really a large, long-tailed babbler. Has an explosive chattering call sometimes likened to diabolical laughter

Red-billed leiothrix
Leiothrix lutea,
family Timaliidae

Bearded tit
Panurus biarmicus,
family Timaliidae

♂

Occurs across middle Asia to far west China. Females are plain brown

MOUNTAINS

In high alpine mountains worldwide, birds survive on the edge. Not many species live there, but those that do are hardy and often specialized, and some occur nowhere else. Songbirds, in particular, are adapted to individual niches. In temperate zones, they are adept at taking advantage of flushes of food over summer, whether insects, fruit, seeds, or warm-blooded prey. Habitats range from conifer and beech forest at lower levels, to alpine meadow above, where it is too cold for trees to grow. Rock outcrops are everywhere, and some birds work their crevices with great efficiency.

Preying from the air Eagles and ravens spend much of the day in prospective soaring, especially where crags provide thermal uplift.

The treeline Above the treeline temperatures are too cold for trees. Some birds, such as the Eurasian coal tit (above) and crested berrypecker in New Guinea, are adapted to its edges.

Cliffs and screes Habitat for rock-foraging specialists, such as the common rock thrush (below), alpine accentor, and elusive wallcreeper.

Watching while resting A golden eagle sits on a vantage rock from where it can scan the valley.

Alpine meadows Productive foraging for choughs and other ground-feeding birds whenever free of snow.

Snow patches Melting snow patches expose seeds and shoots that citril finches capitalize on.

FACT FILE

Family Troglodytidae Wrens—small, brown and barred, with stubby cocked tails—are birds of hidden places. They thread their way through their habitat on strong legs, and use their slender, curved bills to probe and glean for insects and spiders. At night, they often roost communally, particularly in winter when males call birds into dormitory nests. Wrens avoid migration and hold to permanent territory. Males frame domed nests to attract mates; approving females contribute to the finishing. Eggs are white, speckled brown, and incubated by females. Males, and some-times helpers, assist in feeding young.

Genera 17
Species 77

North & South America, temperate Eurasia to Japan

Winter wren A male sings at the entrance of its domed nest, lined with feathers.

Family Polioptilidae Gnatcatchers are tiny, cock-tailed birds, plumaged in grays and browns, with long, slender bills. They live in undergrowth around marshes and swamps, forever twitching their long tails, and hopping and darting to pick off small insects. Solitary and monogamous, gnatcatchers give a soft, reedy territorial song. Both sexes share nesting duties, building cup-shaped nests perched on branch forks in trees. Eggs, four to five per clutch, are pale blue, speckled with reddish brown.

Genera 3
Species 14

Temperate North America to South America & Cuba, Bahamas

Confined to Panama and Colombia in Central America

White-headed wren
Campylorhynchus albobrunneus, family Troglodytidae

Found in the cactus deserts of southwest USA and Mexico. Flips over stones and mud pats in search of food

Cactus wren
Campylorhynchus brunneicapillus, family Troglodytidae

Wrens are birds of undergrowth. All are confined to the Americas, except for the winter wren which occurs in Eurasia

Tropical gnatcatcher
Polioptila plumbea, family Polioptilidae

♂

Male gnatcatchers may don a black bar across the forehead when breeding

Lives on rocky hillsides and canyons from temperate western North America to Mexico

Long-billed gnatwren
Ramphocaenus melanurus, family Polioptilidae

Canyon wren
Catherpes mexicanus, family Troglodytidae

Marsh wren
Cistothorus palustris, family Troglodytidae

Bay wren
Thryothorus nigricapillus, family Troglodytidae

Male marsh wrens lead prospective mates to their nests with soft singing and wing fluttering. Widespread in temperate North America

Gray-breasted wood-wren
Henicorhina leucophrys, family Troglodytidae

Found in mountains from south Mexico to Bolivia

Stripe-headed creeper
Rhabdornis mystacalis,
family Rhabdornithidae

One of two species
in a family confined
to rain forests of
the Philippines

Fairly sedentary,
like other nuthatches,
subsists mostly on
nuts in winter

Eurasian nuthatch
Sitta europaea,
family Sittidae

Goldcrest
Regulus regulus,
family Regulidae

**White-breasted
nuthatch**
Sitta carolinensis,
family Sittidae

Widespread in pine
forests across boreal
Eurasia; migratory

Firecrest
Regulus ignicapillus,
family Regulidae

**Golden-crowned
kinglet**
Regulus satrapa,
family Regulidae

One of two North
American kinglets,
and the only other
migratory species
in the family

Inhabits mostly
pine forests
in west Euraisa

Confined to
high mountains
in Eurasia

Wallcreeper
Tichodroma muraria,
family Sittidae

Widespread
in Eurasia

In display, males flutter
around females with
wings spread to show
off their rich red, black,
and white patterning

Eurasian treecreeper
Certhia familiaris,
family Certhiidae

FACT FILE

Family Regulidae Kinglets are tiny, brown, warbler-like insectivores. They have vivid splashes of erectile yellow or orange on the crown. Working alone or in family packs, they hop-glean and flutter actively about the outer foliage of mostly conifers. They build domed nests of moss and cobweb in treetops. Spotted eggs are brooded by both sexes.

Genera 1
Species 5

Eurasia & North America, N.W. Africa

Family Sittidae The tree-living nuthatches work alone, sidling up and down branches and trunks, probing crevices and under bark for insects, or hammering open nuts. Their straight bills, long, clinging toes, and short tails are adapted for such foraging. They nest in cavities in trees and cliffs—often shoring them up with mud—and lay three to ten white, freckled eggs.

Genera 2
Species 25

North America, Eurasia to Japan, Philippines & Gr. Sundas

Family Certhiidae Slender, brown treecreepers have spiny-tipped tails used as a prop as they creep jerkily up over trunks, branches, and twigs in spirals. Probing for insects with their slender, curved bills, they feed alone. Nests are rough cups of fiber wedged into tree crevices, crotches, or cracks in bark. Eggs, in clutches of three to seven, are usually white and spotted reddish.

Genera 2
Species 8

Temperate North America & Eurasia to India & N. Indo-China, subtropical Africa

Spot-winged starling
Saroglossa spiloptera,
family Sturnidae

Breeds in fields and forest edges in the Himalayan foothills, migrating to Myanmar and Thailand in winter. Females are duller brown and streaked underneath

Amethyst starling
Cinnyricinclus leucogaster,
family Sturnidae

Metallic starling
Aplonis metallica,
family Sturnidae

Confined to upland scrubs in northwest South America

Builds globular hanging nests in trees in large colonies throughout the New Guinea region

Golden-breasted starling
Lamprotornis regius,
family Sturnidae

Gray catbird
Dumatella carolinensis,
family Mimidae

This North American migrant has a cat-like call

Occurs in open bushland and savannas on the horn of Africa; nests in tree holes

Long-tailed mockingbird
Mimus longicaudatus,
family Mimidae

Superb starling
Lamprotornis superbus,
family Sturnidae

A common and beautiful visitor to safari campsites in east Africa, in search of pickings

Golden-crested myna
Ampeliceps coronatus,
family Sturnidae

Rosy starling
Sturnus roseus,
family Sturnidae

♂

Hill myna
Gracula religiosa,
family Sturnidae

Mynas are mainly dull
brown, with patches
of naked yellow skin
on the head and bold
white flashes in the wing

European starling
Sturnus vulgaris,
family Sturnidae

Yellow-billed
oxpecker
Buphagus africanus,
family Sturnidae

Bali myna
Leucopsar rothschildi,
family Sturnidae

♂

Common myna
Acridotheres tristis,
family Sturnidae

Wattled starling
Creatophora cinerea,
family Sturnidae

A widespread south Asian
bird of towns and villages,
feeds on scraps and nests
in buildings. Has been
introduced widely from
Africa to Australia

Occurs in open woodlands
and pastures of Africa.
Males develop extensive
wattling on the face and
crown when breeding

FACT FILE

Hill myna Popular cage-birds in
Southeast Asia because of their talking,
hill mynas live in pairs or small flocks in
hill forests, regrowth, and plantations.
They forage for both fruit in trees and
insects on the ground, walking about
sedately and probing here and there.
At night, they gather in noisy colonies
to roost in trees. Pairs stuff loose
collections of grass, twigs, and leaves
into holes in trees or buildings as nests.
The female incubates her pale blue
eggs unaided.

⚊ Up to 10½ in (27 cm)
◗ 2–4
∥ Sexes alike
⊘ Sedentary
♦ Common

India, S.E. Asia, Sunda arc

European starling Widely introduced
throughout North America, South
Africa, Australia, and New Zealand,
this species is a bird of the fields. It
walks about on the ground probing
for small invertebrates, but also eats
fruit seasonally. It gathers in large,
noisy flocks to feed and to roost at
night. New, non-breeding plumage
each autumn is tipped with white, but
as breeding approaches, the tips wear
off and expose glossy, black plumage
beneath. Pairs build rough cup-nests
of straw in holes in trees and buildings.
Eggs are plain, pale blue and are
brooded by the female alone.

⚊ Up to 8½ in (21 cm)
◗ 3–8
∥ Sexes alike
↻ Local migrant
♦ Common

W. Eurasia

Yellow-billed oxpecker Oxpeckers
spend most of the day clinging to the
hides of large mammals of the African
plains, such as buffaloes, giraffes, and
rhinoceroses. Moving around with
jerky, woodpecker-like motions, they
use their stiff tails as a prop, and scissor
or pluck with their bills to pick off
parasites, such as blood-filled ticks
and flies. They even lap up secretions
from eyes and wounds. Gregarious
when feeding, pairs nest alone with
several helpers. Nests are untidy pads
of straw and feathers stuffed in tree
holes. The female alone incubates
her bluish white, and sometimes
brownish spotted, eggs.

⚊ Up to 9 in (23 cm)
◗ 2–3
∥ Sexes alike
∿ Local nomad
♦ Locally common

Sub-Saharan Africa

FACT FILE

Family Cinclidae Dippers are small, dusky-gray songbirds with an unusual habit: they feed underwater. They plunge into quick-flowing, stony-bottomed streams and move rapidly about under the water to pick up aquatic insects and occasionally fishes. They then emerge from the water with prey and stand briefly on rocks, to catch their breath before the next dive. For this special kind of feeding they have short wings and tails, and long, sturdy feet; wings are used to swim and feet to grip the stream bed. Dippers hold territory—a section of stream bank—year-round. Nests are large, domed structures of fiber, lined with a cup of leaves, and fitted into rocky banks over water. Eggs are plain white and both sexes share nesting tasks.

Genera 1
Species 5

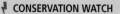

W. North & N.W. South America, Eurasia

Thrushes, chats, and Old World flycatchers The next two families, distributed worldwide, are of small to mid-sized, monogamous songbirds that have an upright stance, hopping gait, and large, dark eyes. The chats are often included in the thrush family, but are placed here with the flycatchers. The three groups are closely related; all have a unique "thumb" on the muscles of the voice box, and spotted young. They include such brilliant summer singers as the Eurasian blackbird and common nightingale.

Sharing the field
A male and female (top and center) common stonechat, and a winchat (bottom) share a shrub in a European field. They use perches like this one for spying insect prey in the open.

⚑ CONSERVATION WATCH

Dippers dip out There are only five species of dippers worldwide, but already the rufous-throated dipper (*Cinclus schulzi*), which is confined to northwest Argentina, is listed as vulnerable.

White-capped dipper
Cinclus leucocephalus,
family Cinclidae

The only dipper with both white cap and throat, this species is endemic to South America

Black-throated thrush
Turdus atrogularis,
family Turdidae

Green cochoa
Cochoa viridis,
family Turdidae

Sedentary and uncommon in evergreen montane forest, from the Himalayas to south China, and through Southeast Asia

♂

White-browed shortwing
Brachypteryx montana,
family Turdidae

A familiar North American bird, bounding in stop-start fashion over the ground in parks, gardens, natural woodlands, and forest

American robin
Turdus migratorius,
family Turdidae

Vaired solitaire
Myadestes coloratus,
family Turdidae

Confined to the hill forests of east Panama

♂

Eastern bluebird
Sialia sialis,
family Turdidae

Common in open woods of east North America, where it is migratory

Blue whistling thrush
Myophonus caeruleus,
family Turdidae

Lives in hill forests along
streams from the Tien
Shan in central Asia to
Myanmar, central China,
Southeast Asia, and Java

Eyebrowed thrush
Turdus obscurus,
family Turdidae

Siberian thrush
Zoothera sibirica,
family Turdidae

Females are brown with
barred breasts. Breeds from
central Eurasia to Japan;
migrates to Southeast Asia
and Sunda arc in winter

♂

Slaty-backed
nightingale-thrush
Catharus fuscater,
family Turdidae

Varied thrush,
Ixoreus naevius,
family Turdidae

Found in forests
and scrubs flanking
the north Andes

Chestnut-capped thrush
Zoothera interpres,
family Turdidae

Endemic to south
Thailand and the
Sunda arc, where
it is sedentary

White's thrush
Zoothera aurea,
family Turdidae

Scaled plumage
camouflages this thrush
on the forest floor

Old World chats This large group of birds, of 161 species, forms a distinct group of Old World flycatchers (family Muscicapidae), with mostly unscaled "legs" and shrike-like perch and pounce manner of feeding. They are solitary foragers, and males are usually more brightly plumaged than females.

Common redstart This bird lives in undergrowth around the edges of forests and woodlands, diving on to insect prey from mostly under cover perches. It flies in undulating swoops from point to point, and quivers the tail when perched. Brown females build cup-nests of fiber in holes in trees, stumps, or on the ground. They lay plain, pale blue eggs.

- Up to 6 in (15 cm)
- 4–6
- Sexes differ
- Migrant
- Common

N. Africa, temperate Eurasia

Common rock thrush A bird of sunny, stony hillsides, this thrush hops along, perches on top of vantage rocks, and dives on to invertebrate prey. It also eats fruit. Flight is low and floating, and the tail is quivered on landing. Females build cup-nests in crevices under rock over-hangs and brood immaculate, blue eggs.

- Up to 8½ in (21 cm)
- 4–6
- Sexes alike
- Partial migrant
- Common

N.W. Africa, S. Europe to E. Asia

Pied bushchat This species lives in open habitats—mostly regrowth and grassland—perching on exposed vantage perches, diving on to insect prey, and singing sweetly to advertise territory. It flies from perch to perch in jerky undulations. Females are dull gray and build simple cup-nests of fiber in earth banks and cliffs. They brood alone.

- Up to 6 in (15 cm)
- 2–4
- Sexes differ
- Sedentary
- Locally common

South Asia to Philippines & New Guinea

White-winged redstart
Phoenicurus erythrogaster,
family Muscicapidae

Orangeflanked bush robin
Luscinia cyanura,
family Muscicapidae

European robin
Erithacus rubecula,
family Muscicapidae

White-starred robin
Pogonocichla stellata,
family Muscicapidae

Common redstart
Phoenicurus phoenicurus,
family Muscicapidae

Common stonechat
Saxicola torquata,
family Muscicapidae

White-crowned forktail
Enicurus leschenaulti,
family Muscicapidae

Northern wheatear
Oenanthe oenanthe,
family Muscicapidae

Common rock thrush
Monticola saxatilis,
family Muscicapidae

White-rumped shama
Copsychus malabaricus,
family Muscicapidae

Bluethroat
Luscinia svecica,
family Muscicapidae

Pied bushchat
Saxicola caprata,
family Muscicapidae

Gray-headed canary flycatcher
Culicicapa ceylonensis,
family Muscicapidae

Found from India to the Sunda arc

Rufous-bellied niltava
Niltava sundara,
family Muscicapidae

Migrant of mountain forest undergrowth from the Himalayas to north India, Southeast Asia, and Sumatra

Rufous-gorgeted flycatcher
Ficedula strophiata,
family Muscicapidae

Large niltava
Niltava grandis,
family Muscicapidae

♂

♂

Mugimaki flycatcher
Ficedula mugimaki,
family Muscicapidae

♂

Asian verditer flycatcher
Eumyias thalassinus,
family Muscicapidae

♂

Breeds in woodlands and forest edges from southern Siberia to Sakhalin; migrates to Southeast Asia and the Sunda arc. Females are brown

♂

Sapphire flycatcher
Ficedula sapphira,
family Muscicapidae

A flycatcher of upper strata open forest and clearings, from the Himalayas and south China, through Southeast Asia to Sumatra

White-eyed slaty flycatcher
Melaenornis fischeri,
family Muscicapidae

Occurs in mountain forests from central China and Himalayas to Southeast Asia; females are cinnamon

FACT FILE

Family Muscicapidae Old World flycatchers and chats are small insectivores that forage alone in lower to upper strata of open woodlands and forest. They capture prey on the wing, picking it off from leaves and branches or in midair. Their short, narrow bills are broadened at the base for this purpose and surrounded by short bristles for protection. Feet are small, fitted for perching. Few feed on the ground or in grassland. Most species in the boreal temperate zone are migratory, wintering in the tropics. Males, commonly the brighter colored sex, defend breeding territory while females build cup-nests of fiber and incubate alone, brooding large clutches of two to eight blue-green eggs. Both parents rear the young.

Genera 48
Species 275

W. Alaska, N.E. Canada, Africa, Eurasia to W. Melanesia

White-eyed slaty flycatcher A typical flycatcher, this species forages on the edges of lower strata of dense montane forests. It hawks out from perches or dives, shrike-like, on to the ground to seize prey. When taking bees, it squeezes out the sting before eating. Unusually, both sexes look alike and both brood, building a cup-nest of moss in tree crotches and incubating pale green, umber-freckled eggs

⤒ Up to 6 in (15 cm)
● 2–4
⫽ Sexes alike
⊘ Sedentary
⤓ Locally common

C.E. Africa

Pied pairs *Pied flycatchers (female at the nest and male below) are small, insect-eating birds that live in wooded areas. They often sit on low perches under cover, then fly off to catch insects in flight.*

⚡ CONSERVATION WATCH

Failing flycatchers Fifteen flycatchers are listed as threatened, of which ten are vulnerable, four endangered, and one critical. The critical species is Rück's blue flycatcher (*Cyornis ruecki*), from the diminishing rain forests of north Sumatra.

FACT FILE

Family Promeropidae Sugarbirds are long-tailed, brownish, nectar-eating songbirds. They specialize in perching on the flower heads of Proteas and probing to mop up nectar with their protrusible, brush-tipped, near-tubular tongues. For this, they congregate in loose colonies in stands of Proteas, and take insects as well. In display, males make spectacular flights, whirring up on drumming wings caused by modified primary flight feathers. Then, at the top of the arc, they whipcrack their long tail up and down before diving back to cover. Calls are tinny and twangy. The female builds a cup-nest of fiber in shrubberies, lining it with layers of wiry stems and Protea down. She alone incubates clutches of two gray, dark-blotched eggs, but the male helps to rear chicks.

Genera 1
Species 2

S. Africa

Family Dicaeidae Tiny flowerpeckers hop-forage in the upper strata of rain forests and tropic woodlands. Though taking some nectar and protein-rich insects for feeding to young, they pick mostly small fruit, particularly the viscid berries of mistletoes. After squeezing the seed from its skin with their finely toothed bills, they swallow it whole. A modification of the alimentary tract allows the seed to by-pass the stomach and move quickly through the simple intestine, where nutrients are absorbed from surrounding flesh. The seed is then voided in under an hour. Females, dull and gray-green in comparison to their brilliantly colored mates, hang felted, purse-like nests from twigs in outer foliage. They incubate their clutches of two to three, plain white eggs unaided. Both sexes rear the chicks.

Genera 2
Species 44

India, S.E. Asia
& its archipelagos to
Melanesia & Australia

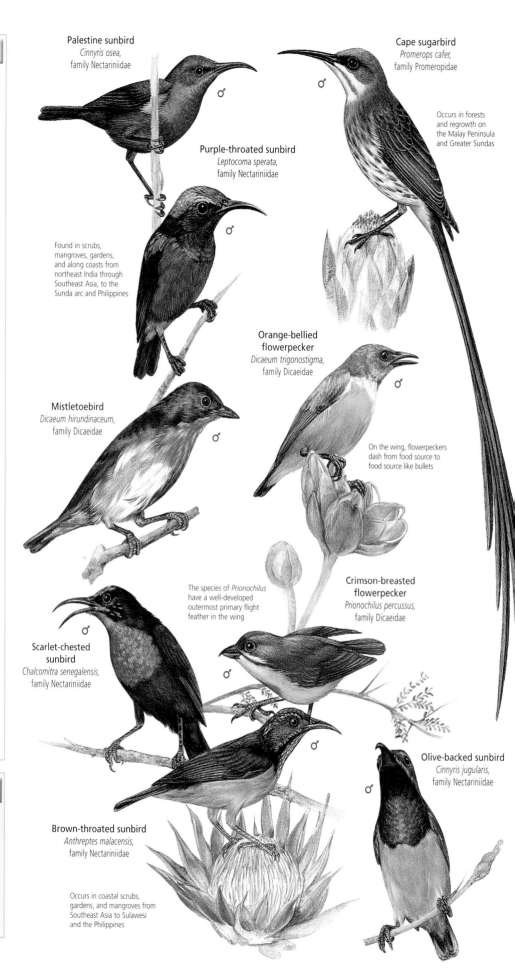

Palestine sunbird
Cinnyris osea,
family Nectariniidae
♂

Cape sugarbird
Promerops cafer,
family Promeropidae
♂

Occurs in forests
and regrowth on
the Malay Peninsula
and Greater Sundas

Purple-throated sunbird
Leptocoma sperata,
family Nectariniidae
♂

Found in scrubs,
mangroves, gardens,
and along coasts from
northeast India through
Southeast Asia, to the
Sunda arc and Philippines

**Orange-bellied
flowerpecker**
Dicaeum trigonostigma,
family Dicaeidae
♂

Mistletoebird
Dicaeum hirundinaceum,
family Dicaeidae
♂

On the wing, flowerpeckers
dash from food source to
food source like bullets

**Crimson-breasted
flowerpecker**
Prionochilus percussus,
family Dicaeidae

The species of *Prionochilus*
have a well-developed
outermost primary flight
feather in the wing

**Scarlet-chested
sunbird**
Chalcomitra senegalensis,
family Nectariniidae
♂

♂

Olive-backed sunbird
Cinnyris jugularis,
family Nectariniidae
♂

♂

Brown-throated sunbird
Anthreptes malacensis,
family Nectariniidae

Occurs in coastal scrubs,
gardens, and mangroves from
Southeast Asia to Sulawesi
and the Philippines

Golden-fronted leafbird
Chloropsis aurifrons,
family Chloropseidae

Orange-bellied leafbird
Chloropsis hardwickei,
family Chloropseidae

Male leafbirds sing rich, melodious songs while concealed within the forest canopy

Asian fairy-bluebird
Irena puella,
family Irenidae

Found from India and Nepal through Southeast Asia to the Sunda arc and Palawan

Crimson sunbird
Aethopyga siparaja,
family Nectariniidae

Variable sunbird
Nectarinia venusta,
family Nectariniidae

Regal sunbird
Cinnyris regius,
family Nectariniidae

Locally common in mountain forests of the central Rift Valley, central east Africa

Takes nectar from tubular flowers, and insects and spiders from under leaves, dashing through the forest at speed. Sexes are alike

Sunbirds hover almost as much as perching and take nectar from flowers by capillary action

Southern double-collared sunbird
Cinnyris chalybeus,
family Nectariniidae

Little spider hunter
Arachnothera longirostris,
family Nectariniidae

Long-tailed widowbird
Euplectes progne, family Ploceidae

Males molt into short-tailed, brown plumage when not breeding; distinguished from females by their red-and-white shoulder sash

Red-billed quelea
Quelea quelea, family Ploceidae

Can swarm, locust-like in millions—doing serious damage to grain crops throughout sub-Saharan Africa. Males don a black mask when breeding

Red-billed buffalo weaver
Bubalornis niger, family Ploceidae

Village weaver
Ploceus cucullatus, family Ploceidae

Females are white-breasted and grayish-backed. Flocks throughout the savannas of sub-Saharan Africa

Black-throated accentor
Prunella atrogularis, family Prunellidae

Breeds in high mountains from northeast Europe to the Urals and central Asia. Migrates to southwest Asia in winter

Common in southern Africa; males don red and black only for breeding. Nests are balls of interwoven grass attached to reeds

Gregarious and endemic to the dry thornveldt and desert watercourses of southern Africa. Sexes are alike

Scaly-fronted weaver
Sporopipes squamifrons, family Ploceidae

Streaked weaver
Ploceus manyar, family Ploceidae

Southern red bishop
Euplectes orix, family Ploceidae

Gouldian finch
Erythrura gouldiae,
family Estrildidae

Once widespread and abundant in savannas across north Australia, this species has declined alarmingly

Chestnut-breasted munia
Lonchura castaneothorax,
family Estrildidae

This popular cage bird comes from Java and adjacent islands to the east, where it has declined greatly

Java sparrow
Lonchura oryzivora,
family Estrildidae

Zebra finch
Taeniopygia guttata,
family Estrildidae

A characteristic bird of Australia's inland, and now kept in captivity worldwide

♂

Common waxbill
Estrilda astrid,
family Estrildidae

Star finch
Neochmia ruficauda,
family Estrildidae

Moderately abundant in northwest Australia, this grassfinch has all but disappeared in the northeast

A bird of riverside grasslands and reed beds throughout sub-Saharan Africa

Red-cheeked cordon-bleu
Uraeginthus bengalus,
family Estrildidae

♂

Occurs in woodlands throughout sub-Saharan Africa and urban areas in Zimbabwe

Painted firetail
Emblema picta,
family Estrildidae

♂

A reclusive species found around waterholes in rocky ranges throughout arid inland Australia

Red-billed firefinch
Lagonosticta senegala,
family Estrildidae

FACT FILE

Family Estrildidae Waxbills and grass-finches, the smallest of all finches, are brilliantly colored in reds, blues, greens, and yellows. They feed mainly on seeds, often in flocks. Like other finches, they have a crop and muscular stomach for storing and grinding food. Some species also take insects, such as ants and termites. Males court by hopping about an intended mate, holding a feather or piece of grass in the bill, and singing. Both sexes share nesting duties. They build rough, domed nests of stems and fiber in shrubberies and incubate clutches of four to six plain, white eggs. Dormitory nests are built for sleeping. Nestlings have luminous mouth-spots that signpost feeding parents to their mouths. Adults have the rare ability to regurgitate whole crop contents in a single movement.

Genera 26
Species 130

Sub-Saharan Africa, Madagascar, S. Asia to Australia & S.W. Pacific

Zebra finch Easily kept in captivity, this species is perhaps the world's most widely used bird in studies of bird physiology and behavior. In the wild, it lives in arid woodlands, following rains and seeding grasses. It concentrates in small flocks around water holes because, being a seed-eater, it needs to drink daily to maintain its water balance. Despite such a precarious existence, this finch is widely abundant.

Up to 4 in (10 cm)
4–6
Sexes differ
Nomad
Locally common

Inland Australia, Lesser Sundas

Termite runways
The green-winged pytilia uses its sharp bill to dig into covered termite "runways" on the ground and tree trunks, feeding on termites inside.

CONSERVATION WATCH

Grassed grassfinches Eight species of grassfinches are listed as vulnerable, and two as endangered. Among them is the beautiful gouldian finch (*Erythrura gouldiae*), of northern Australia. Degradation of habitat by cattle and respiratory infections by mites have caused its decline.

FACT FILE

Family Viduidae Indigobirds and whydahs are both small, African brood parasites. The groups lay their clutches of two to three white eggs in the nests of waxbills and grassfinches. Unlike nestling cuckoos, indigobird chicks do not eject their hosts' chicks but are reared alongside them, and as in waxbills, indigobird nestlings have luminous, colored mouth spots. Adults are small, finch-like birds with bills like waxbills. Flocks feed together on the ground, mainly on seed scratched up with the feet. In plumage this family resembles the weavers. When breeding, males don spectacularly long tails and striking black, yellow, white, and chestnut patterned plumage. After breeding, they molt out into dull brown and streaked female plumage with short tails.

Genera 2
Species 20

Sub-Saharan Africa (except rain-forested Congo & Namibian desert)

Family Passeridae Snowfinches and sparrows are small, chunky songbirds with conical, finch-like bills. They differ from other finches in having a unique bone in the tongue, to stiffen it for husking the seeds that they eat. Like many other finch-like birds, they flock and feed on the ground but unlike most, they often breed colonially. The group builds rough, domed nests of straw bound in tree foliage or wedged into crevices in cliffs or buildings. Their eggs are whitish, marked with grays and blacks. Plumage is usually dull, in streaked browns and whites, and males often resemble females. Both sexes share nesting duties.

Genera 11
Species 40

Africa, Eurasia to Sunda arc, Sulawesi

Dustbathing
The house sparrow (Passer domesticus) often gathers in groups to dust-bathe in order to clean their skin and plumage.

⚡ CONSERVATION WATCH

Sparrows spark It says much for the adaptability of both sparrows and snowfinches that not a single species in their family is currently listed as threatened; nor are any indigobirds and whydahs.

Pin-tailed whydah
Vidua macroura,
family Viduidae

Widespread in woodlands and about cultivation in sub-Saharan Africa. Polygamous, males mate with diverse females

♂

Eastern paradise whydah
Vidua paradisaea,
family Viduidae

♂

Often feeds on east African roadsides. Females look like small, striped sparrows

Straw-tailed whydah
Vidua fischeri,
family Viduidae

♂

White-browed sparrow weaver
Plocepasser mahali,
family Passeridae

Gray-headed social weaver
Pseudonigrita arnaudi,
family Passeridae

Builds weaver-like nests in colonies in woodlands throughout central east Africa

Sudan golden sparrow
Passer luteus,
family Passeridae

♂

White-winged snowfinch
Montifrigilla nivalis,
family Passeridae

Occurs in dry woodland and steppe in a narrow band between equatorial Africa and the Sahara

An alpine bird of high mountains, from the Pyrenees to the Himalayas and central Asia

Male is in full breeding plumage. Out of breeding it loses the long tail, and the red bill and feet become more pale

Chaffinch
Fringilla coelebs,
family Fringillidae

♂

Lacks a crop to hold
seeds, feeds its young
entirely on insects

Hawfinch
Coccothraustes coccothraustes,
family Fringillidae

The massive bill of
this Eurasian migrant
is used to crack large,
strong nuts

Water pipit
Anthus spinoletta,
family Motacillidae

Gray wagtail
Motacilla cinerea,
family Motacillidae

♂

Wagtails are patterned
in yellow, dark gray, and
white, in contrast to pipits
which are brownish and
streaked with black

Fire-fronted serin
Serinus pusillus,
family Fringillidae

Brambling
Fringilla montifringilla,
family Fringillidae

♂

Lives on alpine moors
from China to the
Himalayas. Males rise
singing into the air in
display, then descend
on spread wings

Rosy pipit
Anthus roseatus,
family Motacillidae

♂

Madagascan wagtail
Motacilla flaviventris,
family Motacillidae

Differs from other
yellow-bellied wagtails
in having a black breast
band and no dull, non-
breeding plumage

Red-throated pipit
Anthus cervinus,
family Motacillidae

♂

FACT FILE

Family Motacillidae Wagtails and
pipits are small, slender, long-tailed
insectivores. They run here and there
over the ground to pick up food, then
stop and wag the tail up and down.
Flight is swift and undulating, and
many species are migratory. They
congregate in loose groups then, but
when breeding, they break up into
solitary pairs. Male and female court
in song-flights, then either both, or
the female alone, build a cup-nest of
fiber on the ground or in a rock crevice.
They incubate a clutch of two to seven
whitish eggs that have gray markings.

Genera 5
Species 64

Widespread (only one species
in North America)

White wagtails White wagtails
(*Motacilla alba*) are seen
here in two
different adult
races, with a
juvenile at left.

Gray wagtail This species frequents
the margins of stony streams and
ponds, darting over the ground or
flitting from rock to rock for insects,
never far from freshwater. Breeding
males display in flights from perch to
perch, flickering their wings rapidly,
spreading the tail, and puffing up
their plumage. Females build the nest,
usually in rock crevices along streams,
and do most of the brooding.

⤒ Up to 7½ in (19 cm)
● 3–6
✳ Sexes differ (breeding)
↻ Migrant
↟ Locally common

Africa, Eurasia to New Guinea & N. Australia

⚡ CONSERVATION WATCH

Pipits in peril Apart from the
endangered Sharpe's longclaw
(*Macronyx sharpei*), all threatened
members of the family Motacillidae
are pipits. Three are vulnerable and
the sokoke pipit (*Anthus sokokensis*),
is endangered. Both endangered
species are Kenyan—their habitat is
small, fragmented, and diminishing.

FACT FILE

Family Fringillidae "True" finches have short, cone-shaped bills for picking up and husking small seeds. Seeds wedged into a groove in the palate are cracked by the heavily muscled lower bill, then husked by manipulation of the tongue. Bill shapes differ for different types of seed. This family also has specialized wings, having aborted the outermost, tenth primary flight feather. Feeding in shrubbery or trees, they flock after breeding, but nest in pairs. Males, many brilliantly colored, display in song flights over nesting space. Females build neat, cup-shaped nests in trees or shrubs. Eggs are bluish white spotted red-black.

Specialized bill The parrot crossbill (Loxia pytyopsittacus) uses its large, cross-tipped bill to extract the nuts from hard pine cones.

Genera 42
Species 168

North & South America, Africa, Eurasia to S.E. Asia

Greater akialoa The adaptability of the bill in finches culminates in a group of 32 honeycreepers, endemic to Hawaii. Some have conical, seed-cracking beaks, but others have evolved long, curved bills used to probe bark and wood for insects, or flowers for nectar. In nesting habits and traits they resemble other members of the family Fringillidae, a relationship confirmed by DNA evidence.

⚊ Up to 8 in (20 cm)
● 2–3
⁄⁄ Sexes alike
⊘ Sedentary
⚑ Rare, possibly extinct

Central Hawaiian Is.

⚡ CONSERVATION WATCH

Honeycreeper disaster Of the 27 fringillid finches listed as threatened, 18 are honeycreepers—most of the species in that Hawaiian group. Not only are eight considered critical, but a further ten are not listed at all because they are already extinct. Loss of habitat and disease once more expose the plight and vulnerability of island birds.

European goldfinch
Carduelis carduelis,
family Fringillidae

Greater akialoa
Hemignathus ellisianus,
family Fringillidae

Growing up Young European goldfinches bulge out of their nest as they are about to fledge. Their dull plumage will molt into brilliant adult dress in their first autumn.

Uses its tweezer-like bill to probe into thistles and other seed heads and pick out tiny seeds

American goldfinch
Carduelis tristis,
family Fringillidae

♂

Common redpoll
Carduelis flammea,
family Fringillidae

♂

Crimson-winged finch
Rhodopechys sanguinea,
family Fringillidae

Red crossbill
Loxia curvirostra,
family Fringillidae

Pine grosbeak
Pinicola enucleator,
family Fringillidae

Rounded bill, adapted to picking buds and shoots. Lives in boreal forests of the Northern Hemisphere

♂

♂

♂

Works around branches like a parrot, extracting seeds from ripe pine cones with its cross-tipped bill. Lives in boreal forests

Great rosefinch
Carpodacus rubicilla,
family Fringillidae

Uses its sparrow-like bill to pick up seeds, flowers, and plant material from the ground, on scree slopes amid low shrubberies

FACT FILE

The nine-primaried songbirds
Related to the "true" finches, the last six advanced families of songbirds have only nine primary flight feathers instead of the usual ten. It is evidence that they all evolved from a common North American ancestor, 15 or more million years ago. Centered in the Americas, they radiated there into forms matching those in the Old World—into warbler, sparrow, lark, oriole, and thrush-like birds.

Family Parulidae New World warblers are small insect-eaters of foliage. They don yellow or sometimes reddish plumage patterns when breeding—males more than females. Their short, slender bills are adapted to gleaning, but some have broader, bristled bills and catch prey on the wing. Many are migratory. Females build cup-nests and brood alone.

Genera 26
Species 116

North America to South
America, West Indies

BREEDING PLUMAGE

In New World warblers, sexual differences in breeding plumage vary with the species, particularly in those that migrate.

Variety is spice In the orange-crowned warbler, Vermivora celata, (top), sexual differences in breeding plumage hardly exist; in the magnolia warbler, Dendroica magnolia, (bottom right), they are slight but clear; and in the American redstart, Setophaga ruticilla, (bottom left), they are striking, the male black-and-reddish. After breeding, both sexes molt into similar drab winter dress. They need camouflage then, not bright plumage for display.

⚡ CONSERVATION WATCH

Warbler threats in the New World
Three American warblers are critically endangered, five endangered, and eight vulnerable. Two of the critically endangered, Bachman's warbler and Belding's yellowthroat, breed in the USA. The third, Semper's warbler, is confined to the Lesser Antilles.

Golden-winged warbler
Vermivora chrysoptera,
family Parulidae

Breeds in eastern United States and migrates as far as northern South America for winter

Northern parula
Parula americana,
family Parulidae

MacGillivray's warbler
Oporornis tolmiei,
family Parulidae

Most New World warblers build cup-shaped nests. Only the female incubates her two to six cream, speckled, or plain eggs

Lives in marsh and woodland thicket from east and west Canada to Mexico

Canada warbler
Wilsonia canadensis,
family Parulidae

Common yellowthroat
Geothlypis trichas,
family Parulidae

Elegant patterns of red and yellow on head and breast characterize wood warblers in breeding plumage

Yellow-rumped warbler
Dendroica coronata,
family Parulidae

Occurs in mixed woodland in North America

Collared redstart
Myioborus torquatus,
family Parulidae

Out of breeding, New World warblers forage in flocks of mixed species, each keeping to its own niche; but when breeding, pairs hold individual territory

Nests in cavities in trees; breeds in eastern United States and winters south to northern South America

Prothonotary warbler
Protonotaria citrea,
family Parulidae

Red-winged blackbird
Agelaius phoeniceus,
family Icteridae
♂

Eastern meadowlark
Sturnella magna,
family Icteridae

Shiny cowbird
Molothrus bonariensis,
family Icteridae
♂

♂

Giant cowbird
Molothrus oryzivorus,
family Icteridae
♂

Males jump up
in display to expose
breast marks. Lives in
east and central North
American prairies

Breeds in woodlands
of temperate east
North America and
migrates south to
Central America and
Colombia for winter

♂

Bobolink
Dolichonyx oryzivorus,
family Icteridae
♂

The longest-distance
migrant in its family,
breeds in North American
prairies and winters in
Argentinian pampas

Baltimore oriole
Icterus galbula,
family Icteridae

Yellow-headed blackbird
Xanthocephalus xanthocephalus,
family Icteridae
♂

Lives in mountain scrubs
and rain forests of
Central and northern
South America

Scarlet-rumped cacique
Cacicus uropygialis,
family Icteridae

Crested oropendola
Psarocolius decumanus,
family Icteridae

Occurs in rain forests
of northern South
America, from Panama
to northern Argentina

FACT FILE

Family Icteridae New World blackbirds are more diverse in form and habits than any other family of birds. It is a sign of great evolutionary radiation; most species are found in the tropics. In form, they range from the small, finch-like bobolink; through multicolored New World orioles; to large, black, crow-like grackles, cowbirds, and oropendolas. Males are commonly much larger and more brightly colored than females. In habits, there are seed-eaters, fruit-eaters, and insect-eaters, with variable bills to match. Some feed in trees and others, such as the meadow larks, on the ground where they resemble Old World pipits. Bills are pointed and un-notched, and grackles have a special ridge in the palate that works like a can opener to shell acorns. Most species are gregarious when not breeding, commonly roosting in great flocks. They nest communally and polygamously. Females carry out all nesting duties (except in cowbirds which are brood parasites like cuckoos) and are master-architects at nest-building. The New World orioles construct delicate felted pouches in foliage; the tropical caciques and oropendolas pensile grassy sleeves up to 6 feet (2 m) long, high up in open trees; the grackles complex cup-nests in foliage and stony crevices; and the bobolink and meadow larks similar nests in cavities on the ground. Eggs, in clutches of two to six, are white to pale greenish blue, marked with red-browns and black.

Genera 26
Species 98

North America to South
America, West Indies

Feeding young
*A female Baltimore
oriole (*Icterus galbua*)
attends her nest
slung in shrubbery.
Brightly colored males
display in trees to
attract mates but
take no further part
in rearing the young.*

⚑ CONSERVATION WATCH

Black news Eleven New World blackbirds are listed as threatened. Four are vulnerable, five endangered, and two critical. The critical species are the Montserrat oriole (*Icterus oberi*) of Montserrat Island, and mountain grackle (*Macroagelaius subalaris*) of central Colombia.

FACT FILE

Family Emberizidae Buntings and American sparrows are small, finch-like birds in common brown, dusky-streaked plumage, the males usually brighter than females. White is patchily present. Their stout, conical bills are adapted to seed-eating and have a humped palate against which seeds can be cracked for shelling. They also take fruit and vegetable matter, and, although insects are minor in adult diet, they are fed to protein-needy nestlings. Most feed on the ground or in low shrubberies and scrub. Like other finches, buntings congregate to feed and roost in large flocks when not breeding but split into territory-holding pairs to nest. Most species are monogamous, and males chase their mates in headlong flights and tumbling in the lead-up to nesting. Females bear the brunt of nesting duties with some help from males. They build cup-shaped, or in the tropics, domed nests in crevices and cavities on the ground or in low rock faces and shrubberies. Eggs, in clutches of three to six, are pale, spotted, and scrolled with black and brown.

Genera 73
Species 308

Widespread except Madagascar, Indonesia & Australasia

Dark-eyed junco variation
Three different forms of the male North American dark-eyed junco are shown here, the slate colored (left), the Oregon (center), and the juvenile (right).

⚡ CONSERVATION WATCH

No breaks for buntings Thirty-five species of buntings are listed as threatened: 19 are vulnerable, 11 are endangered, and five are critical. The critical species—on the verge of extinction—are South American. They are the pale-headed bush finch (*Atlapetes pallidiceps*), the hooded seedeater (*Sporophila melanops*), the Tumaco seedeater (*Sporophila insulata*), the Narosky's seedeater (*Sporophila zelichi*), and the Mangrove finch (*Camarhynchus heliobates*), found in the Galápagos.

The five species of Inca finches are endemic to the Peruvian Andes. This species is confined to the Marañon valley

Buff-tailed Inca finch
Incaspiza laeta,
family Emberizidae

Canary-winged finch
Melanodera melanodera,
family Emberizidae

One of a group of two species confined to cold, temperate southern South America and the Falkland Islands

Mourning sierra finch
Phrygilus fruticeti,
family Emberizidae

Saffron finch
Sicalis flaveola,
family Emberizidae

Ranges from northwest to central South America

Wedge-tailed grass finch
Emberizoides herbicola,
family Emberizidae

Rusty-collared seedeater
Sporophila collaris,
family Emberizidae

Occurs in rank grassland from Costa Rica to central South America

White-crowned sparrow
Zonotrichia leucophrys,
family Emberizidae

Stripe-headed sparrow
Aimophila ruficauda,
family Emberizidae

A temperate North American bunting

Chestnut-bellied seed finch
Oryzoborus angolensis,
family Emberizidae

Occurs along the
eastern rim of the
northeast Andes, from
Colombia to north
Argentina and Paraguay

Chestnut-capped brush finch
Buarremon brunneinuchus,
family Emberizidae

One of "Darwin's
finches" from the
Galápagos Islands

Occurs along the mountain
spine of Central America,
from east Mexico to
Venezuela and Ecuador

Chestnut bunting
Emberiza rutila,
family Emberizidae

Common cactus finch
Geospiza scandens,
family Emberizidae

Pine bunting
Emberiza leucocephalos,
family Emberizidae

Occurs in
temperate
central and
east Asia

Yellowhammer
Emberiza citrinella,
family Emberizidae

♂

Crested bunting
Melophus lathami,
family Emberizidae

Named for its elongated
hind claw, this species is
gregarious and breeds
on the arctic tundra

♂

♂

Snow bunting
Plectrophenax nivalis,
family Emberizidae

Lapland longspur
Calcarius lapponicus,
family Emberizidae

After breeding, snow
buntings become gregarious
and both sexes molt into
similar, brownish plumage

FACT FILE

Family Emberizidae Only 14 percent
of bunting species occur outside the
Americas. Their greater numbers in
eastern Asia, and the presence of most
South American species along the
Andes, is evidence that buntings arose
in North America as part of the nine-
primaried radiation. From there they
crossed the Bering bridge to Asia.

Yellowhammer This woodland species
feeds mainly on grass seeds. It flocks
when not nesting, but disperses into
territory-holding pairs to breed, males
singing in defense. Females build cup-
nests of dry grass. Both sexes molt into
duller plumage in winter.

⤒ Up to 6½ in (16.5 cm)
● 3–5
✍ Sexes alike
↻ Partial migrant
↟ Common

Europe to W. Siberia & C. Asia

Lapland longspur Foraging on shrub
and hummock moss fields, the longspur
runs to pick up seeds, flies, and gnats.
Females build tight cup-nests of grass on
the ground. In winter, both sexes molt
into dull plumage and migrate south.

⤒ Up to 6½ in (16 cm)
● 5–7
✍ Sexes differ
↻ Migrant
↟ Locally common

Arctic & temperate Eurasia & North America

Snow bunting Nesting farther north
than any other land bird, the snow
bunting reaches northern Greenland. It
breeds on stony, often ice-bound terrain,
feeding on insects and seeds. Out of
breeding, it moves to more temperate
habitats and takes more seeds.

⤒ Up to 6½ in (17 cm)
● 4–6
✍ Sexes differ
↻ Partial to full migrant
↟ Locally common

Arctic & temperate Eurasia & North America

FACT FILE

Family Coerebidae Resembling a small New World warbler in color, but with a honeycreeper's bill, the bananaquit is the only member of its family. Its thin, curved bill is specialized for taking nectar from flowers and has a frayed tongue with two slit tubes at the tip. It also eats small, sweet fruits and insects, visiting a wide range of shrubbed and treed habitats in search of food, even urban gardens. Both sexes are alike. Built in low foliage, their nests are unusual globular structures with a down-facing entrance, and are constructed in numbers not only for breeding but also sleeping. Eggs are white, speckled brown. The young are fed on insects by regurgitation.

Genera 1
Species 1

S. Mexico to
W.C. South America

Family Thraupidae Tanagers and honeycreepers, small to medium in size, are centered in the northern Andes. Compensating for poor song, their plumage vies with the birds-of-paradise and cotingas as the most brilliant in passerine birds. Males are usually more brightly colored than females. Shortish-tailed and long-legged, they live mostly in trees and shrubs, using bills of diverse form to take various foods in outer foliage. Some have finch-like bills for seed-eating; many straight, narrow bills to pick fruit or catch insects; and still others slender, curved bills for rifling nectar from flowers. They roost in trees and bushes, and flock only loosely. Both sexes, or the female alone, construct the nest, usually a cup of fiber or sometimes a dome, in trees and shrubs. Eggs are brooded by the female. Both parents feed young on insects carried in the mouth or by regurgitation.

Genera 62
Species 271

North America to
South America

Deep-blue flowerpiercer This bird's short, hooked upper bill, needle-like lower bill, and tubular tongue are specialized for piercing tubular flowers at the bottom, and stealing nectar without pollinating the flower. There are 18 species of flowerpiercers.

⤓ Up to 4 in (10 cm)
◗ 2–3
⫽ Sexes differ
⊘ Sedentary
⫚ Uncommon

Mexico to central South America

Bananaquit
Coereba flaveola,
family Coerebidae

The yellow rump is
a diagnostic trait

Red-legged honeycreeper
Cyanerpes cyaneus,
family Thraupidae
♂

Green honeycreeper
Chlorophanes spiza,
family Thraupidae

**Deep-blue
flowerpiercer**
Diglossa glauca,
family Thraupidae
♂

Giant conebill
Oreomanes fraseri,
family Thraupidae

Golden-hooded tanager
Tangara larvata,
family Thraupidae

In this species, older
siblings of the year and
other adults may help
parents feed nestlings.
Ranges from Mexico
to Ecuador

♂

Swallow-tanager
Tersina viridis,
family Thraupidae

A flycatching
tanager of northern
South America

Found in upper foliage
on rain-forest edges at
low altitudes in northern
South America

Paradise tanager
Tangara chilensis,
family Thraupidae

Scarlet-and-white tanager
Chrysothlypis salmoni,
family Thraupidae

Occurs in hill
forests of Colombia
and Ecuador

♂

Seven-colored tanager
Tangara fastuosa,
family Thraupidae

Endemic to east
Brazil in upper
forest strata

Yellow-backed tanager
Hemithraupis flavicollis,
family Thraupidae

♂

Widespread in outer forest
foliage, from Panama to
Brazil and Peru

Scarlet tanager
Piranga olivacea,
family Thraupidae

♂

**White-throated
shrike-tanager**
Lanio leucothorax,
family Thraupidae

♂

Rosy thrush-tanager
Rhodinocichla rosea,
family Thraupidae

♂

One of the few songsters
in the tanager family, and
then not a brilliant singer

Sooty ant tanager
Habia gutturalis,
family Thraupidae

Strong legs, rounded
wings, and long tail
make for maneuverability
in tight spaces

FACT FILE

Scarlet tanager One of the few migratory tanagers, the scarlet breeds in temperate North American woodlands and migrates to winter in northwest South America. Breeding males are brilliant scarlet and black, but when wintering, molt into drab green female dress. Females alone build the nest and incubate, but both sexes bring insect food to young, carried in the bill. Adults eat fruit as well.

Seasonal change
Two male scarlet
tanagers (bottom)
molt into female
plumage (top)
for winter.

⤒ Up to 6½ in (16.5 cm)
● 3–5
✀ Sexes differ
↺ Migrant
⚘ Locally common

Temperate E. North America to
N.W. South America

Rosy thrush-tanager This large, ground-foraging insectivore and fruit-picker has no clear relatives among the tanagers. It lives in the underbrush of scrubs and monsoon forests, from west Mexico to Venezuela, where it is resident year-round. It sings regularly, and its songs are rich and sustained for a tanager. The rich, rosy flush over the breast in males is dulled in females.

⤒ Up to 8 in (20 cm)
● 2
✀ Sexes differ
⊘ Sedentary
⚘ Locally common

Central & N.W. South America

Sooty ant tanager Like other ant tanagers, this species sings a persistent song at dawn. It is one of five species of ant tanagers which live in the foliage of woods and shrubberies from Mexico, to southeast Brazil and northern Argentina. Unlike other tanagers, they give distraction displays if their nests are threatened.

⤒ Up to 8 in (20 cm)
● 2
✀ Sexes differ
⊘ Sedentary
⚘ Uncommon

N.W. Colombia

Golden-browed chlorophonia
Chlorophonia callophrys,
family Thraupidae

Builds domed nests like euphonias, constructed by duller plumaged females, and has similarly large clutches

♂

White-vented euphonia
Euphonia minuta,
family Thraupidae

Diademed tanager
Stephanophorus diadematus,
family Thraupidae

Localized in central northeast South America

Carmiol's tanager
Chlorothraupis carmioli,
family Thraupidae

Fulvous-crested tanager
Tachyphonus surinamus,
family Thraupidae

Occurs in hill forests in northern South America

♂

Silver-beaked tanager
Ramphocelus carbo,
family Thraupidae

Hooded mountain tanager
Buthraupis montana,
family Thraupidae

Blue-gray tanager
Thraupis episcopus,
family Thraupidae

Endemic to mountain forests in northwest South America

Blue-black grosbeak
Cyanocompsa cyanoides,
family Cardinalidae

♂

Lives in tropical
forests from
southwest Mexico
to west Argentina

Slate-colored grosbeak
Saltator grossus,
family Cardinalidae

♂

Plush-capped finch
Catamblyrhynchus diadema,
family Cardinalidae

Ranges from Venezuela,
along the Andes, to
northwest Argentina

Black-thighed grosbeak
Pheucticus tibialis,
family Cardinalidae

♂

Local in Costa
Rica and Panama

Northern cardinal
Cardinalis cardinalis,
family Cardinalidae

♂

Painted bunting
Passerina ciris,
family Cardinalidae

♂

Breeds in woodlands
of southern United
States and migrates
to Central America for
winter. Males do not
molt into duller plumage

Indigo bunting
Passerina cyanea,
family Cardinalidae

♂

Breeds in temperate east
North American woods
and winters in South
Amercia. Males molt
into partial cinnamon
winter plumage

EVOLUTION OF BILLS

The size and shape of birds' bills vary, adapted to their diets and food-gathering methods. It was Charles Darwin who first offered convincing evidence that such physical features are not immutable, and that species change over time in response to their environments. He theorized that Galápagos Islands finches, which differed most noticeably in bill size and shape, were all descended from a common ancestor and had evolved to exploit different ecological niches that were not being used by other animals. Genetic mutations that helped certain birds thrive were likely to be passed on to successive generations. This adaptive radiation is most noticeable on remote islands, where outside influences and competitor species are few or absent.

A productive relationship The brilliantly colored iiwi, one of the Hawaiian honeycreepers, has a bill that allows it to reach nectar easily in the tropical blooms on which it feeds. It can often be seen hanging upside down while feeding.

Isolated habitats Left to right: Hawaii; Galápagos Islands; Madagascar.

Rapid spread Specialized species that also eat insects (H1 and H3) or seeds (H2) developed rapidly—perhaps within a few hundred thousand years—to fill Hawaii's untapped ecological niches.

Special skills One Darwin finch species (G1) has learned to extract insects from under bark or cracks in wood using a cactus spine or twig. The largest of the ground finches (G2) uses its sturdy bill to eat large seeds.

Different appetites Nectar specialists such as H4 evolved long, curved bills that allowed them to probe and extract nectar, whereas seed-eaters such as H5 were better served by strong, stout bills that could crack hard shells.

Limitations Despite having bills that allowed them to eat well on the Hawaiian islands, many honeycreepers such as H6 went extinct. Evolutionary change could not keep pace with introduced predators and disease.

A rainbow of differences The Hawaiian honeycreepers belong to the subfamily Drepanidinae, which includes more than 30 species (many now extinct) that look and behave very differently from each other, despite the fact that they all trace their lineage back to a single founder species. Their ancestor appears to have been a flock of Eurasian rosefinch-like (*Carpodacus*) birds that flew by chance 2,500 miles (4,000 km) across open ocean, possibly with the aid of storm winds, to settle on this volcanic archipelago millions of years ago. There they diversified, evolving bills not only fitted for eating different seeds and insects, but also nectar from flowers of different form. The pictured Hawaiian honeycreepers (above) are: H1: anianiau (*Hemignathus parvus*); H2: Laysan finch (*Telespyza cantans*); H3: crested honeycreeper, or akohekohe (*Palmeria dolei*); H4: iiwi (*Vestiaria coccinea*); H5: Maui parrotbill (*Pseudonestor xanthophrys*); H6: black mamo (*Drepanis funerea*, extinct).

Diversity on a large island The vangas (family Vangidae) are a diverse group of songbirds found only on the island of Madagascar, a long isolated island of diverse habitats the size of California. The 22 species all prey on invertebrates or small reptiles, but, to avoid competition, have each evolved different bills to take prey of different size from different niches. The vangas pictured are: M1: sickle-billed vanga (*Falculea palliata*); M2: Lafresnaye's vanga (*Xenopirostris xenopirostris*); M3: helmet vanga (*Euryceros prevostii*); M4: red-shouldered vanga (*Calicalicus rufocarpalis*); M5: blue vanga (*Cyanolanius madagascarinus*).

M2

M3

M1

M4

M5

Niche filler A Chabert's vanga (*Leptopterus chabert*) perches on a branch in Madagascar. This bird is an insectivore that catches its prey by flying forth from a perch, rather like a woodswallow (*Artamus*).

A variety of roles
The vangas have specialized so much that there are almost as many genera as species in this group. The long bill of M1 is ideal for feeding in spiny forests; M2 probes in dead wood; M4 gleans insects from bushes and in flight.

Similarities to other birds
Individual vanga species have filled niches similar to those exploited by other birds elsewhere and have thus grown to resemble them. The M3, for example, recalls a small hornbill.

G4

Bloodsucker One finch (G5) is also known as the "vampire finch" due to its habit of pecking roosting or breeding seabirds in order to drink their blood.

Versatile bird One of the ground finches (G6) evolved a longer bill, which allows it to feed on cactus flowers and fruits as well as seeds. Diet diversification is especially important in lean times.

G6

G5

G3

Few predators
A Galápagos hawk (*Buteo galapagoensis*) soars above Fernandina Island. It is one of the few land birds, apart from the finches, that has managed to colonize these remote islands. Only three raptor species are found there.

Spawning a scientific revolution Modern genetic analyses have proven Darwin right, showing that the 14 species of Galápagos-based birds now known as Darwin's finches are indeed descended from one species, a seed-eating bunting that arrived there from the South American mainland. The Galápagos birds pictured are: G1: woodpecker finch (*Camarhynchus pallidus*); G2: large ground finch (*Geospiza magnirostris*); G3: warbler-finch (*Certhidea olivacea*); G4: masked booby (*Sula dactylatra*); G5: sharp-beaked ground finch (*Geospiza difficilis*); G6: common cactus finch (*Geospiza scandens*).

GLOSSARY

adaptation A change in a bird's behavior or body that allows it to survive and breed in new conditions.

adaptive radiation A situation in which birds descended from a common ancestor evolve to exploit different ecological niches that are not being filled by other animals, as in the finches of the Galápagos Islands.

algae The simplest forms of plant life.

altricial Helpless at birth. Describes newly hatched chicks of some birds.

arboreal Living all or most of the time in trees.

avian Of or about birds. Birds form the class Aves in the animal kingdom.

basic plumage The plumage worn by adult birds outside the breeding season.

barb A part of a feather vane. Barbs emerge from the central shaft of a feather in a parallel arrangement, like the teeth on a comb.

beak see bill.

bib A small region of contrasting color on the upper breast.

bill The horny covering of the jaws of a bird, comprising two halves—the maxilla (upper) and the mandible (lower). Sometimes called a beak.

biodiversity The total number of species of plants and animals in a particular location.

birds of prey Flesh-eating land birds that hunt and kill their prey. Hawks, eagles, kites, falcons, buzzards, and vultures are diurnal birds of prey; owls are nocturnal birds of prey.

bronchii The two branches of the windpipe that go to the lungs.

brood A number of young birds hatched in one clutch or group. As a verb, "to brood" means to shelter young birds from the Sun, heat, or cold.

brood parasite A bird that tricks another species into raising its young, as some cuckoos do. A young brood parasite often kills all its nestmates so that they do not compete with it for food or care.

call A sound uttered by a bird that is often unconnected with either courtship or announcement of territory.

camouflage The colors and patterns of a bird that enable it to blend in with the background. Camouflage conceals birds from predators and helps them ambush prey.

caudal Relating to the tail.

cephalic Of, relating to, or situated on or near the head.

cloaca An internal chamber in birds, into which the contents of the reproductive ducts and the waste ducts empty before being passed from the body.

clutch The full, completed set of eggs laid by a female bird in a single nesting attempt.

conspecific Of the same species.

convergent evolution The situation in which totally unrelated birds develop similar traits to cope with similar evolutionary pressures.

courtship The behavior patterns that male and female birds display when they are trying to attract a mate.

crest A line of emergent feathers on the top of the head. Many birds can raise or lower the crest to communicate with others.

cursorial Roams widely on foot.

dabbling Using the bill in a rapid, nibbling motion to sieve food from mud or water, a method of feeding so characteristic of certain ducks that they are defined by the term.

deforestation The cutting down of forest trees for timber, or to clear land for farming or building.

dimorphic Having two distinct forms within a species. Sexual dimorphism is the case in which the male and female of a species differ in appearance.

display Behavior used by a bird to communicate with its own species, or with other animals. Displays can include posturing and exhibiting brightly colored parts of the body, and may signal threat, defense, or readiness to mate.

distraction display A pattern of behavior used by adults of some species to lure a predator away from the nest.

diurnal Active during daytime.

divergent evolution The situation in which two or more similar species become more and more dissimilar due to environmental adaptations.

DNA A molecule, found in chromosomes of a cell nucleus, that contains genes. DNA stands for deoxyribonucleic acid.

domestication The process of taming and breeding a bird for human use. Domesticated birds include pets, as well as birds used for sport or food.

echolocation A system of navigation that relies on sound rather than sight or touch. Some birds use echo-location to tell them where they are, where their prey is, and if an obstruction is in their way.

ecosystem A community of plants, animals, and the environment to which they are adapted.

egg The large, rounded shell that contains a yolk and a white, laid by a female bird. If it has been fertilized, the egg contains a tiny embryo that will grow into a chick, using the yolk and white as food. When mature, the chick will break out of the eggshell.

egg tooth A sharp, tooth-shaped calcium deposit that grows on the tip of the bill of an embryonic bird. The bird uses the tooth to help it break through the shell when it is hatching.

embryo An unborn animal in the earliest stages of development. An embryo may grow inside its mother's body, or in an egg outside her body.

endothermic Able to regulate the body temperature internally, as warm-blooded animals do.

estivate To spend a period of time in a state of inactivity to avoid unfavorable conditions.

evolution Gradual change in plants and animals, over many generations, in response to adaptations.

exotic A foreign or non-native species of animal or plant, often introduced into a habitat by humans.

feather The components of a bird's covering or plumage. A feather is made of a horny substance called keratin, and has a long shaft with two vanes on either side. The vanes, made up of many closely spaced barbs, give the feather its shape and color. Feathers have many uses. They keep birds warm and dry and help them to fly.

feral A wild animal or plant, or a species that was once domesticated but has returned to its wild state.

fledgling A young bird that has grown its first true feathers and has just left its nest.

food chain A system in which one organism forms food for another, which in turn is eaten by another, and so on. The first organism is usually an alga or other single-celled life form in an aquatic food chain, and a plant in a terrestrial food chain.

fossil A remnant, impression, or trace of a plant or animal from a past geological age, usually found in rock.

frugivore A fruit-eater.

gizzard In birds, the equivalent of the stomach in mammals. Grit and stones inside the gizzard help to grind up food. Food passes from the gizzard to the intestine.

global warming The increase in the temperature of Earth and its lower atmosphere due to human activity such as deforestation, land degradation, intensive farming, and the burning of fossil fuels. This causes the absorption of heat by water vapor and "greenhouse" gases, including carbon dioxide and methane. The trapped heat, which would otherwise be radiated out to space, may cause the polar icecaps to melt and ocean levels to rise. Global warming is also known as "the greenhouse effect."

Gondwana Ancient southern supercontinent, comprising the present-day continents of Australia, India, Africa, South America, and Antarctica.

gorget A patch of brilliantly colored and often iridescent feathers on the throat of some birds (especially in hummingbirds).

granivore A seed-eater.

guild A loose group made up of several species of birds that usually share the same habitat.

gullet In birds, the gullet is the equivalent of the esophagus in mammals. This tube passes food from the bill to the gizzard.

habitat The area in which an animal naturally lives. Many different kinds of animals live in the same environment (for example, a rain forest), but each kind lives in a different habitat within that environment. For example, some animals in a rain forest live in the trees, while others live on the ground.

hatchling A bird that has recently hatched from its egg.

hawking To forage by catching and eating food on the wing.

herptiles Any type of reptile or amphibian.

hybrid The offspring of parents of two different species or races.

imprinting A process in which hatchlings identify with and attach themselves to a parental figure.

incubate To keep eggs in an environment, outside the female's body, in which they can develop and hatch. Most birds incubate their eggs by warming them with body heat.

insectivore An animal that eats insects or invertebrates. Some insectivores also eat small vertebrates, such as frogs, lizards, and mice.

introduced An animal or plant species imported from another place by humans and deliberately or accidentally released into new habitat.

iridescent Showing different colors as light strikes from different angles, as in a soap bubble or oil on a pool of water. The plumage of some birds is iridescent.

juvenile A young bird wearing its first set of fully functional feathers.

keratin The protein from which feathers are constructed.

Laurasia Ancient northern super-continent, comprising present-day Asia, North America, and Europe.

lek An arena or place where male birds of certain species congregate to compete in display to attract females for mating.

mandible The lower part of a bird's bill, often smaller than the upper part.

maxilla The top part of a bird's bill, usually larger than the lower part.

migration A usually seasonal journey from one habitat to another. Many birds migrate vast distances between locations to find food, or to mate and lay eggs.

molt To shed the outer layer of the body and limbs: the feathers.

monogamous Describes male and female which pair to form a single couple.

morph A color or other physical variant within, or a local population of, a species.

niche The ecological position occupied by a species within an animal community.

nocturnal Active at night. Nocturnal birds have special adaptations, such as large, sensitive eyes or ears, to help them find their way in the dark. All nocturnal birds rest during the day.

nomad A bird which lacks fixed territory, and wanders instead from place to place in search of food and water.

omnivore A bird that eats both plant and animal food.

order A major group used in taxonomic classification. An order forms part of a class, and comprises one or more families.

oviparous Reproducing by laying eggs. Little or no development occurs within the mother's body; instead, the embryos develop inside the egg.

pair bond A partnership maintained between a male and a female bird through one or several breeding attempts. Some species maintain a pair bond for life.

paleontology The scientific study of life in past geological periods.

Pangea Ancient supercontinent in which all the present-day continents were once joined.

parallel evolution The situation in which unrelated groups living in isolation develop similar structures to cope with similar evolutionary pressures.

parasitism The situation in which an animal or plant lives and/or feeds on another living animal or plant, sometimes with harmful effects.

passerine Any species of bird belonging to the order Passeriformes. A passerine is often described as a songbird or a perching bird.

plumage The sum total of feathers on a bird's body.

polygamous Describes which males mate, usually temporarily, with more than one female at breeding time and vice versa.

precocial Active and self-reliant at birth. Describes newly hatched chicks of some birds, such as ducks and chickens.

predator A bird that lives mainly by killing and eating other animals.

preen To clean, repair, arrange, and maintain plumage.

prehensile Grasping or gripping. The prehensile tongue of parrots enables them to extract kernels from shells.

rain forest A tropical forest that receives at least 100 inches (250 cm) of rain each year. Rain forests are home to a vast number of plant and animal species.

raptor A diurnal bird of prey, such as a hawk or falcon. The term is not used to describe owls.

regurgitate To bring food back up from the stomach to the mouth. Many birds regurgitate partially digested food to feed their chicks.

roost A place or site used by birds for sleeping. Also, the act of settling at such a place.

rudimentary Describes a simple, undeveloped, or underdeveloped part of a bird, such as an organ or wing. The rudimentary parts of some modern-day birds are the traces of the functional parts of an early ancestor, which now serve no purpose.

sallying To forage by flying out from a perch to pick up food from surfaces or in the air, then returning to a perch to eat.

savanna Open grassland with scattered trees. Most savannas are found in subtropical areas that have a distinct summer wet season.

scansorial Clambers about on a range of surfaces: trunks, rocks, logs, shrubbery.

scavenger A bird that eats carrion—often the remains of animals killed by predators.

sedentary Having a lifestyle that involves little movement; also used to describe birds that do not migrate.

social Living in groups. Social birds can live in breeding pairs, sometimes together with their young, or in colonies of up to thousands of birds.

song Any vocalization of a bird with the particular purpose of obtaining a mate or announcing a territory.

species A population of birds with very similar features that are able to breed together and produce fertile young.

stereoscopic vision Vision in which both eyes face forward, giving an animal two overlapping fields of view and thus allowing it to judge depth.

sternum The breastbone. Flying birds have a large, deeply keeled sternum to anchor their powerful flight muscles.

stylet A sharp mouthpart used for piercing plants or animals.

sub-antarctic Of the oceans and islands just north of Antarctica.

symbiosis An alliance between two species that is usually (but not always) beneficial to both. Animals form symbiotic relationships with plants, microorganisms, and other animals.

sympatric Of two or more species, occurring in the same area.

syrinx The 'voice box' of birds at the junction of the trachea and bronchii on the windpipe. Muscles work the air passing through this chambered structure to produce the calls and songs made by birds.

taxonomy The science of classifying living things into various groups and subgroups according to similarities in features and adaptations.

temperate Describes an environment or region that has a warm summer and a cool winter. Most of the world's temperate regions are located between the tropics and the polar regions.

territory An area defended by a bird for its own exclusive use against intruders of its own species (or, occasionally others). The area often incorporates all living resources needed by the bird, such as food and a nesting and roosting site.

thermal A column of rising air, used by birds to gain height, and on which some birds soar to save energy before gliding slowly downward again.

torpid In a sleep-like state in which bodily processes are greatly slowed. Torpor helps birds to survive difficult conditions such as cold or lack of food. Estivation and hibernation are types of torpor.

trachea A breathing tube in an animal's body. In vertebrates, there is one trachea (or windpipe), through which air passes to the lungs.

transient A migrant bird in transit across the area between its normal breeding and wintering distributions.

tropical Environments or regions near the Equator that are warm to hot all year round.

tundra A cold, barren habitat where much of the soil is frozen and the vegetation consists mainly of mosses, lichens, and other small plants adapted to withstand intense cold. Tundra is found near the Arctic Circle and on mountain tops.

vagrant Any individual bird outside the normal distribution of its species.

vane The plumed part of the feather that grows from the central shaft.

vertebral column The series of bony vertebrae running from head to tail along the back of vertebrates, and which encloses the spinal cord.

vertebrate An animal with a backbone. All vertebrates have an internal skeleton of cartilage or bone. Birds are vertebrates.

vestigial Relating to an organ that is non-functional or atrophied.

vortex Circular air currents made by the movement of a bird's wingtips.

zygodactylous Of birds, having two of the four toes pointing forward, and the other two pointing backward.

INDEX

Page numbers in italics refer
to illustrations, photographs,
and to information in captions.
Species are listed by both their
common name/s and scientific
name, although page references
to scientific names often relate
only to mentions in the text of
common names.

ACKNOWLEDGMENTS

t=top; l=left; r=right; tl=top left; tcl=top center left; tc=top center; tcr=top center right; tr=top right; cl=center left; c=center; cr=center right; b=bottom; bl=bottom left; bcl=bottom center left; bc=bottom center; bcr=bottom center right; br=bottom right

APL = Australian Picture Library; APL/CBT = Australian Picture Library/Corbis; APL/MP = Australian Picture Library/Minden Pictures; ARL = Ardea London; AUS = Auscape International; BCC = Bruce Coleman Collection; GI = Getty Images; NHPA = Natural History Photographic Agency; PL = photolibrary.com.

PHOTOGRAPHS

Front cover tl PL tc, tr, c GI

1c GI 2c NHPA 4c NHPA 6c GI 8cl GI 12c GI 14b, cr GI 15c PL 16b APL/CBT 18b APL/CBT 19b, tl GI tc PL tr APL/MP 20cr APL/CBT 21br PL 22br GI tr APL/CBT 23tc NHPA tcl, tcr, tl, tr GI 24b GI 25bl BCC br APL/MP t APL/CBT 26bl NHPA br APL/CBT tr PL 27c APL 28b GI 29b PL tr APL/CBT 30bl NHPA br PL tr GI 31c GI 32t APL/CBT 33bl, tr GI cl APL/CBT tl NHPA 34l PL tr APL/CBT 35b APL/CBT 36bl APL br NHPA tl GI 37c PL 38br PL tr APL/MP 39b APL/CBT t PL 40b APL/CBT 41bl, br, tr APL/CBT 42b APL/CBT t NHPA 43bl PL cr, t APL/CBT 44c GI 46cl APL/CBT 46cr PL 48c APL/CBT 50cl GI 51br GI 54c APL/MP cl PL 56cr, l GI 62bcr APL/MP bl APL/CBT c PL 63tl APL/MP 65c, cl APL/CBT 68cl PL 70cl GI 72tl, tr APL/CBT 73c APL/MP 74c, cl GI 77br, c PL 82cr, l APL/MP 84bc, c, cr PL 87c PL 92cr, tr PL 99br, r GI 101bc, br PL cl GI 107cr APL/CBT 110cr GI c PL 114bl PL c GI 120c PL 121br, cl APL/CBT 123bc APL/CBT cl APL/MP 124c GI 125br GI 128bl, br, cr, tl APL/CBT 129bl, br, tl, tr APL/CBT 130c, cl APL/CBT 132bl ARL/Jean-Paul Ferrero br GI cl APL/MP 135c APL/MP 141br GI cl APL/CBT 142cl APL/CBT 144c PL 147cl APL/CBT c NHPA 148c PL cl APL/MP 152br APL/MP cl APL/CBT tr GI 153bl, c, tr APL/MP br APL/CBT tl PL 154bc NHPA bl APL/MP br PL 155bc Frank Park/ANTPhoto.com br J.M. Soper/ANTPhoto.com bl Graeme Chapman br GItr NHPA 164br GI tl APL/MP 169b, bl, tl, tr William S. Peckover 174tr APL/MP 175tl, tr APL/MP 178bl, tl AUS br, cl, tr Graeme Chapman 179tr Cyril Webster/ANTPhoto.com 189tl PL 205c APL 214tl VIREO/Peter La Tourette 215br APL/MP cl ARL.

ILLUSTRATIONS

All illustrations © MagicGroup s.r.o. (Czech Republic) - www.magicgroup.cz; except for the following:

Mike Atkinson/Garden Studio 47b, 122bl; **Gerald Driessen** 200cl; **Lloyd Foye** 166bl; **Gino Hasler** 23bcl bcr cr; **David Kirshner** 17bl tl, 18tr, 20cl, 21cl, 58bl, 63bcr bl, 64br cl cr tr, 80bl, 95br, 112bl, 116br, 119br, 123bl, 143bc, 146b, 150tr, 157br, 166cl, 173br, 201br; **Frank Knight** 86bl, 165br; **Frits Jan Maas** 81br, 194bl, 203cr, 60bl, 103bc, 111br; **Rob Mancini** 14cl, 46br, 63cl cr, 101bl, 125c cr tr, 131br, 190cl, 192cl, 195cr, 202bl, 207br, 208bl, 211cr; **Map Illustrations/Laurie Whiddon** 70cr; **Karel Mauer** 103bl, 146bl, 197br; **Rob Morton** 106c; **Erik van Ommen** 98c cl, 131br, 151cr, 189c; **Maurice Pledger** 104bl; **Tony Pyrzakowski** 84bl, 86bcl, 93t; **Trevor Ruth** 139br; **Guy Troughton** 72b, 92c, 164c, 174c, 179c, 214c; **Trevor Weekes** 65br, 125cr, 143br, 151br, 213cr; **Wildlife Art Ltd.** 17br cr tr, 21tc, 40tr, 47bl, 66t, 70c, 71tr, 84br, 85br, 114bc, 116bl, 117br, 119br, 139l.

MAPS AND GRAPHICS

All maps by **Andrew Davies/Creative Communication**.

INDEX

Sarah Plant/Puddingburn Editorial Services.

The publishers would like to thank Helen Flint and Chris Spence for their assistance in the preparation of this volume.

CAPTIONS

Page 1 The sociable, keel-billed toucan, endemic to Honduras, is often found in flocks of six or more birds.

Page 2 Tapered wings allow the large, colorful scarlet macaw to fly quickly through Central and South American forests.

Page 4–5 A male Japanese crane displays its tall, graceful body to attract a female mate.

Page 6–7 Perched on a holly berry branch, northern cardinals are sedentary and endure harsh winter climates.

Page 8–9 A seagull soars over treacherous, stormy water in search of food.

Page 12–13 The color of a flamingo's feathers varies with species and is derived from its diet, which is high in carotenoid pigments.

Page 44–45 A whooper swan takes a nap with one eye open, on the lookout for predators.